W9-CXT-518

COMPREHENSIVE BIOCHEMISTRY

ELSEVIER PUBLISHING COMPANY

335 Jan van Galenstraat, P.O. Box 211, Amsterdam

AMERICAN ELSEVIER PUBLISHING COMPANY, INC.

52, Vanderbilt Avenue, New York, N.Y, 10017

ELSEVIER PUBLISHING COMPANY LIMITED

12B, Rippleside Commercial Estate, Ripple Road, Barking, Essex

Library of Congress Catalog Card Number 62–10359

With 46 illustrations and 25 tables

COMPREHENSIVE BIOCHEMISTRY

COMPREHENSIVE BIOCHEMISTRY

SECTION I (VOLUMES 1–4)

PHYSICO-CHEMICAL AND ORGANIC ASPECTS OF BIOCHEMISTRY

SECTION II (VOLUMES 5–11)

CHEMISTRY OF BIOLOGICAL COMPOUNDS

SECTION III (VOLUMES 12–16)

BIOCHEMICAL REACTION MECHANISMS

SECTION IV (VOLUMES 17–21)

METABOLISM

SECTION V (VOLUMES 22–26)

CHEMICAL BIOLOGY

GENERAL INDEX (VOLUME 27)

COMPREHENSIVE BIOCHEMISTRY

EDITED BY

MARCEL FLORKIN

Professor of Biochemistry, University of Liège (Belgium)

AND

ELMER H. STOTZ

Professor of Biochemistry, University of Rochester, School of Medicine and Dentistry, Rochester, N.Y.

VOLUME 12

ENZYMES

GENERAL CONSIDERATIONS

ELSEVIER PUBLISHING COMPANY

AMSTERDAM · LONDON · NEW YORK

1964

CONTRIBUTORS TO THIS VOLUME

RAMAPRASAD BANERJEE

Maître de Recherches au Centre National de la Recherche Scientifique, Institut de Biologie Physico-Chimique, 13, rue Pierre Curie, Paris-5e (France)

JOSEPH E. COLEMAN, B.A., M.D., PH.D.

Assistant Professor of Biological Chemistry, Department of Biological Chemistry, Yale University Medical School, New Haven 11, Conn. (U.S.A.); Formerly Research Associate, Biophysics Research Laboratory, Harvard Medical School, Boston 15, Mass. (U.S.A.)

EDWIN A. DAWES, PH.D., D.SC., F.R.I.C.

Reckitt Professor of Biochemistry, Department of Biochemistry, The University, Hull (Great Britain)

C. H. W. HIRS, B.SC., PH.D.

Department of Biology, Brookhaven National Laboratory, Associated Universities, Inc., Upton, Long Island, N.Y. (U.S.A.)

HANS HIRSCHMANN

Professor of Biochemistry, Department of Medicine, Lakeside Hospital, Western Reserve University, Cleveland, Ohio 44106 (U.S.A.)

JOHN M. REINER, PH.D.

Professor of Biophysics, Department of Microbiology, Division of Basic Health Sciences, Emory University, Atlanta 22, Ga. (U.S.A.)

BERT L. VALLEE, B.SC., M.A., M.D.

Professor of Biological Chemistry, Harvard Medical School, Biophysics Research Laboratory, Peter Bent Brigham Hospital, 721 Huntington Avenue, Boston 15, Mass. (U.S.A.)

EDWIN C. WEBB, M.A., PH.D.

Professor of Biochemistry and Head of the Department of Biochemistry, The University of Queensland, St. Lucia, Brisbane (Australia)

IRWIN B. WILSON, M.A., PH.D.

Professor of Biochemistry, College of Physicians and Surgeons, Department of Neurology, Columbia University, 630 West 168th Street, New York 32, N.Y. (U.S.A.)

RENÉ WURMSER

Professeur honoraire à la Faculté des Sciences de Paris, Institut de Biologie Physico-Chimique, 13, rue Pierre Curie, Paris-5e (France)

GENERAL PREFACE

The Editors are keenly aware that the literature of Biochemistry is already very large, in fact so widespread that it is increasingly difficult to assemble the most pertinent material in a given area. Beyond the ordinary textbook the subject matter of the rapidly expanding knowledge of biochemistry is spread among innumerable journals, monographs, and series of reviews. The Editors believe that there is a real place for an advanced treatise in biochemistry which assembles the principal areas of the subject in a single set of books.

It would be ideal if an individual or small group of biochemists could produce such an advanced treatise, and within the time to keep reasonably abreast of rapid advances, but this is at least difficult if not impossible. Instead, the Editors with the advice of the Advisory Board, have assembled what they consider the best possible sequence of chapters written by competent authors; they must take the responsibility for inevitable gaps of subject matter and duplication which may result from this procedure.

Most evident to the modern biochemist, apart from the body of knowledge of the chemistry and metabolism of biological substances, is the extent to which he must draw from recent concepts of physical and organic chemistry, and in turn project into the vast field of biology. Thus in the organization of Comprehensive Biochemistry, the middle three sections, Chemistry of Biological Compounds, Biochemical Reaction Mechanisms, and Metabolism may be considered classical biochemistry, while the first and last sections provide selected material on the origins and projections of the subject.

It is hoped that sub-division of the sections into bound volumes will not only be convenient, but will find favour among students concerned with specialized areas, and will permit easier future revisions of the individual volumes. Toward the latter end particularly, the Editors will welcome all comments in their effort to produce a useful and efficient source of biochemical knowledge.

Liège/Rochester

M. Florkin
E. H. Stotz

PREFACE TO SECTION III

(VOLUMES 12–16)

Following Section II of Comprehensive Biochemistry on the Chemistry of Biological Compounds, and preceding sections on Metabolism and Chemical Biology, Section III is devoted primarily to Enzymes. Recognizing the encyclopedic nature of any effort to provide even a minimal treatment of all known enzymes, the Editors have chosen instead to select examples from modern enzymology in which advances in reaction mechanisms have been made. Certainly a well-established biochemical reaction mechanism is the carrier function of coenzymes which serve as the prosthetic groups of enzymes, and Section III has a primary purpose of providing treatment of both the chemistry and function of the coenzymes. Other chapters, however, treat thermodynamic and kinetic aspects of enzyme catalysis, hydrolytic enzymes displaying "active center" characteristics, and chelation and stereochemical considerations in enzyme catalysis. A considerable portion of the Section deals with biological oxidation mechanisms. Finally, Section III would seem incomplete without inclusion of the recommendations of the Enzyme Commission of the International Union of Biochemistry and the classified list of Enzymes.

Liège/Rochester
November 1964

M. FLORKIN
E. H. STOTZ

CONTENTS

VOLUME 12

ENZYMES — GENERAL CONSIDERATIONS

Chapter III. Oxidation–Reduction Potentials
by R. Wurmser and R. Banerjee

Chapter IV. Enzyme Kinetics
(Optimum pH, Temperature and Activation Energy)
by Edwin A. Dawes

Chapter V. Quantitative Aspects of Enzymes and Enzyme Systems
by JOHN M. REINER

Chapter VI. Metal Coordination and Enzyme Action
by BERT L. VALLEE AND JOSEPH E. COLEMAN

Chapter VII. Newer Aspects of Enzymatic Stereospecificity
by H. HIRSCHMANN

Chapter VIII. Enzyme Structure and Function with Particular Reference to Bovine Ribonuclease and Chymotrypsin
by C. H. W. HIRS

Chapter I

Introduction, Historical, Definitions, General Concepts, Isoenzymes

EDWIN C. WEBB

Department of Biochemistry, University of Queensland, Brisbane (Australia)

The metabolism of a living organism is a complicated interlocking pattern of sequential chemical reactions. With very few exceptions each separate metabolic step is catalyzed by an enzyme, so that it is not surprising to find that a very large proportion of work published in the biochemical literature is concerned with enzymes. It has been calculated that around two out of every three papers published in the current issues of the *Journal of Biological Chemistry* can be regarded, in the widest sense, as contributions to enzymology.

The study of enzymes includes many types of investigation, and is a field which overlaps with many other disciplines. However, in a general way one can say that interest in an enzyme is of one of two types: interest in the actual reaction catalyzed, or interest in the enzyme as a catalyst. The study of intermediary metabolism belongs essentially to the former type; it is the basis for the tabulation, classification and nomenclature of enzymes, which are dealt with in Volume 13. This Volume will be concerned with the more general problem of the nature of enzymatic catalysis, for it has long been clear that all enzymes have much in common.

1. Enzyme kinetics

An enzyme may be defined as "a protein with catalytic properties due to its power of specific activation"[1]. The first part of the definition is a generalization about enzymes as substances which will be discussed later in this Chapter; it relates to comparatively recent studies, since until some enzymes had been obtained in a more or less pure state they could not be studied as substances, except very indirectly. The central part of the definition is that enzymes are true catalysts, speeding up chemical reactions without

References p. 17

themselves being involved in the overall process. Enzyme kinetics is a study of the quantitative characteristics of this catalysis; it is a study almost as old as that of non-biological catalysis, and has contributed immeasurably to our understanding of the fundamental nature of enzyme action. An excellent review of the history of enzyme kinetics has been written by Segal[2].

The concept of catalysis was put forward by Berzelius[3] in 1836, some time before the first measurements of chemical reaction rates. This was only three years after the first clear recognition of an enzyme by Payen and Persoz[4], who gave the name "diastase" to an alcohol precipitate of malt extract which converted starch into sugar. Berzelius was aware of this work and included the action of diastase among his examples of "catalytic force". It was only late in the nineteenth century that the idea arose that enzymes acted by means of some "vital force" which was not subject to the physical chemical laws applicable to non-biological systems, an idea which lingered on for some decades.

Between 1850 and 1880 a number of chemists made quantitative studies of chemical changes, which led up to the concept of chemical equilibrium as a balance between two rate processes, each dependent on a mass law. In the next 30 years many investigators extended these studies to enzyme-catalyzed reactions, in the hope that "the light thrown on the mode of action . . . of one member of the group will be a key to the wider knowledge of the others"[5]. Many of these experiments were extremely unsatisfactory, because the effects of hydrogen ion concentration could not be properly controlled, although the importance of the acidity of the incubation mixtures was well recognized[5]. It was not until Sörensen[6] in 1909 introduced the concepts of pH and buffers that this variable could be standardized. This not only made all enzyme kinetic studies more reliable and meaningful, but also opened a new field in the effect of pH on enzyme activity, which has helped in the identification of functional groups in the enzyme protein. This topic is discussed in Chapter IV.

The conclusions drawn by different workers from these early experiments were often contradictory. Some found that the progress curves for enzyme-catalyzed reactions fitted first-order kinetics and concluded that enzyme action followed the normal mass action law. Others found marked departures from the results expected, particularly in the variation of apparent first-order velocity constant with substrate concentration. An extreme view was that of Duclaux[7], who presented kinetic equations based on a primary zero order reaction, with velocity independent of substrate concentration, modified by product inhibition. Several other empirical equations were put forward in the period 1890–1905.

The theory that forms the foundation stone of all enzyme kinetic theory that enzymes function through the formation of an enzyme–substrate intermediate complex, was first proposed in a qualitative way by A. J. Brown[8]. It was Victor Henri, however, who first developed the quantitative theory based on this idea, in contributions[9] which have not always received the recognition they deserved. Henri assumed that a rapid equilibrium step leading to the formation of a complex was followed by a rate-limiting breakdown of the complex with liberation of the product of the reaction; he also assumed that the product inhibited the reaction. He obtained the expression for initial velocity often referred to as the Michaelis–Menten equation:

$$v_0 = \frac{ks_0}{1 + s_0/K_s}$$

where v_0 and s_0 are the velocity of the enzyme-catalyzed reaction and substrate concentration at zero time; in addition he gave an equation for the rate at time t:

$$\frac{dx}{dt} = \frac{k(s_0 - x)}{1 + (s_0 - x)\ K_s + x/K_i}$$

where x is the amount of substrate which has reacted at time t. By integration of this equation he obtained an equation for the progress curve which he was able to check with the published data for sucrase and amylase.

Michaelis and Menten[10] confirmed and extended the work of Henri. They gave graphical methods for evaluating the constants of the rate equation (V and K_m), and applied them to their own data for sucrase obtained under carefully controlled conditions. Most studies of the effect of substrate concentration on enzyme activity still use the Michaelis–Menten equation, although a number of more convenient methods for plotting the results graphically are available[11–13]. A statistical method for obtaining the parameters of the Michaelis–Menten equation from experimental data has also been published[14].

The concept of an enzyme–substrate intermediate complex (often referred to as a "Michaelis complex") as the theoretical basis of enzyme kinetics has proved extremely fruitful. Extensions of the theory have dealt with the effects of competitive and non-competitive inhibitors, activators, and excess substrate inhibition, and they have been applied to a wide range of enzymes. These matters are discussed in more detail in Chapter V.

There are two main directions in which enzyme kinetic theory has departed significantly from the basis laid down by Henri and by Michaelis. The first concerns the equilibrium between enzyme, substrate and complex, which was originally supposed to be established very rapidly, so that the equilibrium position was not appreciably disturbed by the breakdown of the

References p. 17

enzyme–substrate complex to give the reaction products. It was first shown by Briggs and Haldane[15] that an equation formally similar to that of Michaelis and Menten could be obtained without making this assumption, by postulating a "steady state" or "dynamic equilibrium" in which all the processes leading to formation or breakdown of the complex are balanced:

$$E + S \underset{k_{-1}}{\overset{k_{+1}}{\rightleftharpoons}} ES \overset{k_{+2}}{\rightarrow} E + P$$

It can be shown that the Michaelis–Menten equation is a special case, obtained when k_{+2} is small compared with k_{-1}, of the more general Briggs–Haldane equation*:

$$v = \frac{k_{+2}s}{s + \dfrac{k_{-1} + k_{+2}}{k_{+1}}}$$

For nearly 20 years the steady-state treatment remained a purely academic curiosity, since it gives the same general equation:

$$v = \frac{Vs}{s + K_m}$$

differing only in the meaning given to the experimental parameter K_m. According to Michaelis and Menten

$$K_m = \frac{k_{-1}}{k_{+1}}$$

whereas according to Briggs and Haldane

$$K_m = \frac{k_{-1} + k_{+2}}{k_{+1}}$$

In 1943, however, Chance[16] devised methods for measuring the separate velocity constants k_{+1} and k_{+2} for horseradish peroxidase, whose complex with H_2O_2 can be detected spectroscopically. The results were used to verify the Briggs–Haldane relationship in a very elegant manner. The most interesting discovery, however, was that in this case the Michaelis–Menten equilibrium assumptions were certainly not applicable; on the contrary, the experimental K_m approximated to k_{+2}/k_{+1}. K_m was not, as had been generally supposed, an equilibrium constant defining the affinity of the enzyme for its substrate, but the ratio of the velocity constants for two successive steps in the reaction mechanism.

* The symbols used in this section are those recommended by the I.U.B. Commission on Enzymes[17], not those of the original authors.

The two decades since Chance's work may be regarded as the "steady-state" phase of enzyme kinetics. A number of methods have been invented for the measurement of the separate kinetic constants of enzyme reactions, even in cases where the ES complex cannot be detected directly. They depend primarily on the measurement of changes in very small time intervals, and developments in electronic techniques have helped greatly in this direction. For some of the enzymes investigated K_m does correspond fairly closely to K_s, the equilibrium dissociation constant of ES, and it is clear that peroxidase, discussed above, is probably an extreme case.

The steady-state theory has been extended to cover more complicated situations than those discussed hitherto. For example, the product is presumably formed in combination with the enzyme, and the rate of dissociation can be taken as finite, so that one may consider the situation:

$$E + S \rightleftharpoons ES \rightleftharpoons EP \rightleftharpoons E + P$$

In an extreme case the dissociation of product may be the "limiting step" in the reaction sequence. There may be more intermediate steps than these; the enzyme may exist in more than one form (*e.g.* oxidized and reduced forms in the case of oxidoreductases) or the products may be liberated in two stages. As an example of the latter point one may mention that many enzymes hydrolyzing acyl substrates are themselves acylated during the reaction; representing enzyme as EH and the substrate as $R \cdot CO \cdot R'$, one may write:

$$EH + R \cdot CO \cdot R' \rightleftharpoons EH\text{—}R \cdot CO \cdot R' \rightleftharpoons E \cdot CO \cdot R + R'H$$

$$E \cdot CO \cdot R + H_2O \rightleftharpoons EH\text{—}R \cdot COOH \rightarrow EH + R \cdot COOH$$

Kinetic treatments of many such mechanisms have been published; in the majority of cases (but not all) they lead to rate equations formally similar to the Michaelis–Menten equation, but with complex kinetic meanings for both V and K_m. Comparison of the theory with experimental data, especially if this covers both the overall kinetics and the rate constants of separate stages, may be expected to throw light on the actual mechanism of the reaction. This type of work is actively proceeding in many places.

The second important development of kinetic theory has been its extension to systems of more than two components. All the earlier treatments formulated the overall enzyme-catalyzed reaction as

$$S \rightarrow P$$

whereas in fact almost all enzyme reactions involve two substrates, or occasionally three (see Volume 13). In addition many enzymes only function in the presence of an activator (*e.g.* a metal ion) whose concentration must also be taken into account.

References p. 17

Steady-state rate equations for two-substrate reactions were published more or less independently by a number of workers (*e.g.* Refs. 1, 18, 19). They reduce to Michaelis-type expressions with linear reciprocal plots only under certain conditions, *e.g.* if there is an obligatory order of reaction, one substrate always combining with the enzyme before the other.

In the last few years attempts have been made to write a general rate equation for an enzyme reaction, incorporating all possible mechanisms, and involving more than one substrate and possibly activators and inhibitors in addition (*e.g.* Refs. 20–22). The results are very complicated, and new mathematical techniques and new types of symbolism have been introduced to deal with them. At first sight it appears to be a sterile academic exercise, since the general equations themselves are far too complex to relate directly to experimental measurements. On the contrary, however, in the opinion of the writer they may lead to a new flowering of the subject of enzyme kinetics. From such general equations it is possible to write down simple expressions which are unambiguously associated with particular mechanisms; an obligatory order of combination, for example, or the exclusion of certain possible intermediates. To prove conclusively from kinetic results that an enzyme reaction proceeds by one particular mechanism it is necessary not only to show that they are compatible with that mechanism (as has often been done), but also that they are incompatible with all other possible mechanisms. Starting from a general theory, one can set out the minimum experimental results required for this. Thus the theory not only helps in the interpretation of kinetic results in terms of reaction mechanism, but also helps in the design of experiments by stating what kinds of results are required. The use of more sophisticated theory, coupled with the greatly improved methods of investigation now available, such as recording equipment for physico-chemical measurements, will ensure that the subject of enzyme kinetics continues to contribute to our knowledge of how enzymes work.

2. Enzymes as substances

The nineteenth century biochemists used crude extracts, or even whole cells, and thought of enzymes as properties rather than as substances. It was not until 1920 that any serious attempt to purify enzymes began, with the work of Willstätter and his colleagues. Many other biochemists regarded this approach as unprofitable, since the separated enzymes were "unphysiological", and their action was regarded as having little relevance to the activity of the intact cell or tissue.

In 1926 Sumner obtained crystals of urease from Jack bean meal[23]. These first crystals were, in fact, not much more than 50% pure, but they

were dismissed entirely by Willstätter and others as being merely a protein "carrier" of the enzyme. Other enzymes were soon crystallized, however, particularly by Northrop and his school, who purified a series of digestive enzymes[24]. Recrystallization increased the specific activity of these enzymes to a constant value, and physical methods of investigation proved conclusively that the preparations were homogeneous. In these cases, in fact, enzymes had been obtained as pure substances and each activity was due to a single molecular species of protein.

Following Northrop's work, a good deal of effort was put into the purification of enzymes, and many more were crystallized. They were at first largely extracellular enzymes, but in the late 1930's the more important intracellular enzymes of metabolism were tackled, the first successes in this group being achieved by Warburg and his school. At the same time attention was given to criteria of purity of protein preparations, and the development of electrophoretic techniques and the ultracentrifuge facilitated the assessment of purification procedures. At the time of writing around 100 enzymes have been obtained in an acceptable state of purity, most of them crystalline[1].

All enzymes which have been obtained in a pure state have been found to be proteins, sometimes with a non-protein prosthetic group attached to the protein molecule. (From time to time claims are made that highly purified enzyme solutions contain no detectable protein (*e.g.* Ref. 25), but these are probably due to the sensitivity of the detection methods used and the high specific activity of the particular enzymes.) The molecular weights of purified enzymes vary from 9000 to 1 000 000 or more.

Once enzymes can be obtained in quantity in the pure state (a number can be purchased from commercial organizations by the gram!) it is possible to investigate them as chemical substances. A good proportion of the literature of protein chemistry has in recent years been concerned with enzymes. Amino acid analyses have been published for about two dozen enzymes, and in one case, ribonuclease, the amino acid sequence is completely known[26] (see Chapter VIII).

The non-protein prosthetic groups mentioned above have received a good deal of attention. They are frequently firmly-bound reactants which couple two enzymatically catalyzed reactions; many examples are found among the oxidoreductases, and are discussed in later Chapters. A coloured prosthetic group (*e.g.* haem or flavin) can sometimes be used to follow the purification of the enzyme, and once the latter has been obtained reasonably pure, the concentration of the prosthetic group can be used to estimate the minimum molecular weight.

Destruction of the tertiary structure of an enzyme protein by denaturation usually leads to irreversible loss of activity, as does any kind of proteolysis.

References p. 17

With a small number of hydrolytic enzymes it is possible to show that minor parts of the protein can be removed without any appreciable effect on the catalytic efficiency. A very exceptional case is ribonuclease, which can be split by subtilopeptidase A into two inactive fragments; activity is restored by simply mixing the fragments[27].

Many lines of evidence have led to the idea of an "active centre", a special configuration at some point on the protein molecule being responsible for enzyme–substrate interaction at that point. The facts of specificity, in particular, could hardly be explained in any other way. Much of the chemical work with pure enzymes has been directed towards the elucidation of the structure of this active centre. If a potent inhibitor can be shown to attack specifically a single residue in the enzyme, without disturbing the spatial arrangement of the peptide chains, it seems reasonable to infer that that particular residue is associated with the active centre. Koshland has given a critical review of chemical methods for determining the nature of the active centre[28].

A group of enzymes, often referred to as "SH enzymes", are particularly sensitive to inhibition by thiol reagents, such as iodoacetate, chloroacetophenone and *p*-chloromercuribenzoate. The essential —SH group sometimes takes part in the enzyme reaction, as in the case of glyceraldehydephosphate dehydrogenase, where a labile thiolester intermediate is formed by oxidation of the substrate. Not all of the so-called "thiol reagents" are completely specific, and it has been shown that inhibition of ribonuclease by iodoacetate and bromoacetate is due to reaction with a single histidine residue. Histidine has been identified in the active site of quite a few enzymes[29].

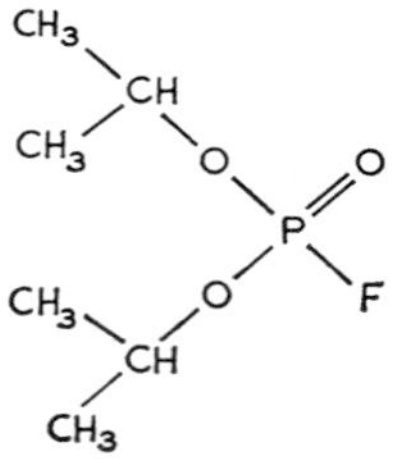

$$(CH_3)_2CH{-}O{-}P(=O)(F){-}O{-}CH(CH_3)_2$$

Fig. 1. Structure of diisopropyl phosphorofluoridate (DFP).

One of the most productive chemical investigations using an inhibitor stemmed from the wartime interest in the "nerve gases", a group of organophosphorus compounds of which diisopropyl phosphorofluoridate (DFP) is the most widely used. Its structure is shown in Fig. 1. It is an extremely potent irreversible inhibitor of cholinesterases and also of some other enzymes which can catalyze esterolysis, including the proteolytic enzymes chymotrypsin and trypsin. The stoichiometry of the inhibition of chymotrypsin by DFP has been carefully studied; one molecule of DFP reacts with one molecule of enzyme, liberating fluoride and leaving a diisopropylphosphoryl (DIP) radical substituted on a serine residue, and completely inactivating the enzyme. Only one of the many serine residues in chymotrypsin is able to react in this way. The DIP–serine link is resistant to mild hydrolysis, so that it is possible to use DFP as an active centre marker, to identify the particular serine involved. The techniques which have been developed for determining amino acid sequences in proteins can be applied to the peptides containing DIP obtained by partial hydrolysis of DFP-inactivated enzymes, thus obtaining an amino acid sequence at or near the active centre. Table I shows a number of results obtained in this way. A striking feature is the great similarity of sequence in enzymes whose specificity varies widely.

It is unlikely that purely chemical studies of this type alone will give a complete picture of the reaction mechanism. Trypsin and chymotrypsin are known to have a histidine in the active site, yet no histidines occur in the sequences shown in Table I; presumably more than one portion of

TABLE I

AMINO ACID SEQUENCES AT THE ACTIVE CENTRE OF SOME DFP-SENSITIVE ENZYMES

Enzyme	*Sequence*
Chymotrypsin	Gly-Asp-$\overset{*}{\text{Ser}}$-Gly-Gly-Pro-Leu
Trypsin	$\overset{NH_2}{\text{Asp}}$-Ser-Cys-Glu-Gly-Gly-Asp-$\overset{*}{\text{Ser}}$-Gly-Pro-Val-Cys-Ser-Gly-Lys
Thrombin	Asp-$\overset{*}{\text{Ser}}$-Gly
Subtilopeptidase A	Thr-$\overset{*}{\text{Ser}}$-Met-Ala
Elastase	Asp-$\overset{*}{\text{Ser}}$-Gly
Liver carboxylesterase	Gly-Glu-$\overset{*}{\text{Ser}}$-Ala-Gly-Gly-(Glu, Ser)
Cholinesterase	Phe-Gly-Glu-$\overset{*}{\text{Ser}}$-Ala-Gly-(Ala, Ala, Ser)

$\overset{*}{\text{Ser}}$ represents the serine residue specially reactive with DFP.

peptide chain is involved in the active centre. The possibility that the active centre may be a pattern of groups extending transversely across two or more adjacent peptide chains or sections of one folded chain has been discussed by Dixon[30]. This would explain the great importance of the tertiary

References p. 17

structure mentioned earlier. A complete chemical picture of an enzyme as a substance, which is a prerequisite of an irrefutable theory of enzyme catalysis, must await further advances in our knowledge of the spatial arrangement of peptide chains within protein molecules.

3. The identity of enzymes

The attempt of the Enzyme Commission of the International Union of Biochemistry to draw up a definitive list of enzymes (the results of the attempt are given in Volume 13) raised in an acute form the question of what criteria are needed to decide whether two enzyme preparations contain the "same" enzyme. In this section we shall discuss some of the difficulties encountered.

The definition of an enzyme given on p. 1 stresses the functional aspect, and the nomenclature used in the Enzyme Commission List is a functional one, in which each name describes as clearly as possible the particular reaction catalyzed by that enzyme. Many enzymes are extremely specific, both as to substrate and as to type of reaction catalyzed, and for these naming is quite straightforward. Others can catalyze a range of reactions, and then a choice must be made; to quote the Enzyme Commission (Rule 14): "When an enzyme catalyzes more than one type of reaction or acts on more than one substrate (or pair of substrates), the name will normally refer to only one substrate (or pair of substrates) and one reaction. A general rule has not yet been found for such cases. Each must be considered on its merits, and the choice must be to some extent arbitrary. In certain cases it may be possible to use a term which covers a whole group of substrates, and this is permissible".

It is with these last-mentioned cases that difficulties arise, which may be illustrated by reference to enzymes EC 3.1.1.1 (carboxylesterase) and EC 3.1.1.2 (arylesterase). It is clear that there is a whole group of enzymes which hydrolyze esters of carboxylic acids and are fairly unspecific with regard to the alkyl and acyl groups[31]. They show small variations from one to the other in their detailed specificity patterns, for example in the optimum chain length of saturated aliphatic alkyl or acyl radical in the substrate ester. A single tissue, such as liver, may contain 3 or more esterases all able to hydrolyze the same range of substrates, but distinguishable by their relative activities with pairs of substrates, such as ethyl butyrate and phenyl acetate, or phenyl acetate and naphthyl acetate[32]. Such enzymes may sometimes also be distinguished by their response to inhibitors. The entries 3.1.1.1 and 3.1.1.2 in the Enzyme List represent generalized groupings; the first covers those enzymes, like the so-called "ali-esterase" of liver, which hydrolyze aliphatic and phenolic esters with more or less equal facility, while the latter is reserved for those enzymes which attack phenolic esters very much more efficiently than aliphatic ones. A more detailed classification would be possible only if purified, homogeneous enzyme preparations were examined with a wide range of substrates; single reactions cannot be used for the identification of such enzymes. It may be noted that the reaction given for enzyme 3.1.1.2 is carried out not only by the enzymes discussed in this paragraph, but also by the cholinesterases, chymotrypsin and glyceraldehydephosphate dehydrogenase.

When the same catalytic activity is found in a series of related living organisms, it would seem likely that it is due to similar enzymes with identical or very similar active centres, but they are not necessarily identical proteins. Enzymes from different species which are indistinguishable in their catalytic function can be shown to be different proteins in a number of ways. They may differ in crystalline form, in molecular weight, in sedimentation constant, or in solubility. Pig and ox pepsin are identical in these respects, but each can dissolve in a saturated solution of the other, so they must be different molecules. Proteins from closely related species often show quantitative differences in their reaction with an antibody to one of them prepared in a third species, and such differences in cross-reaction extend to enzymes. In this way a number of enzymes from a range of animals have been distinguished, as have urease from jack bean and soy bean, and alcohol dehydrogenase from brewer's and baker's yeast. The immunological technique is very sensitive, and the differences involved may be very small, and might be merely substitution of a few amino acid residues in an area of the protein remote from the active centre. The only enzyme for which detailed chemical information is available is ribonuclease; the enzymes from the pancreas of ox and sheep differ in only three positions in the peptide chain[33]. One of the differences is a minor one, a replacement of a threonine in ox by serine in sheep; another is more dramatic, a replacement of lysine by glutamic acid, but is at a position far from those residues believed to be in the active site. The nature of the third difference is not yet known.

It is rather more surprising to find that enzymes from different tissues of the same animal can be distinguished as proteins. Yet this has been done by the immunological method for alkaline phosphatase from human bone and intestinal mucosa; for α-amylase from pig liver and pancreas; and for phosphorylase from dog liver and muscle. Liver and muscle phosphorylases differ in a number of respects including molecular weight, vary independently in congenital diseases, and may well be produced under the influence of different genes[34]. In a larger number of cases it has not been possible to distinguish purified preparations of an enzyme from different tissues of the same species in any way.

References p. 17

By some methods of protein separation, and especially by electrophoresis on starch or agar gels, it has been possible to show that in some cases a single enzyme activity in a tissue is due to several distinct protein components. Markert and Møller[35] suggested the name "isozymes" for such groups, although many others workers have preferred the more logical form "isoenzyme". They defined these as "the different molecular forms in which proteins may exist, with the same enzymic activity". This would include the species differences which were discussed above, but workers in this field have tended to restrict the term to multiple forms in a single species, and an *ad hoc* committee of isoenzyme experts who met in New York in 1961 recommended this latter usage[36].

Isoenzymes have been conclusively demonstrated for about 30 enzymes to date; in most cases 2 to 5 forms have been found, but sometimes as many as 10 or more have been claimed. The group of isoenzymes which has received most attention is that of lactate dehydrogenase (L-lactate:NAD

TABLE II

PERCENTAGE DISTRIBUTION OF THE ISOENZYMES OF LACTATE DEHYDROGENASE IN NORMAL HUMAN TISSUES

	Isoenzyme number				
	1	*2*	*3*	*4*	*5*
Plasma	24	34	11	8	8
Heart muscle	44	48	4	2	1
Skeletal muscle	14	16	14	7	43
Liver	1	3	7	—	74
Kidney	38	32	15	—	0
Spleen	9	27	33	20	5
Lung	6	17	32	21	11

N.B. Isoenzyme number 1 represents the component with highest mobility towards the anode.

Figures represent the percentage of the total activity of the tissue recovered as each isoenzyme from starch gel.

oxidoreductase, EC 1.1.1.27). Wróblewski and his group have examined the activity of the enzyme in many human tissues in health and disease, and its electrophoretic mobility on starch gel. (For a summary of their results see Ref. 37). Five isoenzymes were detected; all are present (in low concentration) in normal blood plasma, but each tissue has a more or less characteristic distribution, and not all of the five are necessarily present. Heart muscle contains mainly isoenzymes 1 and 2; skeletal muscle a moderate level of isoenzymes 1–4, and a high level of 5; liver mainly 5; and so on (Table II). In many kinds of disease the level of this enzyme in blood plasma rises, and this has proved to be of great clinical importance, as the isoenzyme distribution in the plasma may indicate which tissue has contributed the extra activity. Thus a myocardial infarction produces a specific rise in isoenzymes 1 and 2 in the plasma.

The isoenzymes of lactate dehydrogenase can be separated in other ways, for example by chromatography on DEAE-cellulose, and are undoubtedly real entities and not artefacts. The question arises: how closely related are these proteins? They show enzymatic differences as well as physical differences, and in kinetic properties such as optimum substrate concentration, sensitivity to inhibition, thermostability etc. the five isoenzymes can be arranged in a series showing gradual changes[38]. By making elegant use of immunological techniques, Kaplan and his colleagues have shown that the isoenzymes of lactate dehydrogenase are probably formed by the combined action of two different genes[42]. In many species there are definite differences between the enzymes from heart and skeletal muscle, and these workers showed that during the development of the chick, the lactate dehydrogenase in breast muscle gradually changes from the heart type to the normal muscle type. During this transition three other forms are present which are intermediate in properties (both immunological and enzymatic) between the heart and skeletal-muscle enzymes. Both heart and muscle enzymes are composed of four identical sub-units, and the results can be explained if it is assumed that the sub-units of the two enzymes (denoted by H and M respectively) are formed under the influence of two different genes. The three intermediate forms are then hybrid enzymes which can be represented by HHHM, HHMM and HMMM, the extreme forms being HHHH and MMMM.

In the case of lactate dehydrogenase the existence of the two genes (and hence of the five isoenzymes) is probably related to the different physiological function of the enzyme in a tissue with a fairly constant metabolic load, such as heart muscle, and a tissue which has to meet sudden heavy demands for energy, such as skeletal muscle. It is not clear how many of the known examples of isoenzymes can be explained in this way. Instead of tissue differences, some groups of isoenzymes may represent differences in the enzyme from different parts of the same cell. For example, two malate dehydrogenases, with different affinities and slightly different specificities can be isolated from mammalian tissues; one is entirely located in the mitochondria, and the other in the cell sap[39].

Considerable progress has been made in studying the effect of gene mutations on the structure of certain non-enzymatic proteins such as haemoglobin, and it is to be hoped that these studies will soon be extended to enzymes which exist in multiple forms. Among other results the information obtained may help to define the minimum structures in the enzyme protein necessary for the manifestation of a particular catalytic activity.

References p. 17

4. Multi-enzyme complexes

Recent work has raised again the question: how far are purified enzymes to be regarded as separate entities pre-existing in the cell, rather than degradation products of a more complex structure?

Some of the important metabolic systems due to groups of enzymes have a limited localization in the cell. Much of the "tricarboxylic acid cycle" and other oxidation systems discussed in Volume 14 is confined to mitochondria. When mitochondria are disrupted, particles of various degrees of complexity can be prepared. A good account of these has been given by Green[40] (see also Volume 14, Chapter VI), whose school has been responsible for a good deal of the work in this field.

Mild disruption by exposure to sonic vibration produces the "electron transport particle" (ETP), which contains the complete transport chain needed for oxidation of succinate or $NADH_2$, together with the systems for coupling these oxidations to the esterification of inorganic phosphate. More drastic treatment produces non-phosphorylating particles, which can be further disrupted into particles possessing only portions of the respiratory chain. Thus a "red particle" contains a succinate dehydrogenase system but no cytochrome oxidase; but addition of a "green particle" completes the succinate oxidation system. Other particles have been prepared containing the systems for the oxidation of pyruvate or 2-oxoglutarate by NAD, which involve lipoic acid and coenzyme A.

Green has drawn attention to the fact that some of the enzymatic activities of these particles are not present in mitochondria or the ETP; he refers to this as the "opening phenomenon". It is, of course, arguable that this is merely a question of accessibility of the enzyme to substrates. The mitochondria can be regarded as containing an organized set of enzymes catalyzing a series of consecutive reactions; the intermediate metabolites pass on from one enzyme to another. Only when the mitochondria are damaged or torn apart can these intermediates exchange with similar molecules in the suspending medium.

A rather different situation has been disclosed by studies on the biological synthesis of fatty acids. One of the main pathways (though not necessarily the only one) uses malonyl-CoA as a source of two-carbon units. A widely-distributed enzyme (or enzyme system?) catalyzes the formation of one molecule of palmitoyl-CoA from one molecule of acetyl-CoA and 7 of malonyl-CoA, liberating 7 molecules of CO_2 and 7 of coenzyme A. This system has been studied by several groups in the U.S.A. and by Lynen in Munich. Lynen[41] has obtained a highly purified, homogeneous preparation from yeast which catalyzes the overall synthesis, and has called it "fatty acid synthetase". It has a molecular weight of around 2000000, and since

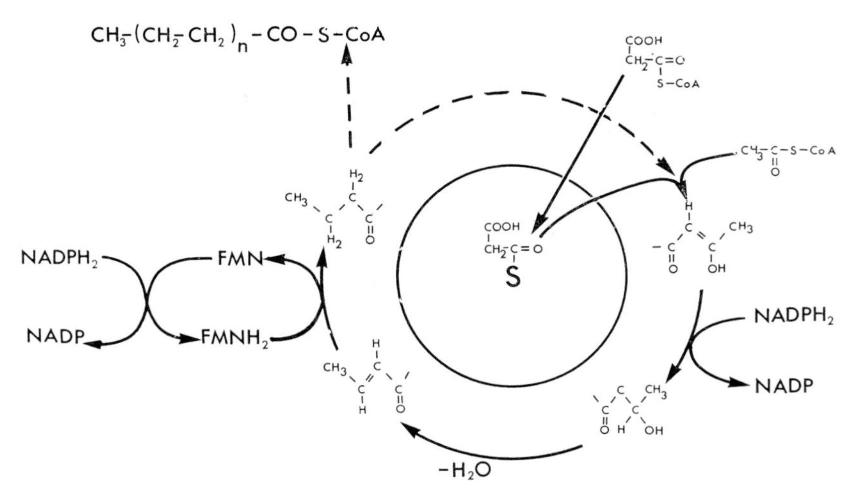

Fig. 2. Reaction scheme for the action of the "fatty acid synthetase" complex. (From Ref. 41.)

it must necessarily catalyze a series of reactions, it might be regarded as a complex of separate enzymes. However, there is good evidence that the first reaction is the transfer of a malonyl group from coenzyme A on to a thiol group on the enzyme, and that the subsequent cycles of condensation, reduction and dehydration take place with radicals covalently bound in thiolester linkage to the enzyme. The reaction sequence postulated by Lynen is shown in Fig. 2, and Fig. 3 shows a hypothetical structure for the enzyme. The acyl group attached to the central —SH group undergoes 7 cycles of reactions, catalyzed by the enzyme sub-units shown, before being

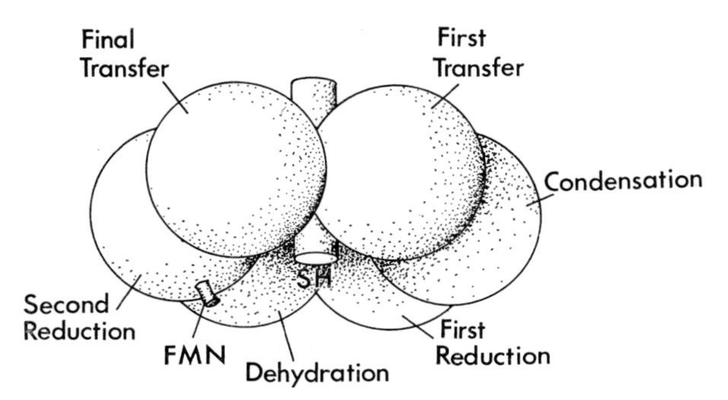

Fig. 3. A hypothetical structure for the "fatty acid synthetase" complex. The sub-units are arranged to correspond with the arrangement of the reactions in Fig. 2. The thiol group to which the substrate is bound is shown on a central "core". (From Ref. 41.)

References p. 17

transferred back to coenzyme A; the component catalyzing the final transfer is specific for acyl residues of from 14 to 20 carbons, which accounts for the predominance of fatty acids of this range in nature. The acyl group re-cycles until it is long enough to leave the enzyme. The individual reactions can be demonstrated by using analogues of the natural intermediates, *e.g.* derivatives of coenzyme A or *N*-acetylcysteamine, but the enzyme has a very low affinity for these analogues. Presumably the sub-units, if isolated, would only be able to catalyze these artificial reactions, and not the physiological one, which involves enzyme-bound intermediates; in this sense the whole complex and not the sub-units represents a single enzyme. This new concept of an enzyme system which is more than a simple addition of separate enzymes may be of great help in our understanding of biosynthesis.

REFERENCES

1 M. Dixon and E. C. Webb, *Enzymes*, Longmans, Green and Co., London, 1958.
2 H. L. Segal in P. D. Boyer, H. Lardy and K. Myrbäck (Eds.), *The Enzymes*, Vol. 1, Academic Press, New York, 1959, p. 1.
3 J. F. Berzelius, *Jahresber. Fortschr. phys. Wiss.*, 15 (1836) 237.
4 A. Payen and J. F. Persoz, *Ann. Chim. (Phys.)*, 53 (1833) 73.
5 C. O'Sullivan and F. W. Tompson, *J. Chem. Soc.*, 57 (1890) 834.
6 S. P. L. Sörensen, *Biochem. Z.*, 21 (1909) 131.
7 E. Duclaux, *Ann. Inst. Pasteur*, 12 (1898) 96.
8 A. J. Brown, *J. Chem. Soc.*, 81 (1902) 373.
9 V. Henri, *Compt. Rend.*, 135 (1902) 916; *Lois générales de l'action des diastases*, Hermann, Paris, 1903.
10 L. Michaelis and M. L. Menten, *Biochem. Z.*, 49 (1913) 333.
11 B. Woolf, quoted in J. B. S. Haldane and K. G. Stern, *Allgemeine Chemie der Enzyme*, Steinkopff, Dresden and Leipzig, 1932, p. 119.
12 H. Lineweaver and D. Burk, *J. Am. Chem. Soc.*, 56 (1934) 658.
13 B. H. J. Hofstee, *Science*, 116 (1952) 329; *Nature*, 184 (1959) 1296.
14 G. N. Wilkinson, *Biochem. J.*, 80 (1961) 324.
15 G. E. Briggs and J. B. S. Haldane, *Biochem. J.*, 19 (1925) 338.
16 B. Chance, *J. Biol. Chem.*, 151 (1943) 553.
17 *Report of the Commission on Enzymes of the International Union of Biochemistry*. Pergamon, Oxford, 1961, p. 12 (See also M. Florkin and E. H. Stotz (Eds.), *Comprehensive Biochemistry*, Vol. 13, *Nomenclature of Enzymes and Coenzymes*, revised edition of the *Report of the Commission on Enzymes of the I.U.B.*, Elsevier, Amsterdam, 1964).
18 H. L. Segal, J. F. Kachmar and P. D. Boyer, *Enzymologia*, 15 (1952) 187.
19 R. A. Alberty, *Advan. Enzymol.*, 17 (1956) 1.
20 J. Botts, *Trans. Faraday Soc.*, 54 (1958) 593.
21 E. L. King and C. Altman, *J. Phys. Chem.*, 60 (1956) 1375.
22 J. Z. Hearon, S. A. Bernhard, S. L. Friess, D. J. Botts and M. F. Morales, in P. D. Boyer, H. Lardy and K. Myrbäck (Eds.), *The Enzymes*, Vol. 1, Academic Press, New York, 1959, p. 49.
23 J. B. Sumner, *J. Biol. Chem.*, 69 (1926) 435.
24 J. H. Northrop, M. Kunitz and R. M. Herriott, *Crystalline Enzymes*, 2nd ed., Columbia University Press, New York, 1948.
25 F. Binkley, *J. Biol. Chem.*, 236 (1961) 735.
26 D. G. Smyth, W. H. Stein and S. Moore, *J. Biol. Chem.*, 238 (1963) 227.
27 F. M. Richards and P. J. Vithayathil, *J. Biol. Chem.*, 234 (1959) 1459.
28 D. E. Koshland, *Advan. Enzymol.*, 22 (1960) 45.
29 E. A. Barnard and W. D. Stein, *Advan. Enzymol.*, 20 (1958) 51.
30 M. Dixon, *Discussions Faraday Soc.*, 20 (1955) 9.
31 B. H. J. Hofstee, in P. D. Boyer, H. Lardy and K. Myrbäck (Eds.), *The Enzymes*, Vol. 4, Academic Press, New York, 1960, p. 485.
32 R. J. Kirkland and E. C. Webb, unpublished observations (1962).
33 C. B. Anfinsen, S. E. G. Åqvist, J. P. Cooke and B. Jönsson, *J. Biol. Chem.*, 234 (1959) 1118.
34 N. Kretchmer, *Proc. Intern. Congr. Clin. Chem., 4th, Edinburgh, 1960*, Livingstone, Edinburgh, 1961, p. 101.
35 C. L. Markert and F. Møller, *Proc. Natl. Acad. Sci., U.S.*, 45 (1959) 753.
36 *Proceedings of the Conference on Multiple Molecular Forms of Enzymes*, New York Academy of Sciences Publication, 1961.
37 F. Wróblewski and K. Gregory, *Proc. Intern. Congr. Clin. Chem., 4th, Edinburgh, 1960*, Livingstone, Edinburgh, 1961, p. 62.
38 B. Hess and S. Walter, *Klin. Wochschr.*, 38 (1960) 1080; 39 (1961) 213.
39 C. J. R. Thorne, *Biochim. Biophys. Acta*, 42 (1960) 175.
40 D. E. Green, *Advan. Enzymol.*, 21 (1959) 73.
41 F. Lynen, *Federation Proc.*, 20 (1961) 941.
42 R. Cahn, N. O. Kaplan, L. Levine and E. Zwilling, *Science*, 136 (1962) 962.

Chapter II

Equilibrium and Thermodynamic Considerations

R. WURMSER AND R. BANERJEE

Institut de Biologie Physico-Chimique, University of Paris (France)

1. Introduction

The purpose of this Chapter is to state some basic principles of thermodynamics and describe ways in which they can become useful tools for the biochemist.

A living cell is the site of continuous physical and chemical changes most of which involve the transformation of energy from one form to another. The system loses energy in many ways: by performing mechanical work, through loss of thermal, chemical and sometimes even of electrical and radiant energy. The intake of energy should not only balance such losses, but should be in excess in the case of growing organisms. The biologist's interest in thermodynamics arises from the possibilities it offers to an understanding of such energy relations.

Laws of thermodynamics tell us whether a given transformation would occur or not, spontaneously or by virtue of its being linked with some energetic process. The laws of thermodynamics can predict whether a given change is energetically possible or not, but little about how it may take place. They have nevertheless served as powerful tools in the study of mechanisms. When a chain of real or supposed events can be described between an effect and its cause, thermodynamic laws can be applied to each of them. Particularly useful examples of such applications in biochemistry are furnished by the theories of intermediary metabolism.

The theory of absolute reaction rates links chemical kinetics to thermodynamics. If one admits that the rate of a reaction depends on a universal constant governing the rate of decomposition of an intermediary (activated) complex, and that this complex is in equilibrium with the initial system, reaction kinetics then become governed by the thermodynamics of this equilibrium.

REFERENCES

1 M. Dixon and E. C. Webb, *Enzymes*, Longmans, Green and Co., London, 1958.
2 H. L. Segal in P. D. Boyer, H. Lardy and K. Myrbäck (Eds.), *The Enzymes*, Vol. 1, Academic Press, New York, 1959, p. 1.
3 J. F. Berzelius, *Jahresber. Fortschr. phys. Wiss.*, 15 (1836) 237.
4 A. Payen and J. F. Persoz, *Ann. Chim. (Phys.)*, 53 (1833) 73.
5 C. O'Sullivan and F. W. Tompson, *J. Chem. Soc.*, 57 (1890) 834.
6 S. P. L. Sörensen, *Biochem. Z.*, 21 (1909) 131.
7 E. Duclaux, *Ann. Inst. Pasteur*, 12 (1898) 96.
8 A. J. Brown, *J. Chem. Soc.*, 81 (1902) 373.
9 V. Henri, *Compt. Rend.*, 135 (1902) 916; *Lois générales de l'action des diastases*, Hermann, Paris, 1903.
10 L. Michaelis and M. L. Menten, *Biochem. Z.*, 49 (1913) 333.
11 B. Woolf, quoted in J. B. S. Haldane and K. G. Stern, *Allgemeine Chemie der Enzyme*, Steinkopff, Dresden and Leipzig, 1932, p. 119.
12 H. Lineweaver and D. Burk, *J. Am. Chem. Soc.*, 56 (1934) 658.
13 B. H. J. Hofstee, *Science*, 116 (1952) 329; *Nature*, 184 (1959) 1296.
14 G. N. Wilkinson, *Biochem. J.*, 80 (1961) 324.
15 G. E. Briggs and J. B. S. Haldane, *Biochem. J.*, 19 (1925) 338.
16 B. Chance, *J. Biol. Chem.*, 151 (1943) 553.
17 *Report of the Commission on Enzymes of the International Union of Biochemistry*. Pergamon, Oxford, 1961, p. 12 (See also M. Florkin and E. H. Stotz (Eds.), *Comprehensive Biochemistry*, Vol. 13, *Nomenclature of Enzymes and Coenzymes*, revised edition of the *Report of the Commission on Enzymes of the I.U.B.*, Elsevier, Amsterdam, 1964).
18 H. L. Segal, J. F. Kachmar and P. D. Boyer, *Enzymologia*, 15 (1952) 187.
19 R. A. Alberty, *Advan. Enzymol.*, 17 (1956) 1.
20 J. Botts, *Trans. Faraday Soc.*, 54 (1958) 593.
21 E. L. King and C. Altman, *J. Phys. Chem.*, 60 (1956) 1375.
22 J. Z. Hearon, S. A. Bernhard, S. L. Friess, D. J. Botts and M. F. Morales, in P. D. Boyer, H. Lardy and K. Myrbäck (Eds.), *The Enzymes*, Vol. 1, Academic Press, New York, 1959, p. 49.
23 J. B. Sumner, *J. Biol. Chem.*, 69 (1926) 435.
24 J. H. Northrop, M. Kunitz and R. M. Herriott, *Crystalline Enzymes*, 2nd ed., Columbia University Press, New York, 1948.
25 F. Binkley, *J. Biol. Chem.*, 236 (1961) 735.
26 D. G. Smyth, W. H. Stein and S. Moore, *J. Biol. Chem.*, 238 (1963) 227.
27 F. M. Richards and P. J. Vithayathil, *J. Biol. Chem.*, 234 (1959) 1459.
28 D. E. Koshland, *Advan. Enzymol.*, 22 (1960) 45.
29 E. A. Barnard and W. D. Stein, *Advan. Enzymol.*, 20 (1958) 51.
30 M. Dixon, *Discussions Faraday Soc.*, 20 (1955) 9.
31 B. H. J. Hofstee, in P. D. Boyer, H. Lardy and K. Myrbäck (Eds.), *The Enzymes*, Vol. 4, Academic Press, New York, 1960, p. 485.
32 R. J. Kirkland and E. C. Webb, unpublished observations (1962).
33 C. B. Anfinsen, S. E. G. Åqvist, J. P. Cooke and B. Jönsson, *J. Biol. Chem.*, 234 (1959) 1118.
34 N. Kretchmer, *Proc. Intern. Congr. Clin. Chem., 4th, Edinburgh, 1960*, Livingstone, Edinburgh, 1961, p. 101.
35 C. L. Markert and F. Møller, *Proc. Natl. Acad. Sci., U.S.*, 45 (1959) 753.
36 *Proceedings of the Conference on Multiple Molecular Forms of Enzymes*, New York Academy of Sciences Publication, 1961.
37 F. Wróblewski and K. Gregory, *Proc. Intern. Congr. Clin. Chem., 4th, Edinburgh, 1960*, Livingstone, Edinburgh, 1961, p. 62.
38 B. Hess and S. Walter, *Klin. Wochschr.*, 38 (1960) 1080; 39 (1961) 213.
39 C. J. R. Thorne, *Biochim. Biophys. Acta*, 42 (1960) 175.
40 D. E. Green, *Advan. Enzymol.*, 21 (1959) 73.
41 F. Lynen, *Federation Proc.*, 20 (1961) 941.
42 R. Cahn, N. O. Kaplan, L. Levine and E. Zwilling, *Science*, 136 (1962) 962.

Chapter II

Equilibrium and Thermodynamic Considerations

R. WURMSER AND R. BANERJEE

Institut de Biologie Physico-Chimique, University of Paris (France)

1. Introduction

The purpose of this Chapter is to state some basic principles of thermodynamics and describe ways in which they can become useful tools for the biochemist.

A living cell is the site of continuous physical and chemical changes most of which involve the transformation of energy from one form to another. The system loses energy in many ways: by performing mechanical work, through loss of thermal, chemical and sometimes even of electrical and radiant energy. The intake of energy should not only balance such losses, but should be in excess in the case of growing organisms. The biologist's interest in thermodynamics arises from the possibilities it offers to an understanding of such energy relations.

Laws of thermodynamics tell us whether a given transformation would occur or not, spontaneously or by virtue of its being linked with some energetic process. The laws of thermodynamics can predict whether a given change is energetically possible or not, but little about how it may take place. They have nevertheless served as powerful tools in the study of mechanisms. When a chain of real or supposed events can be described between an effect and its cause, thermodynamic laws can be applied to each of them. Particularly useful examples of such applications in biochemistry are furnished by the theories of intermediary metabolism.

The theory of absolute reaction rates links chemical kinetics to thermodynamics. If one admits that the rate of a reaction depends on a universal constant governing the rate of decomposition of an intermediary (activated) complex, and that this complex is in equilibrium with the initial system, reaction kinetics then become governed by the thermodynamics of this equilibrium.

REFERENCES

[1] M. Dixon and E. C. Webb, *Enzymes*, Longmans, Green and Co., London, 1958.
[2] H. L. Segal in P. D. Boyer, H. Lardy and K. Myrbäck (Eds.), *The Enzymes*, Vol. 1, Academic Press, New York, 1959, p. 1.
[3] J. F. Berzelius, *Jahresber. Fortschr. phys. Wiss.*, 15 (1836) 237.
[4] A. Payen and J. F. Persoz, *Ann. Chim. (Phys.)*, 53 (1833) 73.
[5] C. O'Sullivan and F. W. Tompson, *J. Chem. Soc.*, 57 (1890) 834.
[6] S. P. L. Sörensen, *Biochem. Z.*, 21 (1909) 131.
[7] E. Duclaux, *Ann. Inst. Pasteur*, 12 (1898) 96.
[8] A. J. Brown, *J. Chem. Soc.*, 81 (1902) 373.
[9] V. Henri, *Compt. Rend.*, 135 (1902) 916; *Lois générales de l'action des diastases*, Hermann, Paris, 1903.
[10] L. Michaelis and M. L. Menten, *Biochem. Z.*, 49 (1913) 333.
[11] B. Woolf, quoted in J. B. S. Haldane and K. G. Stern, *Allgemeine Chemie der Enzyme*, Steinkopff, Dresden and Leipzig, 1932, p. 119.
[12] H. Lineweaver and D. Burk, *J. Am. Chem. Soc.*, 56 (1934) 658.
[13] B. H. J. Hofstee, *Science*, 116 (1952) 329; *Nature*, 184 (1959) 1296.
[14] G. N. Wilkinson, *Biochem. J.*, 80 (1961) 324.
[15] G. E. Briggs and J. B. S. Haldane, *Biochem. J.*, 19 (1925) 338.
[16] B. Chance, *J. Biol. Chem.*, 151 (1943) 553.
[17] *Report of the Commission on Enzymes of the International Union of Biochemistry*. Pergamon, Oxford, 1961, p. 12 (See also M. Florkin and E. H. Stotz (Eds.), *Comprehensive Biochemistry*, Vol. 13, *Nomenclature of Enzymes and Coenzymes*, revised edition of the *Report of the Commission on Enzymes of the I.U.B.*, Elsevier, Amsterdam, 1964).
[18] H. L. Segal, J. F. Kachmar and P. D. Boyer, *Enzymologia*, 15 (1952) 187.
[19] R. A. Alberty, *Advan. Enzymol.*, 17 (1956) 1.
[20] J. Botts, *Trans. Faraday Soc.*, 54 (1958) 593.
[21] E. L. King and C. Altman, *J. Phys. Chem.*, 60 (1956) 1375.
[22] J. Z. Hearon, S. A. Bernhard, S. L. Friess, D. J. Botts and M. F. Morales, in P. D. Boyer, H. Lardy and K. Myrbäck (Eds.), *The Enzymes*, Vol. 1, Academic Press, New York, 1959, p. 49.
[23] J. B. Sumner, *J. Biol. Chem.*, 69 (1926) 435.
[24] J. H. Northrop, M. Kunitz and R. M. Herriott, *Crystalline Enzymes*, 2nd ed., Columbia University Press, New York, 1948.
[25] F. Binkley, *J. Biol. Chem.*, 236 (1961) 735.
[26] D. G. Smyth, W. H. Stein and S. Moore, *J. Biol. Chem.*, 238 (1963) 227.
[27] F. M. Richards and P. J. Vithayathil, *J. Biol. Chem.*, 234 (1959) 1459.
[28] D. E. Koshland, *Advan. Enzymol.*, 22 (1960) 45.
[29] E. A. Barnard and W. D. Stein, *Advan. Enzymol.*, 20 (1958) 51.
[30] M. Dixon, *Discussions Faraday Soc.*, 20 (1955) 9.
[31] B. H. J. Hofstee, in P. D. Boyer, H. Lardy and K. Myrbäck (Eds.), *The Enzymes*, Vol. 4, Academic Press, New York, 1960, p. 485.
[32] R. J. Kirkland and E. C. Webb, unpublished observations (1962).
[33] C. B. Anfinsen, S. E. G. Åqvist, J. P. Cooke and B. Jönsson, *J. Biol. Chem.*, 234 (1959) 1118.
[34] N. Kretchmer, *Proc. Intern. Congr. Clin. Chem., 4th, Edinburgh, 1960*, Livingstone, Edinburgh, 1961, p. 101.
[35] C. L. Markert and F. Møller, *Proc. Natl. Acad. Sci., U.S.*, 45 (1959) 753.
[36] *Proceedings of the Conference on Multiple Molecular Forms of Enzymes*, New York Academy of Sciences Publication, 1961.
[37] F. Wróblewski and K. Gregory, *Proc. Intern. Congr. Clin. Chem., 4th, Edinburgh, 1960*, Livingstone, Edinburgh, 1961, p. 62.
[38] B. Hess and S. Walter, *Klin. Wochschr.*, 38 (1960) 1080; 39 (1961) 213.
[39] C. J. R. Thorne, *Biochim. Biophys. Acta*, 42 (1960) 175.
[40] D. E. Green, *Advan. Enzymol.*, 21 (1959) 73.
[41] F. Lynen, *Federation Proc.*, 20 (1961) 941.
[42] R. Cahn, N. O. Kaplan, L. Levine and E. Zwilling, *Science*, 136 (1962) 962.

Chapter II

Equilibrium and Thermodynamic Considerations

R. WURMSER AND R. BANERJEE

Institut de Biologie Physico-Chimique, University of Paris (France)

1. Introduction

The purpose of this Chapter is to state some basic principles of thermodynamics and describe ways in which they can become useful tools for the biochemist.

A living cell is the site of continuous physical and chemical changes most of which involve the transformation of energy from one form to another. The system loses energy in many ways: by performing mechanical work, through loss of thermal, chemical and sometimes even of electrical and radiant energy. The intake of energy should not only balance such losses, but should be in excess in the case of growing organisms. The biologist's interest in thermodynamics arises from the possibilities it offers to an understanding of such energy relations.

Laws of thermodynamics tell us whether a given transformation would occur or not, spontaneously or by virtue of its being linked with some energetic process. The laws of thermodynamics can predict whether a given change is energetically possible or not, but little about how it may take place. They have nevertheless served as powerful tools in the study of mechanisms. When a chain of real or supposed events can be described between an effect and its cause, thermodynamic laws can be applied to each of them. Particularly useful examples of such applications in biochemistry are furnished by the theories of intermediary metabolism.

The theory of absolute reaction rates links chemical kinetics to thermodynamics. If one admits that the rate of a reaction depends on a universal constant governing the rate of decomposition of an intermediary (activated) complex, and that this complex is in equilibrium with the initial system, reaction kinetics then become governed by the thermodynamics of this equilibrium.

Notable developments in modern enzymology are fruits of this conception.

Moreover, the notion that reaction rate constants near equilibrium should be amenable to treatment by equations valid at equilibrium states has led to the development of what is known as the thermodynamics of irreversible processes; the latter has found applications in the study of autoregulation of stationary states which is so typical of life processes.

The progress of theoretical chemistry has, on the other hand, contributed to widening the scope of thermodynamic methods. Wave mechanics permit an understanding of thermodynamic parameters in terms of molecular structure. While it is true that this has till now been realized only for very simple molecules, this opens nevertheless new perspectives which might one day interest the biochemist.

The aim of the following pages is not to review the applications of thermodynamics to biochemistry or enzymology, but rather to enable the student of biochemistry to handle the current concepts and methods. The fundamental laws of thermodynamics have therefore been stated and, wherever possible, illustrated.

2. The first law of thermodynamics: energy

We are accustomed intuitively to associate a system, for example a given volume of gas under defined conditions, with a definite amount of internal energy. Should the system undergo change, any loss or gain of its internal energy is, according to the first law, equal to the gain or loss of energy by the environment. The change may involve the transfer of heat and also work of any kind (pressure–volume, osmotic, electrical etc.) performed by or upon the system. The first law takes the mathematical form

$$U_2 - U_1 = \Delta U = q - w \qquad (1)$$

where q is the heat *absorbed* by the system and w the work *done* by the system on the environment, U_1 and U_2 being the internal-energy contents of the system before and after the transformation.

When the work term involves only pressure–volume work (mechanical),

$$w = \int_{V_1}^{V_2} P\mathrm{d}V$$

For a change at constant pressure, the relation (1) may be written in the form

$$q = U_2 - U_1 + P(V_2 - V_1) = (U_2 + PV_2) - (U_1 + PV_1) \qquad (2)$$

The quantity $(U + PV)$ is a function of the state of the system and is called the enthalpy or heat content, H. One may write in a general way, including chemical transformations

References p. 60

$$\Delta H = \Delta U + \Delta(PV) \tag{3}$$

The enthalpy change $-\Delta H$ is synonymous with the heat of reaction at constant pressure. In cases where the work term (here $\Delta(PV)$) disappears, for example in the case of a reaction taking place in a bomb calorimeter at constant volume and temperature, the enthalpy change is equal to the internal-energy change ΔU.

Among the events likely to change the internal energy of a system are: change in the state of intra- and intermolecular bonds, change of temperature, introduction or extraction of material from the system. Let us for the moment omit the last two possibilities; the system is at constant temperature and we do not modify the capacity factor. The change of internal energy due to rearrangement of chemical bonds is the difference between the sum of the effects of the new bonds formed and that of the bonds ruptured. This difference, *i.e.* the heat of reaction at constant pressure and at a given temperature represents the sum of two components, namely chemical and thermal.

The chemical component corresponds to ΔH_0, the heat of reaction one would have measured if the reaction could take place at absolute zero. It depends on the difference of the bond energies which are essentially electronic and that of the energies associated with the residual vibrations of the nuclei at absolute zero.

The thermal component of the heat of reaction at a given temperature is due to change in that part of energy represented by translational movements, rotations and vibrations. The amount of heat required to bring the products of reaction from absolute zero to a temperature T may be different from that required by the reactants since the reaction is supposed to have given rise to new molecules and new bonds with different translational, rotational and oscillatory characteristics. The magnitude of this difference determines how far the heat capacities of the products would be different from that of the reactants.

The heat of reaction thus becomes temperature-dependent when it comprises a thermal-energy component.

$$\left(\frac{\partial H}{\partial T}\right)_p = \Delta C_p \tag{4}$$

where ΔC_p is the sum of the heat capacities of the products less the corresponding sum for the reactants.

The heat of reaction at temperature T is thus the sum of ΔH_0 (heat of reaction at absolute zero) and of

$$\int_0^T \Delta C_p \, \mathrm{d}T$$

(a) *Measure of the heat of a reaction*

An obvious method is of course direct experimental determination with the help of a microcalorimeter. Reactions of biochemical interest followed this way are so far rather few; some notable exceptions will be referred to later in this Chapter.

Another experimental procedure applicable to reversible reactions consists in measuring the equilibrium constant at different temperatures and deducing ΔH therefrom. The principle of this method will be discussed later.

In certain cases it is possible to take recourse to thermochemical data. This procedure is based on the principle that changes of internal energy or heat content due to a transformation are governed solely by the final and initial states of the system and not by the way in which the final state is attained. The heat of a reaction at constant pressure can thus be deduced from the heats of formation at constant pressure of participants in the reaction.

The heat of formation of a substance is the quantity of heat evolved in the synthesis of a mole of the substance starting from the constitutive elements taken in their standard states. The standard reference state is the form of the element which is the most stable at room temperature and 1 atm pressure. In principle, for real gases the reference state is at zero pressure, but the heat content is practically the same at 1 atm. The heat of a reaction

$$\mathrm{AB} + \mathrm{CD} \rightarrow \mathrm{AC} + \mathrm{BD}$$

is equal to the sum of the heats of formation

$$\mathrm{A} + \mathrm{C} \rightarrow \mathrm{AC} \qquad (H_{\mathrm{AC}})$$

and

$$\mathrm{B} + \mathrm{D} \rightarrow \mathrm{BD} \qquad (H_{\mathrm{BD}})$$

minus the sum of the heats of formation

$$\mathrm{A} + \mathrm{B} \rightarrow \mathrm{AB} \qquad (H_{\mathrm{AB}})$$

and

$$\mathrm{C} + \mathrm{D} \rightarrow \mathrm{CD} \qquad (H_{\mathrm{CD}})$$

$$\Delta H = (H_{\mathrm{AC}} + H_{\mathrm{BD}}) - (H_{\mathrm{AB}} + H_{\mathrm{CD}}) \qquad (5)$$

Generally, the heats of formation themselves cannot be determined directly. They are then calculated, by applying the same principles as above, from the heats of combustion and the heats of formation of the combustion products.

(b) *Chemical energy from structural data*

The chemical energy associated with a given bond, say between two atoms

References p. 60

A and B, is equal and opposite in sign to the total energy one has to spend in dissociating AB. This energy is entirely electrostatic in nature, since it corresponds to coulombic, covalent or Van der Waals' attractions, depending on the nature of the bond.

It is possible in principle to calculate the chemical energy from structural data. Attractions between opposite charges or dipoles are calculated by applying Coulomb's equation; the contributions of covalent bonds and Van der Waals' forces have in some simple cases been evaluated with the help of quantum mechanics. Complete calculation of all parameters have been made only in the case of the hydrogen molecule. Some compounds of biological interest have recently been treated[1] sufficiently enough to be of use to the biochemist.

In practice, some use is made of bond-energy tables. Estimates of bond energy are obtained from thermochemical and sometimes from spectroscopic data and are usually given for covalent bonds, assuming the equivalence of similar bonds, say the four C–H bonds in methane. Since enthalpy data at 25°C and not 0°K are used for these calculations, the values include not only the energies of dissociation at absolute zero (ΔH_0 used earlier in this Chapter) but also terms corresponding to the rotational, oscillational and translational energy of the molecules and a pressure–volume term. Such bond-energy values, say between atoms A and B, would represent the heat of atomization of AB in the ideal gas state at 298.16°K to the atomic elements in their ground state at this temperature.

Values from bond-energy tables may be used to calculate the heats of formation of molecules to which a single valence-bond structure may be assigned; these agree reasonably well with the experimental results. Similar calculations for certain other types of molecules result, however, in discrepancies, the experimental values being always higher than those calculated on a simple additivity principle. This extra energy corresponds to *resonance energy* in the case of molecules having so-called resonating structures; these are molecules to which no unambiguous valence-bond structures may be assigned, some electrons being supposed to be delocalized. Energy calculations in such cases are facilitated by considering two or more possible electronic configurations said to be resonating between one another. For detailed discussion the reader is referred to Pauling[2].

3. The second law

The essential features of the second law of thermodynamics are expressed in the statement that any system left to itself changes in such a way as to approach, rapidly or slowly, a definite state of rest. This state of rest is also called the state of equilibrium.

When a system is in a state of equilibrium its properties do not change with time if it is mechanically and thermally isolated. These conditions differentiate equilibrium from a steady state. But a system can be in equilibrium without being isolated; in such a case the external forces acting upon it should compensate one another and no heat should be taken from or given to the system by the environment.

(a) *Reversible and irreversible processes*

Some natural processes tending towards their state of equilibrium are familiar: diffusion of material from a concentrated solution to a dilute one resulting in uniformity of concentration, passage of heat from one body to another leading to uniformity of temperature, etc. Such natural phenomena are *irreversible* in the sense that any system undergoing such a change is thereby losing in some manner its capacity for spontaneous change; it is impossible to restore the system to its original state except by furnishing energy from another system which suffers a loss in its own capacity of spontaneous change.

One can, however, conceive of certain processes in which the system can be restored to its initial state without more than an infinitesimal expenditure of energy or change in external conditions. These are *reversible* processes, which though not actually realizable, are nevertheless imaginable.

A mixture of water, ester, acid and alcohol in fixed proportions contained in a closed thermostated vessel may be considered. The system is in equilibrium. Suppose a slight disturbance is produced in external conditions determining the equilibrium: an infinitesimal change of temperature of the thermostat surrounding our multicomponent chemical mixture. The mixture suffers a very slight change in chemical composition. When, however, one restores the initial external conditions, the system returns to its initial state.

Imagine now that instead of restoring the initial conditions we continue to modify them by small steps in the same direction. The system passes through a continuum of equilibrium states; the modification is a reversible process. It is seen that such reversible processes are *ideal* ones and may be considered as the limit of actually realizable processes. In the former there is no *degradation* of the system as a whole whereas in the latter the system may be said to have degraded to a more or less extent; it is implied that processes may differ in the degree of irreversibility.

(b) *Entropy*

A convenient quantitative measure of the extent of irreversibility of a process is furnished by a property called entropy.

References p. 60

Consider the passage of a system from state 1 to state 2 at a constant temperature T; the passage may be reversible or irreversible. In the first case, if the system is returned reversibly to its original state 1, the *total* entropy change dS of the cycle is zero. In the second case, the total entropy change will have a positive value; the magnitude of this value is higher as the irreversibility of the passage from 1 to 2, or in other words, the degradation of energy in course of this passage, becomes greater. This degradation is manifested by an excess of heat q_{12} evolved during the irreversible phase $1 \rightarrow 2$ over that q_{21} absorbed during the reversible return $2 \rightarrow 1$. But corresponding to the fact the transfer of heat from a higher to a lower temperature is an irreversible process, it is not $(q_{12} - q_{21})$ but $(q_{12} - q_{21})/T$ which measures the degree of irreversibility. The quantity

$$\frac{q_{12} - q_{21}}{T} = \frac{q'}{T}$$

is the production of entropy in the irreversible process $1 \rightarrow 2$.

(c) *Statistical interpretation of entropy*

The second law is in fact a statistical law and can be visualized from a molecular kinetic point of view. The drift of a macroscopic system towards its state of rest reflects the fact that the molecules constituting the system acquire velocities or positions and suffer internal modifications in a manner that the disorder on a molecular or intramolecular level becomes maximum. One feels intuitively that this disorder corresponds to a state of higher probability than one where the molecules would be behaving in an ordered restricted fashion. The spontaneous degradation of a system then means a constant change to states of higher and higher probability. Since the evolution of a system towards its most probable state (equilibrium) is accompanied by the production of entropy, entropy should then be related in some manner with probability. This is expressed by the Boltzman relation:

$$S = \kappa \ln W \tag{6}$$

where W is the possible number of states of the system, κ is the Boltzman constant. At equilibrium *i.e.* the state of highest probability, W should have the maximum value.

The evaluation of entropy from the molecular kinetic point of view would thus consist essentially in finding the conditions in which W of a system may be maximum, consistent with its energy and volume. The considerations that follow are guided mainly by this concern.

Consider the system composed of N molecules and characterized by a total internal energy U. These molecules are different from each other in their individual energy contents. The latter comprises the translational and rotational energies as well as the internal energy. The internal energy itself includes the energy associated with atomic vibrations, with the rotation of groups of atoms, and the electronic energy. All these energies, including the translational energy, are quantified. One may therefore consider for each of them certain energy states $\varepsilon_1, \varepsilon_2, \ldots$ respectively populated by $N_1, N_2, \ldots$ molecules. The sum $\Sigma \varepsilon_i N_i$ represents the total thermal energy U. Note that the energies ε_i are computed in excess of the energy at absolute zero.

W, the possible number of complexions of the system, is the number of ways in which the N molecules may be distributed by permutation in various energy levels. This number has been calculated by each of several statistical methods.

In the classical Maxwell–Boltzman theory,

$$W = \frac{N!}{N_1! N_2! \ldots} \tag{7}$$

The argument is the same which serves to calculate the number of ways in which N mutually distinguishable balls can be placed in a certain number of urns.

The statistics thus takes account of the permutation of molecules occupying the same energy level (the balls in the same urn are different from each other). In quantum statistics, on the contrary, molecules having the same energy are considered indiscernable from each other. Different structures are however admitted for the same energy, g_i the number of structures for the energy state ε_i being called its specific weight or its order of degeneration. Taking due account of these restrictions, one obtains the expression

$$\ln W = \sum_i (N_i \ln g_i - N_i \ln N_i + N_i) \tag{8}$$

Now, in order to know how the system is constituted in its most probable state, it is necessary to calculate the values of $N_1, N_2 \ldots$ etc. corresponding to a state where W is maximum. Calculation of variation deals with this sort of problem. Finally one obtains

$$\underset{\substack{\text{number of molecules in the}\\ \text{energy state } \varepsilon_i}}{N_i} = N \frac{g_i \cdot \mathrm{e}^{-\beta \varepsilon_i}}{Q} \tag{9}$$

where Q is equal to the sum $\Sigma g_i \cdot \mathrm{e}^{-\beta \varepsilon_i}$ and is designated by the name *sum of states* or *total partition function*, β is a constant which can be shown to

References p. 60

be equal to $1/\kappa T$. We have then

$$Q = \sum_i g_i \cdot e^{-\varepsilon_i/\kappa T} \tag{10}$$

The total partition function is composite and is made up of the contributions of respectively translational (tr), vibrational (v), rotational (r) and electronic (e) partition functions.

$$Q = Q_{tr} \times Q_r \times Q_v \times Q_e$$

Keeping in mind the most probable distribution of N molecules in their different energy levels one obtains

$$S = \kappa N \ln \frac{Q}{N} + \kappa NT \left(\frac{\partial \ln Q}{\partial T}\right)_v + \kappa N \tag{11}$$

Since the energies ε_i represent those in excess of the energy at absolute zero,

$$U - U_0 = N \Sigma\, \varepsilon_i$$

Hence, entropy per mole

$$S = R \ln \frac{Q}{N} + \frac{U - U_0}{T} + R \tag{12}$$

where U_0 is the energy which molecules possess at absolute zero (zero-point energy); this energy is constant so long as the molecules do not undergo chemical transformations; $U - U_0$ is the thermal energy of the system. Since $PV = RT$ for a perfect gas, one obtains

$$S = R \ln \frac{Q}{N} + \frac{H - H_0}{T} \tag{12a}$$

Note that for a reversible *physical* transformation at constant temperature, *i.e.* one which does not affect the zero-point energy, Eqn. (12a) becomes

$$dS = R \, d \ln \frac{Q}{N} \frac{dH}{T} \tag{12b}$$

4. The third law; absolute measure of entropy

The essence of the third law of thermodynamics is contained in the expression (12a). At absolute zero, when the system contains no thermal energy, the term $(H - H_0)/T$ disappears. The entropy is simply equal to $R \ln (Q/N)$.

At absolute zero all the constituent particles of the system fall into their lowest quantum states. The entropy is given by

$$S_0 = R \ln g_0 \cdot e^{-0} = R \ln g_0$$

If the system can exist in only one configuration, $g_0 = 1$, and the entropy is zero. This is the case of perfect crystals where only one configuration is admitted for the lowest quantum state. There are cases however, where the lowest quantum state might correspond to more than one structure, so that there exists a residual entropy even at absolute zero. If, for example, two structures are admitted, entropy at absolute zero $S_0 = R \ln 2$. Eqn. (12a) is the basis of a method for the measure of the entropy of a substance through measure of specific heat.

Experimental measure of entropy

The relation $dS = dq/T$, valid for any reversible process may be applied to the case of a substance at absolute zero gradually absorbing heat so as to raise the temperature to a value T.

If the absorption of heat takes place at constant pressure,

$$S_T = S_0 + \int_0^T C_p \frac{dT}{T} \tag{13}$$

where C_p is the specific heat at constant pressure.

It is then possible to evaluate $S_T - S_0$ experimentally by measuring the specific heats at constant pressure at different temperatures down to as near to absolute zero as possible and then integrating from temperature 0 to T. For graphical computation it is convenient to express the integral $\int_0^T C_p \, dT/T$ in the form $\int_0^T C_p \, d \ln T$. If any change of state or crystallographic transition occurs between temperatures 0 and T, one should of course take account of the corresponding heats of transition, so that

$$S_T = S_0 + \int_0^T C_p \, d \ln T + \Sigma \frac{\Delta H_i}{T_i} \tag{13a}$$

where ΔH_i is the heat of transition i taking place at temperature T_i.

As examples of the applications of this method may be cited the determination of the entropy of graphite and that of gaseous oxygen. The former does not involve transitions; oxygen on the other hand has three different solid modifications in addition to the liquid and gaseous states. Fig. 1 shows the atomic heat capacity of graphite plotted against log T. The difference of

References p. 60

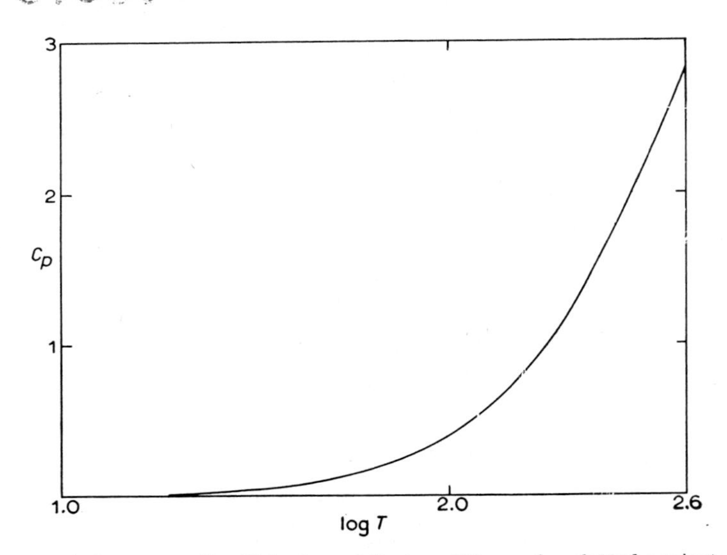

Fig. 1. Atomic heat capacity (C_p) of graphite in cal/deg·mole, plotted against log T. Data of W. DE SORBO AND W. W. TYLER, *J. Chem. Phys.*, 21 (1953) 1660, as represented in G. N. LEWIS AND M. RANDALL, *Thermodynamics*, 2nd ed., McGraw-Hill, New York, 1961.

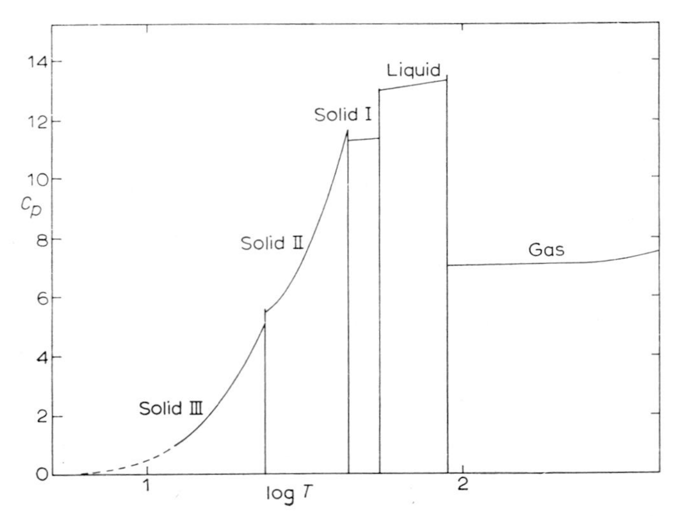

Fig. 2. Plot of molal heat capacity of oxygen against log T. The areas in the graph correspond to terms in the entropy calculation. Data of W. F. GIAUQUE AND H. L. JOHNSTON, *J. Am. Chem. Soc.*, 51 (1929) 2300, as represented in G. N. LEWIS AND M. RANDALL, *Thermodynamics*, 2nd ed., McGraw-Hill, New York, 1961.

entropy between 298°K (log $T = 2.47$) and 0°K is obtained from the area under the curve between log $T = 0$ and log $T = 2.47$ and multiplying by 2.303. One obtains $S_{298} = 1.37$ cal/deg.

The same method applied to oxygen gives heat capacity curves as shown in Fig. 2. The different solid forms have specific heats different from each other. The heats of transition between solid modifications, the heat of fusion and the heat of vaporization (corresponding to the terms $\Sigma\ (\Delta H_i/T_i)$ in Eqn. (13a) have been determined. The entropy is calculated as in Table I.

The entropy of oxygen at higher temperatures for example at 298°K may be readily obtained from the specific heat of the gas.

TABLE I

THE ENTROPY OF GASEOUS OXYGEN

0–14°K, extrapolation	0.54
14–23.66°K, solid III, graphical	1.50
Transition, 22.42/23.66	0.948
23.66–43.76°K, solid II, graphical	4.661
Transition, 177.6/43.76	4.058
43.76–54.39°K, solid I, graphical	2.397
Fusion, 106.3/54.39	1.954
54.39–90.13°K, liquid, graphical	6.462
Vaporization, 1628.8/90.13	18.07
Total, $S_{90°.13}$ (gas, 1 atm.), cal/deg	40.59

5. Free energy

The general criterion of an irreversible process is the relation $dS > 0$ or $\Sigma\ dS > 0$ where the sum covers all the systems affected.

For the study of many problems it is not always easy to follow the change of entropy of all systems involved in a given process. One is therefore led to define certain other thermodynamic functions much easier to manipulate, particularly when the behaviour of a composite system is under study. One of these functions is the free energy.

Consider a spontaneous change undergone by a system at constant temperature and pressure. Any heat evolved or absorbed by the system in course of the change may be supposed to be given to or taken from a large thermostat branched to it. Calling S and S_{ext} the entropies of the system and the thermostat respectively, one may write, in accordance with the second law,

$$dS + dS_{ext} > 0 \tag{14}$$

References p. 60

If the thermostat is very large, its temperature will remain practically unchanged as a result of the heat transfer. The entropy change of the thermostat would then be, when no work is done except against the pressure

$$dS_{ext} = -\frac{dH}{T} \tag{15}$$

where dH is the heat absorbed by the thermostat and evolved by the system. Combining relations (14) and (15),

$$dH - TdS < 0$$

The expression $dH - TdS$ represents the *variation of free energy* and is designated by the symbols dG or dF. The free energy, also called free enthalpy, is a property of the system, as are enthalpy and entropy, and depends on the state of the system and not its history, since by definition free energy is linked to quantities which are themselves properties.

$$G = H - TS \tag{16}$$

A change can be spontaneous if $dG < 0$. Such transformations are called exergonic; those accompanied by an increase of free energy and consequently not spontaneous are called endergonic. Eqn. (12a) may be rearranged to give

$$TS - H = RT \ln \frac{Q}{N} - H_0 \tag{17}$$

whence

$$G = H_0 - RT \ln \frac{Q}{N} \tag{18}$$

The free energy of a system is thus seen to be the algebraic sum of two terms, namely H_0 and $- RT \ln (Q/N)$. In the case of a chemical reaction, where the n's are the stoichiometric coefficients, counted positive for the products, the change of free energy

$$\Delta G = \Delta H_0 - RT \sum n \ln \frac{Q}{N} \tag{18a}$$

The negative value of ΔG represents the maximum work that can be done by the system through a reversible process at constant temperature and pressure against external forces other than pressure.

Reconsider Eqn. (18)

$$G = H_0 - RT \ln \frac{Q}{N}$$

It may be recalled that the volume occupied by the system affects Q_{tr}, the translational partition function. For an ideal system, the total partition function could be written

$$Q/N = Q_0 \times V = Q_0/c$$

where Q_0 is the partition function per unit volume and c the concentration. Expressing the free energy, Eqns. (18) and (18a), in terms of Q_0 one gets

$$G = H_0 - RT \ln Q_0 + RT \ln c \tag{19}$$

$$\Delta G = \Delta H_0 - RT \Sigma n \ln Q_0 + RT \Sigma n \ln c \tag{19a}$$

For a physical change like the isothermal expansion of a perfect gas,

$$\Delta G = RT\Delta \ln P \tag{20}$$

6. Partial molar quantities; chemical potential

In dealing with cases involving addition to or removal of material from a system, or the appearance of new species therein as is the case in chemical reactions, it is convenient to utilize the so-called partial molar quantities.

Many thermodynamic properties are proportional to the mass of the constituents. Such properties are *extensive,* in contrast to *intensive* properties like temperature and pressure which are independent of the amount of material in a phase and have the same value throughout a homogeneous phase.

An extensive property expressed per mole becomes a partial molar quantity; when it is expressed per gram it is a partial specific quantity.

These quantities depend only upon the composition of the system. If the system is formed of many constituents, say n_1 moles of a substance 1, n_2 mols of a substance 2, etc., partial molar quantities do not vary only if new masses of each of the constituents are added in already existing proportions.

If the increase in the volume of a solution resulting upon the addition of an infinitesimal mass dm_i of a particular solute i is dv, the partial specific volume

$$\bar{v}_i = \left(\frac{\partial V}{\partial m_i}\right)_{T,p,m_j} \tag{21}$$

It is a measure of the volume of solvent displaced by the solute. Similarly, the partial molal volume is

$$\bar{V}_i = \left(\frac{\partial V}{\partial n_i}\right)_{T,p,n_j}$$

The total volume of the solution is

$$V = n_1\bar{V}_1 + n_2\bar{V}_2 + \ldots . = \sum_i n_i\bar{V}_i \tag{22}$$

References p. 60

In a similar way, the total heat content of a solution

$$H = n_1\bar{H}_1 + n_2\bar{H}_2 + \ldots. = \sum_i n_i\bar{H}_i \tag{23}$$

where

$$\bar{H}_i = \frac{\partial H}{\partial n_i}$$

Likewise, the free energy of a substance of constant composition at a given temperature and pressure is proportional to the number of moles present as well as the partial molal free energy $\bar{G}_i$ otherwise called *chemical potential* and usually designated by the symbol μ.

$$\bar{G}_i = \mu_i = \left(\frac{\partial G}{\partial n_i}\right)_{T, p, n_j} \tag{24}$$

The chemical potential is obviously equal to the free energy per mole. In a composite system, the total chemical potential

$$\mu = n_1\mu_1 + n_2\mu_2 + \ldots = \sum_i n_i\mu_i \tag{25}$$

where n_i is the number of moles of the ith component having a chemical potential μ_i.

7. Activity

Consider now a type of transformation involving the distribution of a substance between neighbouring phases. If the chemical potential μ_2 corresponding to a phase 2 of the substance is less than that in phase 1 (μ_1,) the substance has a tendency to pass from phase 1 to phase 2, in conformity with the condition that $\Delta G = (\mu_2 - \mu_1)$ be negative. This *escaping tendency* is measured by the *fugacity* in the case of a gas and by *activity* when liquids or solutes are concerned. For a perfect gas, we have, according to (20),

$$\Delta G = \mu_2 - \mu_1 = \bar{G}_2 - \bar{G}_1 = RT \ln \frac{P_2}{P_1}$$

$$\mu = \mu^0 + RT \ln P \tag{20a}$$

For a real gas

$$\mu = \mu^0 + RT \ln f \tag{26}$$

For an ideal solution

$$\mu = \mu^0 + RT \ln c \tag{27}$$

For non-ideal solutions

$$\mu = \mu^0 + RT \ln a \tag{28}$$

μ^0, *the standard chemical potential* is the chemical potential per mole of substance at the *reference state*, which should be specified for each case.

For solutions, the composition can be expressed in concentration c, molality m, or mole fraction x. The activity a is the product of the activity coefficient γ by c, m or x. The activity coefficient reflects non-ideal behaviour, *i.e.* interaction between molecules.

The value of μ^0 is defined when one specifies conditions for which $\gamma = 1$. The usual convention is

for the solvent, $\gamma = 1$ when $x = 1$

for the solute, $\gamma = 1$ when c, m or $x = 0$

8. Equilibrium

(*a*) *Physical*

A solid solute in the presence of its saturated solution constitutes an example of physical equilibrium. The passage of an infinitesimal amount of the crystal into the solution is accompanied by no change of free energy. Hence the process does not involve any change of chemical potential. In a general way, if two phases of a system are in equilibrium, the chemical potential of a constituent distributed between the two phases is the same throughout.

(*b*) *Chemical*

Consider a system of different molecular species A, B, likely to react chemically to give another species AB according to the relation

$$n_A\mathrm{A} + n_B\mathrm{B} \rightleftharpoons n_{AB}\mathrm{AB}$$

The condition of equilibrium is $dG = 0$. In other words, no net work may be furnished by this system in a process taking place at constant temperature and pressure. In an equilibrium system like the above, the addition of infinitesimal amounts of any or all of the constituents does not alter the ratio of the respective molar coefficients n_A, n_B, n_{AB}. Hence, in terms of chemical potentials

$$n_A\,\mu_A + n_B\,\mu_B = n_{AB}\,\mu_{AB} \tag{29}$$

Utilizing the standard chemical potentials μ^0 and rearranging, one gets

$$\Delta G^0 = n_{AB}\mu^0_{AB} - n_A\mu^0_A - n_B\mu^0_B = -RT\ln\frac{(\mathrm{AB})_e^{n_{AB}}}{(\mathrm{A})_e^{n_A}(\mathrm{B})_e^{n_B}} \tag{30}$$

References p. 60

where the sign $(\quad)_e$ refers to the activity of the given component at the equilibrium state. The ratio

$$\frac{(\mathrm{AB})^{n_{\mathrm{AB}}}}{(\mathrm{A})^{n_{\mathrm{A}}}(\mathrm{B})^{n_{\mathrm{B}}}}$$

at equilibrium is called the *equilibrium constant, K*. Hence

$$\Delta G^0 = -RT \ln K \tag{31}$$

ΔG^0 corresponds to the change of free energy accompanying the reaction when the constituents are in their standard states. This corresponds to the work necessary to bring the constituents from unit activity to their respective equilibrium activities. At equilibrium activities, they react, by definition, without change of free energy.

If the constituents are initially not in their standard states, the change of free energy corresponding to the passage of each of them from its actual activity to unit activity has to be added to ΔG^0. One thus gets

$$\Delta G = \Delta G^0 + RT \ln \frac{(\mathrm{AB})^{n_{\mathrm{AB}}}}{(\mathrm{A})^{n_{\mathrm{A}}}(\mathrm{B})^{n_{\mathrm{B}}}} \tag{32}$$

or,

$$\Delta G = -RT \ln K + RT \ln \frac{(\mathrm{AB})^{n_{\mathrm{AB}}}}{(\mathrm{A})^{n_{\mathrm{A}}}(\mathrm{B})^{n_{\mathrm{B}}}} \tag{33}$$

This important expression serves as a basis for the practical measure of free energy change. It is of interest to examine the statistical significance of the equilibrium constant. The term

$$RT \ln \frac{(\mathrm{AB})^{n_{\mathrm{AB}}}}{(\mathrm{A})^{n_{\mathrm{A}}}(\mathrm{B})^{n_{\mathrm{B}}}}$$

is equal to $RT\ \Sigma\ n \ln c$ of Eqn. (19a). Hence

$$\Delta H_0 - RT \Sigma\, n \ln Q_0 = -RT \ln K \tag{34}$$

$$\ln K = \Sigma\, n \ln Q_0 - \frac{\Delta H_0}{RT} \tag{34a}$$

where

$$\Delta H_0 = \Sigma \varepsilon_0 = \varepsilon_{0\mathrm{AB}} - \varepsilon_{0\mathrm{A}} - \varepsilon_{0\mathrm{B}}$$

The equilibrium constant K derives from the number of molecules of each species in the volume of the system at equilibrium. Now, the number of molecules of a given species in a system with a given total energy would be given by its sum of states

$$\sum_i g_i \cdot e^{-\varepsilon_i/KT}$$

only if ε_i included all forms of energy including electronic. As has been pointed out before, in calculations of partition function, the energies are computed from the lowest quantum level, *i.e.* that the zero-point energies are not taken into account. This explains why the equilibrium constant expressed in terms of partition functions is not simply equal to

$$\frac{Q_{0AB}^{n_{AB}}}{Q_{0A}^{n_A} \; Q_{0B}^{n_B}}$$

but a product of two terms. The second term corresponds to zero-point energies. The summation $\Sigma\varepsilon_0$ represents the difference of the zero-point energies of the product AB and those of the reacting species A and B.

Summarizing, the variation of free energy is seen to be the algebraic sum of three quantities:

$$\Delta H_0, \quad -RT\,\Sigma\, n \ln Q_0 \quad \text{and} \quad RT \ln \frac{(AB)^{n_{AB}}}{(A)^{n_A}(B)^{n_B}}$$

A reaction can take place spontaneously at constant pressure and temperature when ΔG is negative; this depends on an interplay of the above three terms. ΔH_0 represents the difference between the energies of AB and (A + B) at absolute zero. This difference results from the electronic adjustments that constitute the reaction. At low temperatures, this term dominates.

The term

$$-RT\,\Sigma\, n \ln Q_0$$

reflects the manner in which the reaction affects the disorder of the system.

A change involving rupture of bonds with consequent increase in rotational and oscillatory movements should be favored.

$$RT \ln \frac{(AB)^{n_{AB}}}{(A)^{n_A}(B)^{n_B}}$$

depends on concentrations. The smaller the ratio the greater are the chances that the reaction proceeds spontaneously in the direction

$$n_A A + n_B B \rightarrow n_{AB} AB$$

When the ratio is greater than K, the reaction can take place only in the direction

$$n_{AB} AB \rightarrow n_A A + n_B B$$

References p. 60

The methods for measuring the free energy G of a substance or the change of free energy ΔG in course of a transformation will be discussed later. The importance of this quantity will be realized when one considers that short of measuring directly the change of entropy, it is the change of free energy and not the heat of a reaction which permits us to predict whether a reaction would take place. The quantities ΔG and ΔH are not equal unless the entropy of the system in question is the same at the beginning and end of an isothermal process. If there is an increase in entropy, the heat liberated due to the readjustment of chemical bonds may be totally or partially masked by the simultaneous consumption of heat due to the creation of additional rotational or oscillatory movements. An example is furnished by the reaction of the total dehydrogenation of glucose.

$$C_6H_{12}O_6 + 6\ H_2O \rightarrow 6\ CO_2 + 12\ H_2$$

From thermochemical data, one has $\Delta H^0 = +146\,720$ cal, the reaction is highly endothermic; judged from ΔH^0 alone a reaction of this type at room temperature is highly improbable. However, the transformation is accompanied by a very large increase in entropy.

$$\Delta S^0_{298} = \left(6\ S^0_{CO_2} + 12\ S^0_{H_2}\right) - \left(S^0_{C_6H_{12}O_6} + 6\ S^0_{H_2O}\right)$$

Taking

$$S^0_{298}CO_2 = 51.1,\quad S^0_{298}H_2 = 31.2,\quad S^0_{298}C_6H_{12}O_6 = 50.7,\quad S^0_{298}H_2O = 16.7$$

one has

$$\Delta S^0_{298} = 534 \text{ cal/deg.}$$

$$\Delta G^0 = \Delta H^0 - T\Delta S^0 = 146\,720 - 298 \times 534 = -12\,000 \text{ cal}$$

The free energy decreases; the reaction should therefore take place spontaneously at 25°C.

9. Standard free energy

Standard states of elements, as already mentioned, are the states in which they occur in the most stable form at ordinary temperature and pressure, for example liquid for mercury, solid for graphite and gas for oxygen. For gaseous elements the standard state is that corresponding to 1 atm pressure. Heats of formation of compounds are usually referred to standard states. Since G is defined in terms of H and S, these conventions should apply also to G. The free energy of a substance taken in its standard state is called the standard free energy.

Thermochemical equations can be added or subtracted. The same arguments justify the combination of standard free energy equations. For example

$$C_{(s)} + O_{2(g)} = CO_{2(g)} \quad \Delta G^0_{298} = -94\,260 \text{ cal}$$

$$CO_{(g)} + \tfrac{1}{2}O_{2(g)} = CO_{2(g)} \quad \Delta G^0_{298} = -61\,452 \text{ cal}$$

The two relations may be combined to give

$$C_{(s)} + \tfrac{1}{2}O_{2(g)} = CO_{(g)} \qquad \Delta G^0_{298} = -32\,808 \text{ cal}$$

10. Measure of enthalpy from change of equilibrium constant with temperature

When one speaks of a free energy change, it is understood that the reactant and the products are at the same specified temperature. It is useful to be able to envisage the manner in which ΔG^0 would change with temperature. This can be attained when K is known as a function of T, *i.e.* at several temperatures. The fundamental expression

$$\Delta G = \Delta H - T\Delta S$$

can be modified and differentiated to yield

$$\frac{\partial(\Delta G/T)}{\partial T} = -\frac{\Delta H}{T^2} \tag{35}$$

Substituting

$$\Delta G^0 = -RT \ln K$$

in Eqn. (35), one gets

$$\frac{\partial \ln K}{\partial T} = \frac{\Delta H}{RT^2} \tag{35a}$$

This very important equation permits the measurement of the enthalpy change of a reaction by measuring K at several temperatures. The relation (35a) also shows that the direction in which an equilibrium is shifted by increasing temperature depends on the exothermic or endothermic nature of the reaction: increasing temperature results in smaller values of K when the reaction is exothermic and larger values of K when it is endothermic.

11. Thermodynamics of activation: theory of absolute reaction rates

The concept of activation introduced by Arrhenius as part of reaction mechanisms has been useful in the understanding of the effect of temperature

References p. 60

on reaction rates. Arrhenius proposed that the rate of a reaction is controlled, not by the average kinetic energy of the reactant molecules, but by the concentration of those molecules having an energy in excess of a threshold, called the energy of activation. The idea is formulated by the relation

$$k = A \cdot e^{-E/RT} \tag{36}$$

where k is the rate constant, E the energy of activation, and A the so-called frequency factor.

The theory of absolute reaction rates provided a means of calculating the frequency factor A, based on the fundamental concept that the reactants combine to form a critical intermediate, called the activated complex, to which equilibrium theories can be applied

$$\mathrm{A} + \mathrm{B} \rightleftharpoons \mathrm{X} \rightarrow \mathrm{AB}$$

Knowledge of the equilibrium constant

$$K^* = \frac{(\mathrm{X})}{(\mathrm{A})\,(\mathrm{B})}$$

should lead to the overall reaction rate, and inversely, the evaluation of K^* by direct kinetic measurements should give indications about the nature of the activated complex.

Considering the equilibrium constant in terms of partition function (*cf.* Eqn. 34a), we have

$$K^* = \frac{Q_{0\mathrm{X}}}{Q_{0\mathrm{A}}\,Q_{0\mathrm{B}}} \cdot e^{-\Delta H_0/RT}$$

Among the degrees of freedom possessed by the activated complex, there must be one corresponding to a rather loose vibration, precisely the one brought into play in the reaction. One could take out the partition function term corresponding to this vibration

$$\frac{1}{1 - e^{-h\nu/\kappa T}}$$

which becomes equal to $\kappa T/h\nu$ when ν tends to zero, *i.e.* in the case of a very loose vibration, and write

$$K^* = \frac{(\mathrm{X})}{(\mathrm{A})\,(\mathrm{B})} = \frac{Q_{0\mathrm{X}}\,(\kappa T/h\nu)}{Q_{0\mathrm{A}}\,Q_{0\mathrm{B}}} \cdot e^{-\Delta H_0/RT} \tag{37}$$

whence

$$\nu(\mathrm{X}) = (\mathrm{A})\,(\mathrm{B})\frac{\kappa T}{h}\,\frac{Q_{0\mathrm{X}}}{Q_{0\mathrm{A}}\,Q_{0\mathrm{B}}} \cdot e^{-\Delta H_0/RT} \tag{38}$$

The product of the frequency ν by (X), the concentration of the activated complex, can then be taken as a measure of the reaction velocity. The *specific* reaction rate k is therefore

$$k = \frac{\kappa T}{h} \cdot \frac{Q_{0X}}{Q_{0A}\, Q_{0B}} \cdot e^{-\Delta H_0/RT} = \frac{\kappa T}{h} K^{\ddagger} \quad (39)$$

$K^{\ddagger}$ is a modified equilibrium constant since it does not include the term corresponding to the degree of freedom involved in the reaction.

Note that one obtains the same expression by considering the passage of molecules across the potential barrier. In this case, the method consists in calculating the number of molecules of the activated complex at the top of the barrier moving in the right direction of the reaction coordinate, and dividing by the time necessary for a molecule to pass across the barrier-width. One gets finally

$$-RT \ln K^{\ddagger} = \Delta G^{\ddagger} = \Delta H^{\ddagger} - T\Delta S^{\ddagger} \quad (40)$$

all substances being in standard states. $\Delta H^{\ddagger}$ is obtained from the experimental values of E by the relation

$$\Delta H^{\ddagger} = E - RT$$

$\Delta H^{\ddagger}$ has the same value as the heat of formation of the true complex, whereas $\Delta S^{\ddagger}$ refers to the formation of the modified complex, but the difference between $\Delta S^{\ddagger}$ and ΔS^{*} is very small. The expression (40) may be rearranged to give

$$K^{\ddagger} = e^{\Delta S^{\ddagger}/R} \cdot e^{-\Delta H^{\ddagger}/RT}$$

Since

$$k = \frac{\kappa T}{h} \cdot K^{\ddagger}$$

we have

$$k = \frac{\kappa T}{h} \cdot e^{\Delta S^{\ddagger}/R} \cdot e^{-\Delta H^{\ddagger}/RT} \quad (41)$$

κ and h, being universal constants, the expression (41) implies that the absolute rate of a reaction is fixed once the structure of the activated complex is known.

12. Procuring and utilizing thermodynamic data

Enthalpy, free energy, and entropy are properties of a system or a substance in a certain state. Thermal and spectroscopic methods used to obtain such values have been mentioned earlier in this Chapter. In systems containing complex molecules, commonly confronted by the biochemist, these methods would hardly be applicable. What is easily measured, on the other hand, is the *variation* of enthalpy, free energy, and entropy as a result of a particular transformation under study. We intend here to illustrate some of the methods commonly utilized to gather such information.

References p. 60

(a) *Determination of enthalpy change*

Applications of direct calorimetry have so far been rare in biochemistry, though some excellent determinations have been reported, for example by Kitzinger and Benzinger[3] in the case of hydrolysis of ATP; the reduction of pyruvate to lactate in the presence of lactic dehydrogenase has been treated by Katz[4]; and the enthalpy change involved in antigen–antibody reaction has been measured by Boyd *et al.*[5] in the case of hemocyanin–antihemocyanin, and by Steiner and Kitzinger[6] in the case of human serum albumin–antiserum albumin.

Evaluation of ΔH is more usually performed through the measurement of equilibrium constants at two or more different temperatures and application of the Van 't Hoff equation (p. 37).

(b) *Determination of free-energy change*

(*i*) *Direct measure of the work performed under reversible conditions*

The maximum work done by a system in the course of a transformation (which is by definition equal to the free-energy diminution) may be furnished only under conditions of reversibility. A direct measure of the free-energy change is thus possible where one can devise experiments approaching these conditions. For a group of reactions particularly important in biochemistry, namely those involving reversible oxidation–reduction, the free-energy change can be measured in the form of electrical work furnished by the reaction mixture in a so-called oxidation–reduction cell. These methods and their applications are discussed in Chapter III.

(*ii*) *From thermal data*

In certain reactions sufficient thermal data exist to allow direct application of the relation $\Delta G = \Delta H - T\Delta S$ for the determination of free-energy change. The enthalpy change can be measured directly in a calorimeter at the temperature T. ΔS, the difference between the entropies of the products of the reaction and that of the reactants, can be calculated when these entropies are available from specific heat data. In some cases, where ΔH corresponding to the reaction is not available, one has to start from ΔH^0, the enthalpy of formation of each reactant and product, usually given at 25°C. Heat capacity or entropy values are then used to calculate the respective ΔG^0 values. Finally the free-energy change of each reactant and product for the transformation from its standard state to its state in the equilibrium system is calculated. The type of procedure employed may be illustrated by calculation of the free-energy change corresponding to the oxidation of the succinate to the fumarate ion[7].

$$\begin{array}{l} CH_2COO^- \\ | \\ CH_2COO^- \end{array} \rightleftharpoons \begin{array}{l} CH—COO^- \\ \| \\ CH—COO^- \end{array} + H_2$$

One mole of succinate ion at unit activity may be considered to have been formed from the elements C, H_2 and O_2 in their standard states, first by combination to give one mole of succinic acid in its standard state (solid), then by dissolution of the acid in water to form a saturated solution, the change of succinic acid from its saturated solution to its solution at unit activity and finally the ionization of the dibasic acid to give the divalent succinate ion at unit activity.

Free energy of formation. This is calculated from standard enthalpy of formation and standard entropy of formation, both known from heat data.

ΔH^0 (standard enthalpy of formation) $= -225\,000$ cal

$\Delta S^0 = S_{\text{succinic acid}} - 4\,S_{\text{carbon}} - 3\,S_{\text{hydrogen}} - 2\,S_{\text{oxygen}} = -155$ entropy units

$\Delta G^0 = -225\,000 - (298 \times -155) = -178\,810$ cal

Free energy of solution. No free-energy change is involved in dissolving the solid acid to its saturated solution since the two phases are in equilibrium, $\Delta G = 0$.

Free energy of concentration change. In the saturated solution, the succinic acid has an activity of 0.615. In order to have the solute at unit activity, the energy to be furnished $= RT \ln (1/0.615) = +288$ cal.

Free energy of ionization. The succinate ion is produced by stripping off 2 moles of proton from 1 mole of the dibasic acid. The work to be performed $= RT \ln K_1K_2$, where K_1 and K_2 are the two dissociation constants. $\Delta G = +13\,420$ cal.

The free energy of formation of a mole of succinate ion at unit activity is thus

$$\Delta G^0 = -178\,810 + 288 + 13\,420 = -165\,102 \text{ cal}$$

By similar reasoning, one gets, for the free energy of formation of a mole of fumarate ion at unit activity

$$\Delta G^0 = -144\,630 \text{ cal}$$

The free energy of formation of hydrogen, the second product of the reaction, is zero by convention, since it is in its standard state.

Thus the standard free-energy change for the oxidation of succinate to fumarate is equal to $\Delta G^0 = +20\,460$ cal. The reaction is *endergonic*; it is not spontaneous under the specified conditions, *i.e.* where all the constituent molecules are in their standard states.

But, by changing the activity of one or more of the constituents it is possible to modify the energetic picture. For example, if the hydrogen is at a pressure of 10^{-16} atmospheres,

References p. 60

$$\Delta G = \Delta G^0 + RT \ln \frac{10^{-16} \times (\text{fumarate})}{(\text{succinate})} = -1\,300 \text{ cal}$$

The reaction becomes *exergonic.*

(iii) From equilibrium data

An obvious method is of course to utilize the relation

$$\Delta G^0 = -RT \ln K$$

If the equilibrium constant K can be determined by analytical methods, the free-energy change corresponding to the given reaction can be calculated. An example is furnished by the experiments of Meyerhof and Green[8] on the reaction involving glucose 6-phosphate, water, glucose and inorganic phosphate in the presence of intestinal phosphatase, at 38°.

$$\text{Glucose 6-phosphate} + H_2O \rightleftharpoons \text{glucose} + P_i$$

$$K = \frac{(\text{inorganic phosphate}) \cdot (\text{glucose})}{(\text{water}) \cdot (\text{ester})}$$

Glucose and inorganic phosphate in known concentrations are incubated in presence of the enzyme. The reaction is followed by estimating inorganic phosphate in aliquots withdrawn at intervals. In a typical experiment, the initial reaction mixture contained 4.2 moles of glucose, 0.675 moles of phosphate and 27.8 moles of water. At equilibrium, the concentration of inorganic phosphate had gone down by 0.0453 mole; the concentration of the ester formed is then 0.0453 mole. By taking into account a little fructose 6-phosphate that was shown to have been formed, the equilibrium concentrations of glucose, glucose 6-phosphate and inorganic phosphate were found to be 3.96, 0.042, 0.63 moles respectively. Assuming that the concentration of water does not change significantly, one has

$$K' = \frac{0.63 \times 3.96}{27.8 \times 0.042} = 2.13$$

This equilibrium constant is apparent, since concentrations are taken into account instead of activities. On the other hand, it is usual to express the activity of water not in moles, but in terms of the reference state which in the case of pure liquids is considered to be unity. Since pure water having a concentration of 55.5 M has unit activity, the activity of water in the above reaction is 27.8/55.5. This makes the equilibrium constant $K' = 118.2$. The standard free-energy change of the reaction is then

$$\Delta G^0 = -RT \ln 118.2 = \text{approx.} -3000 \text{ cal}$$

In certain cases, consideration of data from several equilibria may be necessary. A good example is offered by the manner in which the free energy of the important reaction of hydrolysis of the terminal phosphate group of adenosine triphosphate was determined[9]. The overall reaction is

$$ATP^{4-} + H_2O \rightleftharpoons ADP^{3-} + HPO_4^{2-} + H^+$$

The reaction is studied in three steps. It is known that ammonium glutamate is converted into glutamine in presence of ATP, which is itself hydrolyzed in the process to ADP and phosphate. The reaction takes place only in the presence of Mg^{2+} ions; it may be shown independently that magnesium forms 1:1 complexes with both ATP and ADP. The reaction, known as the glutamine synthetase system reaction may be represented by

$$MgATP^{2-} + NH_4^+ + \text{glutamate}^{+--} \rightleftharpoons MgADP^- + \text{glutamine} + HPO_4^{2-} + H^+$$

At equilibrium, the concentration of different constituents may be determined by direct analysis and inference. Taking into consideration the activity coefficients of glutamine, glutamate ion and NH_4^+ under the experimental conditions, one obtains, at pH 7.0 and 37°C, the ratio

$$K' = \frac{[MgADP^-]\,[HPO_4^{2-}]\,(\text{glutamine})}{[MgATP^{2-}]\,(NH_4^+)\,(\text{glutamate}^{+--})} = 400 \tag{42}$$

Now the ratio

$$\frac{(\text{glutamine})}{(NH_4^+)\,(\text{glutamate}^-)}$$

at equilibrium in the glutamine hydrolysis reaction is known from independent studies of the system

$$\text{glutamine} + H_2O \rightleftharpoons \text{glutamate}^- + NH_4^+$$

in absence of ATP but in the presence of a specific enzyme, glutaminase. The best value for the constant

$$\frac{(\text{glutamate}^-)\,(NH_4^+)}{(\text{glutamine})}$$

at 37°C is 225. Substituting this value in the expression (42) one obtains

$$K' = \frac{[MgADP^-]\,[HPO_4^{2-}]}{[MgATP^{2-}]} = 9 \cdot 10^4\,M$$

at pH 7.0 and 37°C. This corresponds to a free-energy change of −7.0 kcal for the reaction:

$$MgATP^{2-} + H_2O \rightleftharpoons MgADP^- + HPO_4^{2-} + H^+ \tag{43}$$

$$\Delta G^0 = -\,7000 \text{ cal}$$

In order to calculate the free-energy change corresponding to the hydrolysis of free ATP into free ADP, it is necessary to know the formation constants of the magnesium complexes of ATP and ADP, or at least their ratio.

References p. 60

Burton's study[10] of the equilibria gives

$$MgATP^{2-} \rightleftharpoons Mg^{2+} + ATP^{4-}; \quad K_{diss.} = 10^{-4.74}; \quad \Delta G^0 = 6700 \text{ cal} \qquad (44)$$

$$MgADP^{-} \rightleftharpoons Mg^{2+} + ADP^{3-}; \quad K_{diss.} = 10^{-3.52}; \quad \Delta G^0 = 5000 \text{ cal} \qquad (45)$$

at 37°C and ionic strength 0.1. The difference of ΔG, known to be smaller at higher ionic strengths, is taken to be 1.6 kcal at ionic strength 0.2, in order to conform to conditions of other experiments. Combining Eqns. 43–45 together with this small correction, one obtains, for

$$ATP^{4-} + H_2O \rightleftharpoons ADP^{3-} + HPO_4^{2-} + H^+$$

$$\Delta G^0 = -8600 \text{ cal at pH } 7.0 \text{ and } 37°\text{C}$$

Study of equilibria remains until now the method of choice for the measurement of thermodynamic parameters in biochemical transformations. It is useful to point out some cases where significant information can be obtained only when the equilibrium constant is conveniently defined. An example is offered by systems containing molecules having multiple reactive sites (polyfunctional); one may consider the reaction of the given polyvalent molecule with another polyvalent species, or, to simplify matters, with a monofunctional species, as for example is the case in protein ionization.

13. Multiple equilibria, intrinsic constants

Consider a polyfunctional molecule P in solution, in equilibrium with a reactant X, susceptible to combine with m sites on the aforesaid molecule. For the sake of simplicity, the reactive sites on the molecule may be supposed to be identical and independent of one another; the number of sites m may again be taken to be small, say 5.

Short of saturating all the available sites as would be the case in presence of a large excess of the reactant, one can picture different kinds of molecules PX, PX_2, PX_3, PX_4, PX_5 in proportions depending on the concentration of X. Now the notation PX_1 denotes a molecule having one X fixed to one of its five available positions; it does not describe *which* one. If we could find means to identify each of the fixing sites (no matter that they are supposed equivalent), one would find five kinds of complex PX, namely $PX_{(1)}$, $PX_{(2)}$, $PX_{(3)}$, $PX_{(4)}$, $PX_{(5)}$ where the numerical notation within brackets describes the position of attachment of X, ten varieties of PX_2 ($PX_{2(1,2)}$, $PX_{2(1,3)}$, . . .), and so on.

Consider now the reversible reaction of a molecule of X with a molecule PX to give PX_2, the filled-in sites being specified in both PX and PX_2 for example

$$PX_{(2)} + X \rightleftharpoons PX_{2(1,2)}$$

The *intrinsic* association constant is

$$K'_{int} = \frac{[PX_{2(1,2)}]}{[PX_{(2)}]\,[X]} \tag{46}$$

This constant characterizes the affinity of X for a specified site (site 1 in this case) and is obviously different from the classical equilibrium constant

$$K' = \frac{[PX_2]}{[PX]\,[X]} \tag{47}$$

The concentration terms [PX], $[PX_2]$ in Eqn. (47) refer to concentrations of the respective species no matter where the molecule or the molecules of X might be fixed; those in Eqn. (46), on the other hand, refer to concentrations of PX and PX_2 formed only through the sites 2, and 1 and 2 respectively. The classical constant thus depends not only on the nature of the reacting groups, but in addition, on the total number of groups existent as well as the number of those already combined. This can be shown by simple probability considerations.

In the preceding example, n molecules of X can be fixed on the polyvalent species P through successive equilibria to give rise to the species $PX_{n(i)}$ with specified configuration. By applying n times the generalized Eqn. (46), one obtains

$$[PX_{n(i)}] = K'^{\,n}_{int}\,[X]^n\,[P] \tag{48}$$

But the concentration of PX_n with specified configuration (i) is related to the concentration of PX_n without configurational restrictions by the relation

$$[PX_n] = \frac{m!}{n!(m-n)!}\,[PX_{n(i)}] \tag{49}$$

since

$$\frac{m!}{n!(m-n)!}$$

represents the number of ways in which n molecules of X can be arranged on m sites. Hence

$$[PX_n] = \frac{m!}{n!(m-n)!}\,K'^{\,n}_{int}\,[X]^n\,[P] \tag{50}$$

This value may be utilized in the classical expression of the equilibrium constant,

$$K' = \frac{[PX_n]}{[PX_{n-1}]\,[X]}$$

References p. 60

and one obtains

$$K'_n = \frac{1}{n}(m-n+1)\,K_{int} \tag{51}$$

In the example treated earlier ($m = 5$), this gives

$$K'_1 = 5K'_{int}, \quad K'_2 = 2K'_{int}, \ldots K'_5 = \frac{1}{5}K'_{int}$$

Determination of intrinsic constants

The total number of X molecules fixed on the polyfunctional entity (in the form of PX_n, $PX_{n-1}, \ldots$) may be calculated from the relation (50). By dividing this number by the total number of available groups, one obtains the probability (P) of a group being saturated.

$$P = \frac{K'_{int}[X]}{1 + K'_{int}[X]} \tag{52}$$

Consequently, the mean number of X molecules combined per mole of polyfunctional molecules is

$$r = \frac{m\,K'_{int}[X]}{1 + K'_{int}[X]} \tag{53}$$

The relation (53) may be given linear forms

$$\frac{1}{r} = \frac{1}{m} + \frac{1}{m\,K'_{int}[X]} \tag{54}$$

or

$$\frac{r}{[X]} = m\,K'_{int} - r\,K'_{int} \tag{55}$$

either of which may be utilized to obtain K'_{int} graphically from a known set of values of [X] and r (Figs. 3a, 3b). The concentration [X] of the reactant X in the free state has of course to be measured by appropriate techniques, say spectrophotometry or potentiometry.

In the above model the reaction sites are taken to be equivalent and independent of each other; in other words, we have supposed the absence of interactions; the intrinsic association constant with respect to a given site is the same whether or not other sites are saturated. In many cases, however, this condition might not be true. Cu^{2+} and Zn^{2+} form tetravalent complexes with imidazole; the four intrinsic association constants are found to be unequal, decreasing in the order indicated in the case of copper and increasing in the case of zinc, though the four binding sites in each case may no doubt be considered to be equivalent. Similar interactions

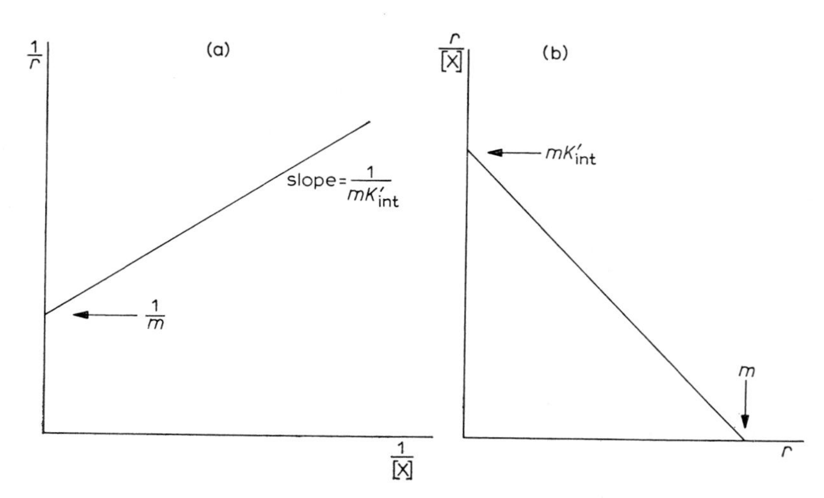

Fig. 3. Two different ways of treating multiple equilibrium data.

are observed in the case of oxygen fixation on haemoglobin[11] and haematin fixation on apohaemoglobin[12]. A procedure conveniently employed for the determination of individual intrinsic constants in such cases has been discussed by Edsall *et al.*[13].

14. Acid dissociation of proteins

Proteins constitute a class of compounds where the proton binding sites may be classified into different categories according to their respective proton affinities, *viz.* carboxyl, imidazole and amino groups. Present methods do not permit the determination of intrinsic dissociation constants with respect to a *specified* proton binding site, say, a given carboxyl group out of many such that may exist (which in other words would amount to determining the dissociation constant of the specific group in a molecule where all other carboxyl, imidazole, amino, or guanidino groups have already fixed their protons); electrometric titration does permit, however, the evaluation of the intrinsic constants corresponding to different categories of sites, namely carboxyl, imidazole and amino groups, assuming the absence of interactions between sites of the same category.

In the pH range characteristic of carboxyl ionization, a given protein molecule will have, at a given instant, some of its carboxyl groups in the ionized state $-COO^-$ and some others in the conjugated acid state $-COOH$. A different molecule of the same protein might not necessarily have the same proportion of its carboxyl groups ionized at the same instant. In fact,

References p. 60

if there is no interaction between the groups of the same molecule, the fixation of a proton on one of the many $-COO^-$ groups available, whether they belong to the same molecule or to different ones, is determined by chance alone. What is measured experimentally is the ratio of the total number of protons fixed to the total number of proton-binding sites available in the solution.

Let $m_1, m_2, m_3 \ldots$ be the number of ionizable groups of categories 1, 2, 3 etc., say carboxylic, histidine and lysine groups of a protein molecule. For each category there exists a pH range where the groups of the given category are only partially saturated. Relation (53) may then be applied to each category of groups. For carboxylic groups, for example,

$$r_1 = \frac{m_1 \left(\frac{1}{K_1'}\right) (H^+)}{1 + \left(\frac{1}{K_1'}\right) (H^+)}$$

K_1' being the apparent intrinsic dissociation constant of the carboxyl groups. A plot of r_1 as a function of pH gives a curve symmetrical about its mid-point; the latter corresponds to the pH at which half the carboxyl groups are ionized and is equal to pK_1'.

The pK of basic thermodynamic significance is one obtained by eliminating different effects of interactions. Introduction of a corrective term ω due to electrostatic effect finally gives the expression

$$pK_1 = pK_1' - \frac{2m_c - m_1}{2.303} \omega \tag{56}$$

where m_c is the sum of all groups existing in the cationic form when groups of the category 1 (of number m_1) are being titrated (as would be the case of imidazole and amino groups of many proteins in the titration range of carboxyl groups).

The knowledge of intrinsic ionization constants and related thermodynamic parameters is useful in understanding protein behaviour in solution. Titration data, besides furnishing the pK values of the different categories of ionizable groups, are as well utilized to determine their respective number. Titrations at different temperatures furnish the ionization constants at the respective temperatures and hence the enthalpy of ionization. This facilitates even more the identification of groups since the heats of ionization of a given category of groups may be deduced from analogy with simple compounds containing such groups. The way in which enthalpy data may be utilized will here be illustrated from the work of Wyman[14] on oxyhaemoglobin.

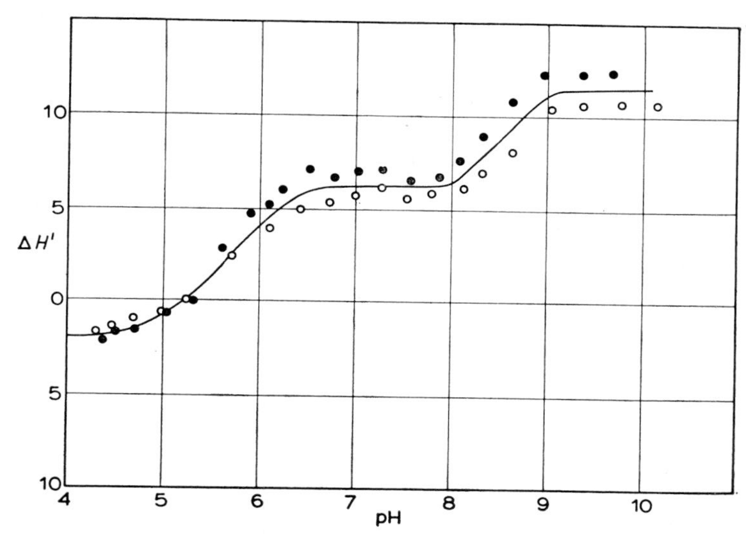

Fig. 4. Apparent enthalpy of ionization (in kcal) of oxyhaemoglobin at different pH values. In full circles: values for 25–37°C; in open circles: values for 6.5–25°C. (From Wyman[15])

The apparent heat of ionization, as calculated from titrations at different temperatures is seen to vary as a function of pH in the manner shown in Fig. 4. The heat of ionization observed in a range of pH corresponds evidently to groups active over the range in question. The enthalpy change is small in the lower range of pH, and since it is known independently that the enthalpy of ionization of carboxyl groups is small, this portion of the curve corresponds in fact to the dissociation of carboxyl groups in the protein. Over the middle range of pH, the enthalpy of ionization is close to 6200 cal, a value attributable to imidazole by analogy to a variety of simple compounds. Finally, at pH beyond 8.5, the high heat of ionization is attributed to amino groups of lysine or to guanidino groups of arginine residues.

Enthalpy data have been utilized by Wyman[15] to identify the so-called oxygen-linked acid groups in haemoglobin.

15. Other protein associations

Reversible fixation of protons is but one though important aspect of protein reactivity. Of equal interest is the dissociation of protein into smaller units, and reactions involving ligands. These phenomena have in many cases been shown to be reversible; treatment in terms of equilibrium considerations has sometimes furnished interesting thermodynamic data.

References p. 60

TABLE II

THERMODYNAMIC PARAMETERS OF SOME MACROMOLECULAR ASSOCIATIONS

System	$-\Delta G^0$ (*kcal/mole*)	$-\Delta H^0$ (*kcal/mole*)	ΔS^0 (*cal/deg/mole*)	*Ref.*
ε-Dinitrophenyllysine–anti-DNP antibody	6.8	1.6	17	16
Terephthalanilide-p,p'-diarsonic acid–rabbit antibody	7.4 ± 0.2	0.8 ± 2.6	22 ± 9	17
Isohaemagglutin β–agglutinogen B				18
β(OO) approx. mol. wt. 125000	8.9	1.7	+ 24	
$\beta(A_1A_1)$ approx. mol. wt. 200000	9.4	6.5	9.7	
$\beta(A_1O)$ approx. mol. wt. 500000	10	16	− 20	
Bovine serum albumin–anti bovine serum albumin	5.5 ± 0.2	0 ± 2	20 ± 8	19
Ovalbumin–antiovalbumin	5.6 ± 0.2	0 ± 2	18 ± 8	20
R-bovine serum albumin–anti R	5.2 ± 0.2	0 ± 2	18 ± 8	21
Insulin self-association	5.2	7.7	− 9	22,23
β-Lactoglobulin A self-association at pH 4.65	14.4 ± 0.4 at 4.5°	53 ± 1	−138 ± 6	24
β-Lactoglobulin B self-dissociation				25
at pH 8.8 ($z = -18$)	4.9 at 20°			
at pH 6.5 ($z = -10$)	7.7 at 20°			
β-Lactoglobulin self-dissociation at pH 3.0 ($z = +28$)	5.8 ± 0.1			26

Interpretation of such data has allowed in some cases an insight into submolecular events accompanying reactions on a molecular level. Table II shows some thermodynamic data relating to various associations.

An interesting aspect of data concerning protein–protein complexes is that the experimentally determined values of ΔS correspond in no case to what one should normally expect. Mutual association of proteins should normally lead to a rather large loss of entropy because of the consequent decrease in the translational and rotational degrees of freedom. For example in the case of insulin self-association, approximate calculations based on plausible molecular dimensions of monomeric and dimeric units show the translational and rotational contributions to ΔS to be respectively -77 and -47 entropy units. The experimental value of -9 is indeed very far from -124, showing that the overall association is accompanied by some other processes likely to contribute a positive entropy change. The entropy gain has sometimes been attributed to a release of bound water, but the possibility of real configurational changes in the protein molecule as a result of association cannot be ruled out.

This seems to be true also in the case of the association of human isohaemagglutinin with agglutinogen B. The combination of human isohaemagglutinin β of a serum with the agglutinogen group β is characterized by widely different enthalpy and entropy changes depending on the genotype of the serum donor, (OO), (A_1A_1) or (A_1O), (Table II). It seems hardly possible to explain the large differences in ΔS between the three groups solely in terms of release of bound water. The specific group anti B should be analogous in all the agglutinins since its structure should be complementary to that of B. The number of bound water molecules released in the course of association should not therefore be much different in one isohaemagglutinin than in another. The molecular dimensions are of course unequal, but their effect on the translation contribution to ΔS has been calculated and found to account for only 25% of the total difference (+44 cal/deg/mol) between types (OO) and (A_1O). The residual difference in the variation of entropy can only be attributed to configurational change in the protein: the combination of isohaemagglutinin β (OO) with the agglutinogen B should result in a complex having a more disordered structure than that obtained with β (A_1O).

16. Enzyme–substrate complex

Extending the Eyring concept of activated complex to the classical scheme of Henri and Michaelis, one gets, for a simplified case, the following succession of events:

References p. 60

$$E + S \underset{k'_1}{\overset{k_1}{\rightleftharpoons}} ES \rightleftharpoons ES^{\ddagger} \overset{k_2}{\rightarrow} E + P$$

Two equilibria are envisaged, one relating to the formation of the enzyme–substrate complex ES and the other corresponding to the passage of this complex from the normal to the activated state $ES^{\ddagger}$. Through some simplifying assumptions it may be shown that in the stationary state.

$$v = \frac{k_2 K[E]\,[S]}{1 + K[S]} \tag{57}$$

where v = rate of reaction, [E] and [S] are the molar concentrations of enzyme and substrate, K the equilibrium constant for the formation of the enzyme–substrate complex, and k_2 the specific rate constant for the decomposition of this complex.

The increase in free energy (ΔG), of enthalpy (ΔH) and of entropy (ΔS) associated with the formation of the complex are of course related to K by the relation

$$K = e^{-\Delta G/RT} = e^{\Delta S/R} \cdot e^{-\Delta H/RT} \tag{58}$$

Combining relations (57) and (58) it may be seen that at low substrate concentration (*i.e.* $K[S] \ll 1$)

$$v = k_2 K[E]\,[S]$$

$$= [E]\,[S] \frac{\kappa T}{h} e^{(\Delta S^{\ddagger} + \Delta S)/R} \cdot e^{-(\Delta H^{\ddagger} + \Delta H)/RT} \tag{59}$$

At low substrate concentration the enzyme is not saturated; one feels intuitively that a change of temperature acts on the overall reaction velocity not only through its effect on k_2 (rate of decomposition of the complex) but also through its action on the formation constant of the complex. The extent of this latter effect depends naturally on the enthalpy change ΔH corresponding to the complex formation. At high substrate concentration (when $K[S] \gg 1$),

$$v = k_2[E]$$

$$= [E] \frac{\kappa T}{h} e^{\Delta S^{\ddagger}/R} \cdot e^{-\Delta H^{\ddagger}/RT} \tag{60}$$

Under these conditions, the enzyme being completely saturated by the substrate, the effect of temperature is limited solely to the activation stage.

From the above relations, it is evident that measures of reaction velocity at low and high substrate concentrations and over a range of temperature at each substrate concentration provide means of determining the thermodynamic parameters of both of the two equilibria envisaged, namely the

TABLE III

THERMODYNAMIC PARAMETERS CORRESPONDING TO THE FORMATION AND ACTIVATION OF SOME ENZYME–SUBSTRATE COMPLEXES

Enzyme	*Substrate*	*Formation of the complex*		*Activation of the complex*		*Ref.*
		ΔH (*kcal/mole*)	ΔS (*cal/deg/mole*)	$\Delta H^{\ddagger}$ (*kcal/mole*)	$\Delta S^{\ddagger}$ (*cal/deg/mole*)	
Trypsin	Benzoyl-L-arginimide			14.9	− 6.2	27
	Sturin			11.8	− 4.7	27
	Benzoyl-arginine ethyl ester			10.6	−17.8	28
	Native lactoglobulin	0	+17	18.5	− 4	29
Chymotrypsin	Benzoyltyrosylglycylamide			10.5	−17.8	27
	Benzoyl-L-phenylalanine methyl ester			11.9	−12.1	30
	Benzoyl-L-tyrosinamide			14.0	−13.7	31
	Acetyl-L-tyrosine ethyl ester			10.9	−12.7	30
	Methyl-L-β-phenyl lactate			10.5	−24.2	30
	Methyl-D-β-phenyl lactate			14.5	−15.1	30
	Denatured pepsin			10.9	− 8.8	27
	Native lactoglobulin			16.2	−13.4	32
Pepsin	Carbobenzoxy-L-glutamyl-L-tyrosyl methyl ester	2.4	20.6	20.7	− 4.5	33
	Carbobenzoxy-L-glutamyl-L-tyrosine	3.0	24.4	17.2	−19.8	33
Urease	Urea	3.3	13.3	9.25	− 7.5	34
Carbonic anhydrase	Carbonic acid	−20.0	−59.8			35
Citric dehydrogenase	Citric acid	−13.4				36
Lactic dehydrogenase	Lactic acid	− 8	−20			37

References p. 60

formation of the enzyme–substrate complex and its activation. Some data are collected in Table III.

The entropy of complex formation (ΔS) is often positive, as in antigen–antibody associations. This again is suggestive of either elimination of several water molecules from the surface of the enzyme, or of real configurational changes. Such change might consist in some unfolding of enzyme structure of the same general character as is supposed to occur in protein denaturation. The negative entropy of activation would be normal in this hypothesis[33], since in going through the activated state to complete reaction, the enzyme must regain its original structure in order to be able to repeat its role of catalyst.

17. Protein configuration and entropy

A molecule of a globular protein in solution may be considered to have been formed from the constituent amino acids first by the formation of a linear chain with the given sequence, followed in turn by the formation of a helix, then folding the helix to the desired configuration, formation of the required number of stabilizing bonds (hydrogen, S–S and electrostatic) and other subsequent reactions such as ionizations, hydration etc. The total free-energy change, referred to the amino acid as the standard state should then be

$$\Delta G = \Delta G_{\text{chain}} + \Delta G_{\text{helix}} + \Delta G_{\text{fold}} + \Delta G_{\text{S-S}} + \Delta G_{\text{elect.}} + \Delta G_{\text{Solution}} + \ldots \text{etc.}$$

Some attempts have been made to calculate the first term. The negative entropy of formation of a chain containing the amino acids arranged in a definite sequence is substantially greater than what would be required if there were no sequence to be respected, for example as in a homopolymer or in a disordered heteropolymer. This additional entropy, called the chain entropy, has been calculated for a straight chain from statistical considerations. For a chain composed of amino acids of ν sorts (ν may be 20 at a maximum), the chain entropy is approximately equal to $-4.57 \log \nu$ for sufficiently long chains[38]. Synthesis of a long peptide chain has therefore to be coupled to energy-yielding reactions, to overcome not only the positive free energy of formation of peptide-bond synthesis, but also this unfavourable entropy effect. Besides, in the course of protein synthesis *in vivo*, the relative concentrations of free amino acids are not necessarily proportional to their respective abundance in the protein formed; some of them will inevitably be at lower concentrations. This calls for an additional amount of favourable standard free energy. For a protein containing 300 amino acids of 20 kinds, Schulz[38] estimates the favourable free energy required at about 10 kcal/mole of amino acid.

The realization of secondary and tertiary structures leading to specific configurations should be accompanied by a diminution of free energy since these structures lead to stable configurations

$$(\Delta G_{\text{helix}} + \Delta G_{\text{fold}} + \Delta G_{\text{S-S}} + \Delta G_{\text{elect.}}) < 0$$

The consequent change of entropy may, however, be expected to be important, since many possible orientations become forbidden as a result. Some attempts have been made to calculate the so-called helical entropy and the configurational (fold) entropy on simplified models by the use of statistical–mechanical methods[39,40].

A fruitful experimental attack has been made through study of reversible denaturation or transconformation, as it is sometimes called. These studies confirm, as could be expected, that the behaviour of proteins is characterized by a large number of geometrical configurations consistent with little difference in free-energy values. As seen from the data in Table IV, the different transconformations are separated by small free-energy barriers though

TABLE IV

THERMODYNAMIC PARAMETERS IN SOME CASES OF REVERSIBLE PROTEIN DENATURATION

Protein	*ΔG (kcal)*	*ΔH (kcal)*	*ΔS (cal/deg)*	*Ref.*
Soybean trypsin inhibitor	−1 (50°)	57.3	180	41
Chymotrypsinogen	−1.2 (46°)	99.6	316	42
Luciferase	+1.6	60.0	196	43
Pepsinogen	1.3	31	93	44
Trypsin	−1.3 (50°)	67.6	213	45
Ribonuclease		37.1	110	46

the entropy and heat changes are very large. There seems to exist a balance between entropy and heat changes so that the positive energy required to break a few bonds in the tertiary structure is balanced by the positive entropy change resulting from increased degrees of freedom. Difficulties in interpreting the increased entropy arise from the fact that the role of water *vis-à-vis* proteins in solution is not known with certainty. Water seems to be involved both in energy and entropy effects; hydration of groups should involve change of free energy, whereas the mobilization or the "binding" of water molecules affects the overall entropy. In denaturation reactions, it is still difficult to assess what part of the total increase of entropy corresponds to real relaxation of the molecules, since any release of "bound" water consequent to change of configuration should also result in an entropy increase.

References p. 60

18. Information and negentropy

The configurational entropy of a protein molecule has in some cases been evaluated in *bits, i.e.* units of information. These are the outcome of studies on the structural basis of hereditary characters, particularly regarding the genes responsible for the biosynthesis of specific proteins.

Information is a measure of the disappearance of uncertainty regarding an event. If there are, before a given message, P_0 possibilities of an event taking place and P_f possibilities after the message, the information received from the message is $K \ln (P_0/P_f)$, where K is a constant. If the message results in the disappearance of all uncertainty, the information (I) received is equal to $K \ln P_0$.

$$I = K \ln P_0 \tag{61}$$

When the disappearance or decrease of uncertainty results from an answer comprising a binary choice, *viz.*: yes or no, — the information received from the answer is $K \ln 2$.

Taking K as equal to $1/\ln 2 = \log_2 e$, one gets

$$I = \frac{\ln 2}{\ln 2} = \log_2 2 = 1 \text{ bit}$$

The researches of Szilard, of Shanon and of Brillouin have led to the understanding of the relation that exists between information and physical entropy. An organized structure is one, which, in the words of Brillouin, contains a large quantity of information; its negentropy is high. Knowing the structure of a molecule amounts to acquiring a quantity of information equivalent to a given number of answers, affirmative or negative, on the nature of the atoms and their positions. The number of answers required is that necessary to reconstitute the molecule itself and not one of its isomers.

By choosing a proper value for K in the relation $I = K \ln P$, the information acquired regarding a particular structure may be made to correspond to the absolute value of the entropy of the molecule. Information in bits/molecule is equal to the entropy in cal/deg/mole multiplied by 0.73.

TABLE V

INFORMATION CONTENT OF SOME ENZYMES

Protein	*Mol. wt.*	*I (bits × 0.69)*
Aldolase	140 000	3482
Triose phosphate dehydrogenase	150 000	3624
Chymotrypsinogen	36 000	855
Pepsin	34 400	743
Ribonuclease	15 000	286

We have seen above that it is possible to estimate the minimum value of the configurational entropy of a protein from the possible number of arrangements of the constituent amino acids in a straight chain. Bramson has made such calculations for some proteins. His results, expressed in bits, for some enzymes are reproduced in Table V.

One might compare the information content of an enzyme, about 10^3 bits, to that of a genome, between 10^9 and 10^{11} bits. Admitting the existence of 600 enzymes, one sees that the genome can very well store the information necessary for the construction of all enzymes.

19. Thermodynamics of irreversible processes: chemical applications

Any real process having a finite velocity is irreversible and, as shown above, is consequently accompanied by a production of entropy. This general principle has led some authors to treat the entropy production as if it were the cause of the irreversible process.

Consider a chemical reaction in a closed system, *i.e.* one in which there is no exchange of material with the outside. Let ξ be a measure of the progress of the reaction

$$n_1 A_1 + n_2 A_2 + \ldots \rightarrow n_1' A_1' + n_2' A_2' + \ldots$$

The reaction velocity is

$$v = \frac{d\xi}{dt}$$

According to the definition of DeDonder, the entropy production is equal to

$$A \frac{d\xi}{dt}$$

where A is called the reaction affinity. This product is equal to q'/T, q' having the same significance as used on p. 24, *i.e.* non-compensated heat, characterizing irreversibility. The affinity is distinct from $-\Delta G$ which depends only on the initial and final states of the system. The affinity A, on the contrary, changes in course of the reaction and depends at each instant on the chemical potentials of the constituents.

$$A = \Sigma\, n_i \mu_i - \Sigma\, n_i' \mu_i' \tag{62}$$

At equilibrium, this affinity evidently disappears. The affinity is related to the equilibrium constant by the relation

$$A = RT \ln \frac{K}{(A_1)^{-n_1} \ldots . (A_1')^{n_1'} \ldots .} \tag{63}$$

References p. 60

At points not far from the equilibrium state, one assumes a linear relation between the reaction velocity and affinity:

$$v = aA$$

where the coefficient a is always positive. In the domain of biochemistry, this concept, in conjunction with what is called the reciprocity principle of Onsager, has been of some interest in treating coupled irreversible reactions. Consider two cases of simultaneous chemical transformation

In both cases A can be transformed reversibly to B and C; the passage of B to C and *vice versa* takes place only in the case II. For case I,

$$v_1 = k_{AB}[A] - k_{BA}[B] = k_{AB}[A]\left(1 - \frac{k_{BA}}{k_{AB}} \cdot \frac{[B]}{[A]}\right)$$

$$v_2 = k_{AC}[A] - k_{CA}[C] = k_{CA}[A]\left(1 - \frac{k_{CA}}{k_{AC}} \cdot \frac{[C]}{[A]}\right)$$

Since the ratios of the rate constants k_{AB}/k_{BA} etc. are equal to the respective equilibrium constants K_1 etc., one may write, for near equilibrium states (*cf.* Eqn. 63),

$$v_1 = k_{AB}\,[A]\,\frac{A_1}{RT}; \quad v_2 = k_{AC}\,[A]\,\frac{A_2}{RT}$$

or

$$v_1 = a_{11}\,A_1; \quad v_2 = a_{22}\,A_2$$

These relations express the idea that the reactions 1 and 2 are linearly independent; only the self-entraining coefficients a_{11} and a_{22} have finite values.

In case II, the existence of the reversible transformation B $\longleftrightarrow$ C should affect the velocities v_1 and v_2 of the reactions 1 and 2. In the expression for velocities,

$$v_1 = a_{11}\,A_1 + a_{12}\,A_2$$

$$v_2 = a_{21}\,A_1 + a_{22}\,A_2$$

it may be shown that the coupling coefficients a_{12} and a_{21} are different from zero, and further that they are equal to one another. In other words, the velocity of the reaction 1 is influenced by the affinity of the reaction 2 exactly in the same manner as the velocity of the reaction 2 is influenced by the affinity of the reaction 1.

This is a particular case of the principle of reciprocity which may be written

$$a_{ij} = a_{ji}$$

and which establishes the dependence between the flux of material caused by one chemical potential gradient and the flux caused by another potential gradient.

This principle has found some interesting applications in biology. Consider *open systems* in a stationary state: the degree of irreversibility termed P by DeDonder is the sum $\Sigma\, Av$ and is always positive.

$$P = A_1 v_1 + A_2 v_2 + \ldots$$

If the intake of material is regulated in a manner so as to maintain A_1 constant and leaving A_2 to change in course of time, and if the change of A_2 conforms to the relation

$$\left(\frac{\partial P}{\partial A_2}\right)_{A_1} = 2(a_{12}A_1 + a_{22}A_2) = 0$$

P then passes through a minimum different from zero. This distinguishes open systems from closed systems where the minimum of entropy is zero and corresponds to equilibrium.

It can be shown that in a state of minimum P, the open system reacts to an increase in the number of moles participating in the reaction 2 by a chemical change in a sense opposite to the perturbation. This constitutes an extension, in the case of irreversible processes, of the Le Chatelier principle according to which any system in chemical equilibrium reacts to a variation of one of the factors of the equilibrium in a manner so that if it were to take place alone, it would produce a change of the considered factor in the opposite sense.

References p. 60

BIBLIOGRAPHY

1 G. N. LEWIS AND M. RANDALL, *Thermodynamics*, 2nd ed., revised by K. S. SPITZER AND L. BREWER, McGraw-Hill, New York, 1961.
2 Y. ROCARD, *Thermodynamique*, Masson, Paris, 1952.
3 I. PRIGOGINE, *Étude Thermodynamique des Phénomènes Irréversibles*, Dunod, Paris, 1947.
4 S. GLASSTONE, K. J. LAIDLER AND H. EYRING, *The Theory of Rate Processes*, John Wiley, New York, 1941.
5 G. S. PARKS AND H. M. HUFFMAN, *Free Energies of Some Organic Compounds*, The Chemical Catalog Company, New York, 1932.

REFERENCES

1 B. PULLMAN AND A. PULLMAN, *Quantum Biochemistry*, Interscience, New York, 1963.
2 L. PAULING, *The Nature of the Chemical Bond*, Cornell University Press, Ithaca, N.Y., 1960.
3 C. KITZINGER AND T. BENZINGER, *Z. Naturforsch.*, 10b (1955) 375.
4 S. KATZ, *Biochim. Biophys. Acta*, 17 (1955) 226.
5 W. C. BOYD, J. B. CONN, D. C. GREGG, G. B. KISTIAKOWSKY AND R. M. ROBERTS, *J. Biol. Chem.*, 139 (1941) 787.
6 R. F. STEINER AND C. KITZINGER, *J. Biol. Chem.*, 222 (1956) 271.
7 H. BORSOOK AND H. F. SCHOTT, *J. Biol. Chem.*, 92 (1931) 535, 559.
8 O. MEYERHOF AND H. GREEN, *J. Biol. Chem.*, 178 (1949) 655.
9 T. BENZINGER, R. HEMS, K. BURTON AND C. KITZINGER, *Biochem. J.*, 71 (1959) 400.
10 K. BURTON, *Biochem. J.*, 71 (1959) 388.
11 F. J. W. ROUGHTON, A. B. OTIS AND R. L. J. LYSTER, *Proc. Roy. Soc. (London), Ser. B*, 144 (1955) 29.
12 R. BANERJEE, *Biochim. Biophys. Acta*, 64 (1962) 385.
13 J. T. EDSALL, G. FELSENFELD, D. J. GOODMAN AND F. R. N. GURD, *J. Am. Chem. Soc.*, 74 (1956) 3054.
14 J. WYMAN, *J. Biol. Chem.*, 127 (1939) 581.
15 J. WYMAN, *Advan. Protein Chem.*, 4 (1948) 466.
16 M. E. CARSTEN AND H. N. EISEN, *J. Am. Chem. Soc.*, 77 (1955) 1273.
17 S. I. EPSTEIN, P. DOTY AND W. C. BOYD, *J. Am. Chem. Soc.*, 78 (1956) 3306.
18 R. WURMSER AND S. FILITTI-WURMSER, *Progr. Biophys. Biophys. Chem.*, 7 (1957) 88.
19 S. J. SINGER AND D. H. CAMPBELL, *J. Am. Chem. Soc.*, 75 (1953) 5577; 77 (1955) 3499.
20 S. J. SINGER AND D. H. CAMPBELL, *J. Am. Chem. Soc.*, 77 (1955) 4851.
21 M. C. BAKER, D. H. CAMPBELL, S. I. EPSTEIN AND S. J. SINGER, *J. Am. Chem. Soc.*, 78 (1956) 312.
22 L. PAULING, D. PRESSMAN, D. H. CAMPBELL, C. IKEDA AND M. IKAWA, *J. Am. Chem. Soc.*, 64 (1942) 2994.
23 P. DOTY AND G. E. MYERS, *Discussions Faraday Soc.*, 13 (1952) 51.
24 R. TOWNEND AND S. N. TIMASHEFF, *J. Am. Chem. Soc.*, 82 (1960) 3168.
25 C. GEORGE AND S. GUINAND, *Biochim. Biophys. Acta*, 59 (1962) 737.
26 R. TOWNEND, L. WEINBERGER AND S. N. TIMASHEFF, *J. Am. Chem. Soc.*, 82 (1960) 3175.
27 J. A. V. BUTLER, *J. Am. Chem. Soc.*, 63 (1941) 2971.
28 G. W. SCHWERT AND M. A. EISENBERG, *J. Biol. Chem.*, 179 (1949) 665.
29 J. YON, *Biochim. Biophys. Acta*, 27 (1958) 111.
30 J. E. SNOKE AND H. NEURATH, *J. Biol. Chem.*, 182 (1950) 577.
31 S. KAUFMAN, H. NEURATH AND G. W. SCHWERT, *J. Biol. Chem.*, 177 (1949) 793.
32 J. YON, *Bull. Soc. Chim. Biol.*, 40 (1958) 45.
33 E. J. CASEY AND K. J. LAIDLER, *J. Am. Chem. Soc.*, 72 (1950) 2159.
34 K. J. LAIDLER AND J. P. HOARE, *J. Am. Chem. Soc.*, 72 (1950) 2489.
35 M. KIESE, *Biochem. Z.*, 307 (1941) 400.
36 W. Y. DANN, *Biochem. J.*, 25 (1931) 177.
37 I. M. SOCQUET AND K. J. LAIDLER, *Arch. Biochem.*, 25 (1950) 171.

[38] G. V. Schulz, *Z. Elektrochem.*, 55 (1951) 569.
[39] H. C. Longuet-Higgins, *Discussions Faraday Soc.*, 25 (1958) 86.
[40] J. A. Schellman, *Compt. Rend. Trav. Lab. Carlsberg, Sér. Chim.*, 29 (1955) 230.
[41] M. Kunitz, *J. Gen. Physiol.*, 32 (1948) 241.
[42] M. A. Eisenberg and G. W. Schwert, *J. Gen. Physiol.*, 34 (1951) 583.
[43] F. H. Johnson, H. Eyring, R. Steblay, H. Chaplin, C. Huber and G. Gherardi, *J. Gen. Physiol.*, 28 (1945) 463.
[44] R. M. Heriott, *J. Gen. Physiol.*, 21 (1938) 501.
[45] M. L. Anson and A. E. Mirsky, *J. Gen. Physiol.*, 17 (1934) 393.
[46] G. Kalinitsky and H. Resnick, *J. Biol. Chem.*, 234 (1959) 1714.

Chapter III

Oxidation–Reduction Potentials

R. WURMSER AND R. BANERJEE

Institut de Biologie Physico-Chimique, University of Paris (France)

1. Introduction

Study of oxidation–reduction potentials provides a convenient way of measuring quantitatively the free-energy change associated with a given oxidative transformation. In heterotrophic organisms drawing their energy from the oxidation of foodstuffs, an important part of cellular activity is associated with oxidation–reduction processes involving intermediate metabolites; thermodynamic criteria applied to such or other postulated intermediates help to chalk out rational pathways in harmony with energy requirements. Oxidation–reduction processes are often coupled with hydrolysis, phosphorylation, etc., but thermodynamic data of these and other reactions are sufficiently linked to the specific oxidation–reduction process to justify particular attention to be given to the latter.

2. Oxidation–reduction

The primary process of oxidation and reduction should be conceived in terms of electron transfer. An oxidizable molecule, in other words an electron donor, is characterized by its tendency to donate one or more electrons to a suitable acceptor. The acceptor becomes thereby reduced, while the donor is simultaneously oxidized; the overall process constitutes an oxidation–reduction. Thermodynamic treatment of oxidation–reduction processes is not concerned with the mechanism of electron transfer though much stimulating work has been done thereon. A collision mechanism involving the formation of an "activated complex" has been conceived; the activated complex is believed to facilitate the transfer of electrons from one molecule to the other. In reactions involving more than one electron, the transfer should normally be stepwise, one electron at a time, with the transient formation of a free-radical intermediate; in certain cases the latter may attain concentrations sufficiently high to be detectable. However, recent work shows many examples where free-radical intermediates, if formed at all, are so short-lived that one might in fact think of two electron transfers.

Whatever might be the mechanism, some oxidation–reduction equilibria are rapid while others are less so. Reactions involving metallic ions or their complexes and most organic dyes are rapid; others, like most of the organic metabolites, may attain equilibrium only in the presence of suitable catalysts in the form of enzymes.

3. Formulation of equilibria

The oxidation of an electron donor A_{red} may be represented by

$$A_{red} \rightarrow A_{ox} + ne \tag{1a}$$

similarly, an electron acceptor B_{ox} may be reduced according to the equation

$$B_{ox} + me \rightarrow B_{red} \tag{1b}$$

An equilibrium involving A and B, supposing that A_{red} and B_{ox} exchange the same number of electrons per molecule, *i.e.*, $n = m$, may take the form

$$A_{red} + B_{ox} \rightleftharpoons A_{ox} + B_{red} \tag{2}$$

In case where $n \neq m$, the stoichiometric relation involves unequal numbers of molecules of A and B.

$$\alpha A_{red} + \beta B_{ox} \rightleftharpoons \alpha A_{ox} + \beta B_{red} \tag{2a}$$

The equation is balanced by the relation $\alpha n = \beta m$.

Except in special circumstances, for example under ionizing radiations, electron transfer from a donor takes place only in the presence of a suitable acceptor. For free-energy calculations, however, it is convenient to break up the overall reaction (for example 2) into two constitutive parts, (1a) and (1b), involving first the loss of electrons by the donor, and then subsequent gain by the acceptor. The procedure is classic in thermodynamics, the free-energy change of the overall reaction is the sum of free-energy changes of each of the consecutive steps. For reaction (1a), the equilibrium constant is

$$K = \frac{(e)^n \, (A_{ox})}{(A_{red})} \tag{3}$$

The determination of the equilibrium constant and the free-energy change

References p. 88

reduces to the problem of measuring the *activity of electrons** at equilibrium for given proportions of donor and acceptor. A convenient means of measuring this activity is furnished by the so-called oxidation–reduction cell.

4. Oxidation–reduction cell

Electroactive substances in solution can exchange electrons with an inert electrode plunged in the medium. The electrode, usually made of some noble metal (platinum, gold), should have negligible *solution pressure* under the conditions, *i.e.* should not liberate or fix cations.

It is customary in electrochemistry to consider half-cells; this is in fact equivalent to dividing a reaction into two half-reactions which are not observable independently of one another, in the same manner as the reaction in Eqn. (2) was represented as the sum of two half-reactions (1a) and (1b). Consider a pair of half-cells containing the reaction mixtures (1a) and (1b) in liquid junction with one another.

$$\mathrm{Pt} \;|\; \underset{a}{\mathrm{A_{ox}, A_{red}}} \;||\; \underset{b}{\mathrm{B_{ox}, B_{red}}} \;|\; \mathrm{Pt}$$

The two platinum electrodes should be at different potentials if the electron activity in the two half-cells is different. We make the assumption that conditions are such that A_{red} is an electron donor with respect to B_{ox}. Let the difference of potential be ΔE.

If the two electrodes are joined externally by a metal conductor, electrons should flow from the negative to the positive terminal and consequently from one half-cell to the other. The substance A_{red} can in this way donate electrons to its acceptor B_{ox} placed in the other compartment in the same manner as it would do if they were really mixed. If the flow of electrons were allowed to proceed, it would continue until the electron activity in the two compartments were the same; the concentration of A_{ox}, A_{red}, B_{ox}, B_{red} in the two half-cells would then be the same as that in an equilibrium mixture corresponding to the reaction (2).

5. Free energy

The free-energy change involved in the reaction considered thus corresponds to the free energy of transfer of n electron-moles from an activity (e_a) to

* There need be no hesitation in considering the electron like any other reacting species that can exist free in solution. Numerous authors have extended the concept of chemical potential to charged particles like protons and electrons, none of which exist free in aqueous solutions; it is usual to include hydrogen ion activity in equilibrium equations. The rigourous treatment of any charged particle would be to consider the so-called *electrochemical potential* made up of two terms, one corresponding to the ordinary chemical potential as if the particle were not charged, the other being linked to the electrostatic potential of the medium and the charge number.

an activity (e_b). Applying the general free-energy equation for such transfers,

$$\Delta G = nRT \ln \frac{(e_b)}{(e_a)} \tag{4}$$

This free-energy change is equal to the maximum work the system is capable of doing, *i.e.* the work done by the system if conditions of reversibility could be maintained. The pair of half-cells considered above corresponds exactly to these conditions provided only an infinitesimal current is allowed to flow, so that the potential difference ΔE does not change. The work *done* in moving n electron-moles across a potential difference ΔE is equal to $nF\Delta E$, where F is the Faraday (96495 coulomb). The work *furnished* by the system, the free-energy change, is therefore given by

$$\Delta G = nRT \ln \frac{(e_b)}{(e_a)} = -nF\Delta E \tag{5}$$

In other words, the free-energy change of a reaction of type (2) may be calculated by measuring the potential difference between inert electrodes plunged in two suitably devised half-cells.

6. Oxidation–reduction potentials

For tabulation purposes, it is usual to record E_h, the potential of individual half-cells with reference to an arbitrarily chosen standard, namely the normal hydrogen electrode, supposed to have a potential zero at all temperatures. It is possible to calculate ΔE for a given pair of half-cells from the difference of the respective E_h values; the free-energy change of a wide variety of reactions can thus be known provided the half-reactions have been studied and E_h values recorded.

E_h represents in fact the difference of potential ΔE between electrodes in the following pair of half-cells

$$\text{Pt} \;|\; \underset{a}{A_{red}, A_{ox}} \;||\; H^+ \text{ (activity} = 1\text{)}, H_2 \text{ (1 atm.)} \;|\; \text{Pt}$$

E_h is, by convention, negative when the system a has a tendency to send electrons to the standard hydrogen half-cell. The electron activity in the latter is equal to unity*. The free-energy change corresponding to the cell

* The half-cell reaction is $H_2 \text{ (1 atm.)} \rightarrow 2H^+(a = 1) + 2\,e$

$$K = \frac{(H^+)^2(e)^2}{(H_2)}; \quad (e) = \sqrt[2]{\frac{K(H_2)}{(H^+)^2}}$$

Since by definition the free-energy change $\Delta G^0 = -RT \ln K$ is zero, K should be unity; hence, since $(H_2) = 1$, $(H^+) = 1$, (e) is also equal to unity.

References p. 88

reaction (a) is then equal to the free energy of transfer of n electron-moles from a solution of electron activity e_a to one of electron activity 1.

$$\Delta G = nRT \ln \frac{1}{(e_a)} = -nRT \ln (e_a) \tag{6a}$$

from consideration of electrochemical potential, and

$$\Delta G = nFE_h \tag{6b}$$

from consideration of electrical work. Hence,

$$E_h = -\frac{RT}{F} \ln (e_a) \tag{7}$$

Now the electron activity in the half-cell a is linked to the equilibrium constant of the half-cell reaction by the relation

$$e_a = \sqrt[n]{\frac{K(A_{red})}{(A_{ox})}} \tag{8}$$

cf. relation (3). Substituting this value in the relation (7), one gets

$$E_h = -\frac{RT}{nF} \ln K + \frac{RT}{nF} \ln \frac{(A_{ox})}{(A_{red})} \tag{9}$$

By putting

$$E_0 = -\frac{RT}{nF} \ln K$$

one gets

$$E_h = E_0 + \frac{RT}{nF} \ln \frac{(A_{ox})}{(A_{red})} \tag{10}$$

In decimal logarithms, at 30°,

$$E_h = E_0 + \frac{0.06}{n} \log \frac{(A_{ox})}{(A_{red})} \tag{10a}$$

The potential of a half-cell containing an electron donor in equilibrium with its conjugated electron acceptor thus depends on two factors: Firstly, E_0, a constant for the system, and secondly the proportion of oxidized and reduced molecules. The constant E_0, being directly linked to the equilibrium constant K expresses a fundamental thermodynamic property of the system and is called the normal oxidation–reduction potential. E_0 constitutes a suitable criterion for the comparison of electron-donor capacity of different systems.

For simple oxidation–reduction systems like the one cited above, E_0 may be determined by measuring E_h of a series of half-cells containing different proportions of A_{ox} and A_{red}, and interpolating to $(A_{ox})/(A_{red}) = 1$. Another convenient procedure is to construct a so-called titration curve; a given quantity of A_{ox} or A_{red} placed in a half-cell is reduced or oxidized in successive steps by the addition of a suitably chosen reducing or oxidizing agent, E_h measurements being made at each step after attainment of equilibrium. The E_h values expressed as a function of the ratio $[A_{ox}]/([A_{ox}] + [A_{red}])$ constitutes a titration curve; the inflexion point in the middle of the curve corresponds to $[A_{ox}]/[A_{red}] = 1$, and permits to calculate E_0, taken due account of the activity coefficients. Note that the above holds only in cases where the stoichiometry of oxidation–reduction conforms to Eqn. (2); *i.e.* where the number of electrons lost during oxidation of 1 molecule of A_{red} is the same as that required to reduce 1 molecule of A_{ox}. The midpoint of a symmetrical titration curve at a given pH, say 7, is often designated by E_{m7}.

In practice, the potential is measured against standard electrodes other than hydrogen, usually against the standard calomel half-cell.

7. Outline of experimental methods

(*a*) *Potentiometry*

(i) Cell design

Titrations are usually performed in cells of the type show in Fig. 1a. Dimensions and other details are adjusted to suit the requirements of the system under study.

One may start with the oxidant in the titration cell and attain different $[A_{ox}]/[A_{red}]$ ratios by progressive addition of a reducing agent from a burette. The reducing agent should be so chosen as to have an electron-donor capacity far superior to that of A_{red}. One may also operate in the reverse order, starting from A_{red} in the titration vessel and oxidizing by a suitably chosen agent. Some authors have also used the so-called method of mixtures, where various $[A_{ox}]/[A_{red}]$ ratios are obtained by direct mixing of different proportions of A_{ox} and A_{red}.

Thunberg–Borsook tubes of the type shown in Fig. 1b are convenient for the study of enzyme-catalyzed transformations (metabolite pairs) and also whenever it is necessary to operate under vacuum.

(ii) Mediators

Certain oxidation–reduction systems do not readily affect the electrode; important progress in the study of such (non-electroactive) systems has

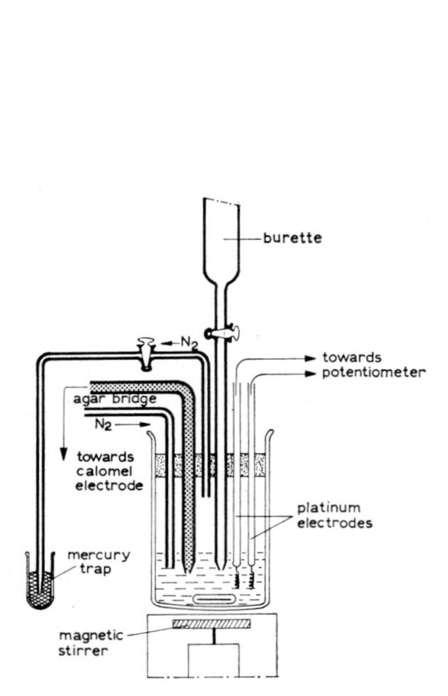

Fig. 1a. Titration vessel.

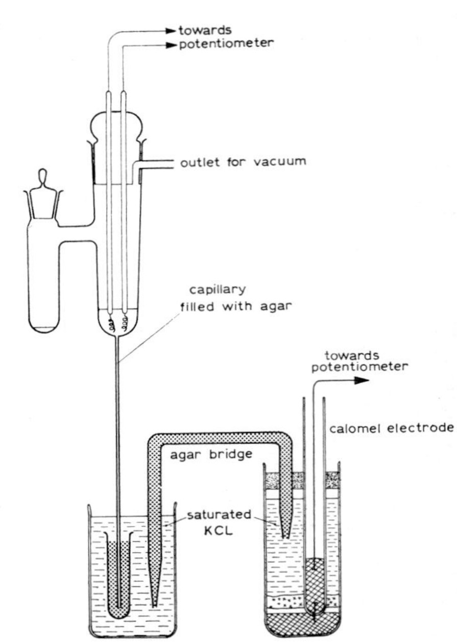

Fig. 1b. Thunberg–Borsook tube assembled with calomel half-cell. (Reproduced from *Techniques de Laboratoire*, Masson, Paris, 1963.)

been made by the use of suitable mediators, themselves usually electroactive dyes which when mixed with the system in relatively small concentrations result in stable potential readings. A mediator should be chosen to have a half-reduction potential, under the conditions used, near that expected for the system under study. The experimental study of oxidation–reduction systems involving metabolites and most of the oxidation–reduction enzymes necessitates the use of suitable mediators. In so far as the mediators act purely as intermediates, only accelerating the attainment of equilibrium, they do not affect the thermodynamic relations.

(*b*) *Colorimetric measure of potential*

E_h of a given oxidation–reduction system can often be measured by colorimetry by the use of the so-called oxidation–reduction indicators. These are electroactive dyes undergoing reversible oxidation–reduction; the oxidant and the reductant have different spectral properties, so that the ratio $[I_{ox}]/[I_{red}]$ can be easily estimated by spectrophotometry. The E_h of a medium containing an oxidation–reduction system under study can thus be determined by colorimetric measurement of $[I_{ox}]/[I_{red}]$ ratio of a suitable indicator of known E_m value added to the medium.

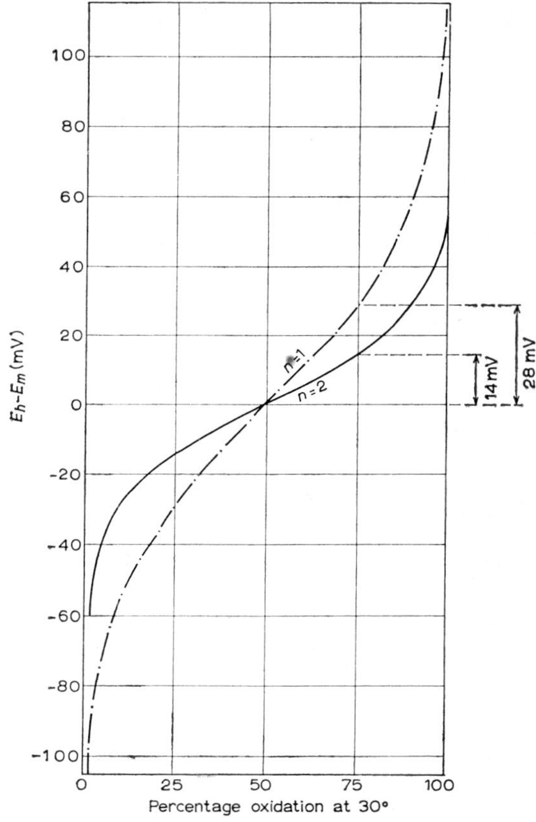

Fig. 2a. Forms of titration curves for systems involving 1 electron (n = 1) and 2 electron (n = 2) transfers. 30°.

Considerable data now exist on the half-reduction potentials of many indicators having a wide spectrum of E_{m7} values. The oxidation–reduction indicators thus constitute a powerful subsidiary tool for the determination of E_h. They have been particularly useful for the study of oxidation–reduction characteristics of living cells.

(c) *Determination of n*

When obtainable, the titration curves have the advantage of permitting to calculate, from the slope at the inflexion point (Fig. 2a), the value of n,

References p. 88

the number of electrons involved in oxidation–reduction. One may also obtain n, if activities are taken as equal to concentrations, from a plot of $E_h - E_m$ for each experimental point against log $(A_{ox})/(A_{red})$ for a system obeying the Eqn. (10), the plot should obviously be a straight line with a slope $2.303 \times RT/nF$ (Fig. 2b): 0.06 V for $n = 1$; 0.03 V for $n = 2$ at 30°.

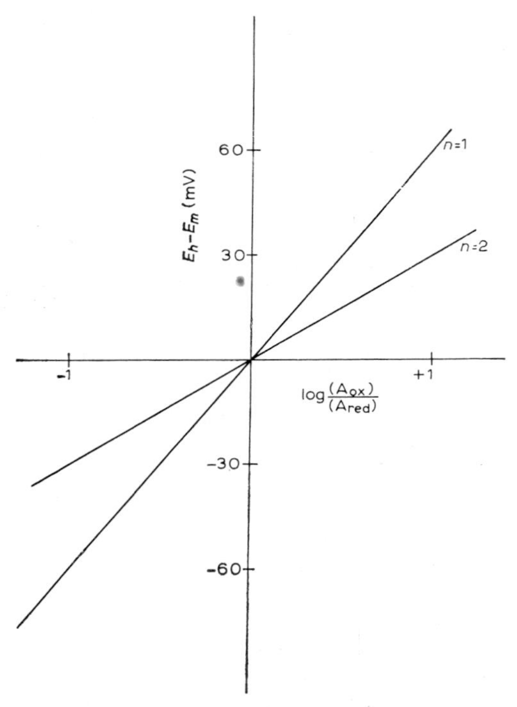

Fig. 2b. Plots of $(E_h - E_m)$ against log $(A_{ox})/(A_{red})$ for systems involving 1 electron ($n = 1$) and 2 electron ($n = 2$) transfers. 30°.

(d) *Measure of potential by coupling*

Potentiometric curves are often hard enough to obtain, particularly with insufficiently pure preparations; for some systems they may not be realizable, for example with particulate enzymes. Flavoenzymes, haemoproteins and similar systems whose absorption characteristics change with the state of oxidation have been successfully treated by studying coupled equilibria with suitable substrate pairs. The principle is the same as in the use of oxidation–reduction indicators, with the difference that metabolite pairs of known oxidation–reduction potential are utilized to obtain that of the system under study.

For example, cytochrome *b* from heart-muscle preparations may be linked to the succinate–fumarate system according to the relation

$$\text{Succinate}^{2-} + 2 \text{ ferricytochrome } b \rightleftharpoons \text{fumarate}^{2-} + 2 \text{ ferrocytochrome } b + 2\,\text{H}^+$$

The equilibrium constant

$$K = \frac{(\text{fumarate}^{2-})\,(\text{ferrocytochrome } b)^2\,(\text{H}^+)^2}{(\text{succinate}^{2-})\,(\text{ferricytochrome } b)^2}$$

may be replaced by an apparent equilibrium constant

$$K'_{ap} = \frac{[\text{fumarate}^{2-}]\,[\text{ferrocytochrome } b]^2}{[\text{succinate}^{2-}]\,[\text{ferricytochrome } b]^2}$$

for experiments conducted at constant pH.

The concentrations of cytochrome *b* respectively in the oxidized and reduced states at equilibrium with the metabolite pair at known concentration ratios may be deduced from spectrophotometric measurements. At a given pH, the half-reduction potential of the cytochrome *b* system, $E_m(b)$ is related to that of the succinate–fumarate system, $E_m(s)$ by the relation

$$E_m(b) = E_m(s) + 0.03 \log K'_{ap} \qquad \text{at } 30^\circ$$

Similarly, for the flavoenzyme D-lactic dehydrogenase

$$\text{Flavo}_{\text{ox}}\text{-enzyme} + \text{D-lactate}^- \rightleftharpoons \text{flavo}_{\text{red}}\text{-enzyme} + \text{pyruvate}^- + \text{H}^+$$

$$E_m(\text{F}) = E_m(\text{L}) + 0.03 \log K'_{ap} \quad \text{where } K'_{ap} = \frac{[\text{FH}]\,[\text{P}]}{[\text{F}]\,[\text{L}]}$$

8. Complex equilibria

(*a*) *Dehydrogenations*

In many reactions of biological interest, for example in metabolic dehydrogenations, electron transfer (oxidation–reduction) is accompanied by simultaneous proton transfer. Consider the lactic acid–pyruvic acid system in presence of the enzyme lactic dehydrogenase and a mediator. The reaction may be represented at very low pH as

$$\text{CH}_3\text{CHOHCOOH} \rightleftharpoons \text{CH}_3\text{COCOOH} + 2\,\text{H}^+ + 2\,\text{e} \tag{11}$$

and at high pH as

$$\text{CH}_3\text{CHOHCOO}^- \rightleftharpoons \text{CH}_3\text{COCOO}^- + 2\,\text{H}^+ + 2\,\text{e} \tag{11a}$$

References p. 88

Consider the last reaction. The equilibrium constant

$$K = \frac{(CH_3COCOO^-)\ (H^+)^2\ (e)^2}{(CH_3CHOHCOO^-)} \tag{12}$$

whence

$$(e) = \sqrt{K\frac{(CH_3CHOHCOO^-)}{(CH_3COCOO^-)}} \cdot \frac{1}{(H^+)} \tag{12a}$$

Applying the general equation of E_h in terms of electron activity (e),

$$E_h = -\frac{RT}{F}\ln(e)$$

$$= -\frac{RT}{2F}\ln K + \frac{RT}{2F}\ln\frac{(CH_3COCOO^-)}{(CH_3CHOH\ COO^-)} + \frac{RT}{F}\ln(H^+) \tag{13}$$

It is necessary to express the electrode equation (13) in terms of experimental quantities, namely S_P, S_L (total concentrations of pyruvic and lactic acids, ionized and non-ionized), K_P and K_L, the ionization constants for the respective acids, and $\gamma_P, \gamma_L, \gamma_{P^-}, \gamma_{L^-}$, the activity coefficients of the specified forms.

$$S_P = \gamma_{P^-}^{-1}(P^-) + \gamma_P^{-1}(P)$$

$$S_L = \gamma_{L^-}^{-1}(L^-) + \gamma_L^{-1}(L)$$

By substituting in Eqn. (13), for (P^-) and (L^-), their values as a function of dissociation constants and activity coefficients, one gets

$$E_h = -\frac{RT}{2F}\ln K + \frac{RT}{2F}\ln\frac{S_P}{S_L} + \frac{RT}{2F}\ln\frac{\gamma_{L^-}^{-1}K_L + \gamma_L^{-1}(H^+)}{\gamma_{P^-}^{-1}K_P + \gamma_P^{-1}(H^+)} \cdot \frac{K_P}{K_L} + \frac{RT}{F}\ln(H^+) \tag{14}$$

The point of half-reduction, E_m, therefore does not correspond in this case to E_0. Moreover, E_m plotted as a function of pH shows segments corresponding to different ionization states (Fig. 3).

The role of ionization exponents may be expected to be still more complex in the case of the succinate–fumarate system, where each component possesses two dissociable protons with different ionization constants (Fig. 3).

Included in Fig. 3 is the classical example of quinol, known to exist in three ionization states.

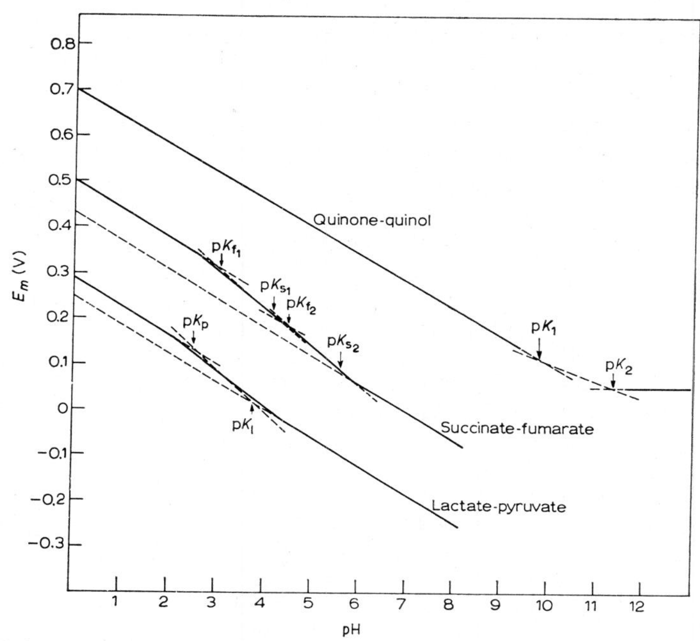

Fig. 3. Relation of half-reduction potential (E_m) to pH for systems lactate–pyruvate, succinate–fumarate and quinone–quinol. Note that ionizing groups are common to oxidant and reductant in the lactic acid–pyruvic acid and in the fumaric acid–succinic acid systems but differ in values of pK'. In the quinone–quinol system, the oxidant does not ionize.

(HO–C₆H₄–OH) ⇌ (O=C₆H₄=O) $+ 2e + 2H^+$ $\quad -\Delta E_m/\Delta pH = 0.06$ V

($^-$O–C₆H₄–OH) ⇌ (O=C₆H₄=O) $+ 2e + H^+$ $\quad -\Delta E_m/\Delta pH = 0.03$ V

($^-$O–C₆H₄–O$^-$) ⇌ (O=C₆H₄=O) $+ 2e$ $\quad -\Delta E_m/\Delta pH = 0$ V

References p. 88

Consider the oxidation–reduction system described by the equation $A^{2-} \rightleftharpoons B + 2\,e$. The reductant A^{2-} arises from quinol A through two successive ionizations, having *apparent* ionization constant K_1', K_2'; the oxidant B, the quinone, is non-ionizable.

Of the three forms A, A^-, A^{2-}, the oxidation–reduction concerns A^{2-} only; its activity or concentration to be introduced in the electrode equation may be derived from the sum of the concentrations of all forms of A (ionized and non-ionized), the ionization exponents and the pH. Thus, let

$$S_O = [B]$$

$$S_R = [A] + [A^-] + [A^{2-}]$$

and let K_1' and K_2' be the first and second apparent ionization constants. Then

$$(A^{2-}) = S_R \cdot \frac{K_1' K_2'}{K_1' K_2' + K_1'(H^+) + (H^+)^2} \cdot \gamma_{A^{2-}}$$

Introduction of this expression for (A^{2-}) in the classical electrode equation gives

$$E_h = E_0 + \frac{RT}{2F} \ln \frac{S_O}{S_R} + \frac{RT}{2F} \ln \left\{(CH^+)^2 + K_1'(H^+) + K_1' K_2'\right\}$$
$$- \frac{RT}{2F} \ln K_1' K_2' + \frac{RT}{2F} \ln \frac{\gamma_B}{\gamma_{A^{2-}}} \qquad (15)$$

By neglecting the activity coefficients

$$E_h = E_0^1 - \frac{RT}{2F} \ln K_1' K_2' + \frac{RT}{2F} \ln \frac{S_O}{S_R} + \frac{RT}{2F} \ln \left\{(H^+)^2 + K_1'(H^+) + K_1' K_2'\right\} \qquad (15a)$$

The above examples underline the importance of secondary effects where they exist and which have to be taken account of in estimating E_0 values. In organic systems, it is usually necessary to undertake determination of E_h values over a wide range of pH. In the case of a simple electron donor–acceptor system without proton transfer, and in the absence of other secondary equilibria (see below), neglecting for the moment the activity coefficients, E_m or E_{m7} is indistinguishable from E_0. In cases where the only secondary reaction is a hydrogen ion dissociation, the mid-point potential E_m becomes equal to E_0 when the activity of hydrogen ions is 1 M, that is when the standardized pH is zero. This value is generally obtained by determining E_m at different pH's and extrapolating to zero pH. In many reactions of biological interest taking place in the presence of enzymes, it may not be practicable to measure E_m in very acid solutions. The slope $\Delta E_m/\Delta$pH obtained in practicable regions of pH is then utilized to calculate E_0. The normal potential thus obtained may not necessarily be the half-reduction potential at pH zero, since ionizations appearing at lower pH might change the slope and consequently the point of intersection on the E_m axis (see example of lactate–pyruvate, Fig. 3). This apparent uncertainty should not trouble us if we keep in mind that the E_0 value calculated from a given slope applies only to the specific equilibrium which determines this slope. For the lactate–pyruvate system, E_0 obtained by extrapolation of E_m at neutral pH corresponds to the free-energy change of the lactate–pyruvate transformation, whereas the value obtained from E_m at very low pH corresponds evidently to the lactic acid–pyruvic acid equilibrium. The free-energy changes of the two systems should obviously be different from each other, since the unequal ionization constants signify different free energies of ionization.

In a general way, the effect of ionization of the oxidant, reductant, or both on the value of E_m at a given pH can be described by taking into account the activities of different species at the pH considered. In systems where activity coefficients or true dissociation constants are not known, the potential is described in terms of concentrations and pH by an equation of the type 15a.

Note on activity coefficients

It should be recalled that the basic electrode equation (10)

$$E_h = E_0 + \frac{RT}{nF} \ln \frac{(A_{ox})}{(A_{red})}$$

requires that activities and not concentrations be taken into consideration. The underlying free-energy relationships $-\Delta G^0 = nFE_0$ supposes that the activity of each substance (A_{ox}, A_{red}, and H^+, if any) considered in an equilibrium equation be unity. The normal electrode potential thus defined is sometimes designated as E^0, but desiring not to multiply symbols, we have written E_0 with the caution that the ratio of oxidant to reductant be the unity in terms of *activities*. The E_0 thus found is equal to the true thermodynamic normal potential E^0, since the free energies of dilution of oxidant and of reductant, each from unit activity to their respective activities in the reaction mixture are equal when $(A_{ox}) = (A_{red})$.

For purpose of free-energy calculations from oxidation–reduction data, it is thus important, whenever possible, to evaluate the activity coefficients of oxidant and reductant under the conditions employed. Note that the use of expressions involving *concentrations* and *apparent* dissociation constants may result in relatively little error if the activity coefficients of the dominant species at a given pH are little different from each other. In the

References p. 88

system lactate–pyruvate, for example, at pH, say 3.2 where the dominant species are the pyruvate ion and the undissociated lactic acid, the correction due to activity coefficients is expected to be more important than at pH 7 where the dominant species are both ionic.

Dehydrogenations considered above are but special examples of cases where the number of reductant molecules differs from that of the oxidant. The treatment here is simplified since hydrogen ion activity is taken care of by pH measurements. In many instances, entities other than hydrogen ion may have to be considered. Consider cases where the reductant is a sulfhydryl compound:

$$2\ \mathrm{RSH} \rightleftharpoons \mathrm{RS{-}SR} + 2\,\mathrm{e} + 2\,\mathrm{H^+}$$

$$K = \frac{(\mathrm{ox})(\mathrm{e})^2\ (\mathrm{H^+})^2}{(\mathrm{red})^2}$$

At 30°C

$$E_h = E_0 + 0.03 \log \frac{(\mathrm{ox})}{(\mathrm{red})^2} + 0.06 \log (\mathrm{H^+}) \qquad (16)$$

$$= E_0 + 0.03 \log \frac{[\mathrm{ox}]}{[\mathrm{red}]^2} + 0.03 \log \frac{\gamma_{\mathrm{ox}}}{(\gamma_{\mathrm{red}})^2} + 0.06 \log (\mathrm{H^+})$$

The midpoint potential, realizing the conditions: (ox) = (red) cannot in this case give E_0 even when E_m values are extrapolated to zero pH, since half-reduction is not sufficient here to eliminate the middle term at right in Eqn. (16). The condition to be realized for obtaining E_0 is obviously:

$$R = (\mathrm{ox})/(\mathrm{red})^2 = 1$$

The absence of activity-coefficient data may result here in considerable error, since the ratio $\gamma_{\mathrm{ox}}/(\gamma_{\mathrm{red}})^2$ is expected to be rather different from unity even when γ_{ox} and γ_{red} are close to each other.

A similar though not identical situation is met with in the case of a group of reactions involving the conversion of an amino group to NH_4^+ ions. A representative of this type is the alanine–ammonium pyruvate transformation.

$$\mathrm{CH_3CHNH_3^+\,COO^-} + \mathrm{H_2O} \rightleftharpoons \mathrm{CH_3COCOO^-} + \mathrm{NH_4^+} + 2\,\mathrm{H^+} + 2\,\mathrm{e} \qquad (17)$$

At 30°C

$$E_h = E_0 + 0.03 \log \frac{[\mathrm{pyruvate}]\ [\mathrm{NH_4^+}]}{[\mathrm{alanine^{+-}}]} + 0.03 \log \frac{\gamma_p\, \gamma_{\mathrm{NH_4^+}}}{\gamma_{\mathrm{ala^{+-}}}} + 0.06 \log(\mathrm{H^+}) \quad (18)$$

E_0 is obtained by measuring E_h for different (pyruvate) (NH_4^+)/(alanine^{+-}) ratios (R) at pH around 7, interpolating to $R = 1$ for each pH, and extrapolating to zero pH by using a 0.06 V/pH slope. Note that the E_0 thus obtained corresponds to the free-energy change of the reaction represented by Eqn. (17).

In brief, the general formulation of half-cell potential (E_h) in terms of the ratio of oxidant to reductant activities has to be modified so as to conform to valid stoichiometric relations. Clark has cited many examples of reactions complicated by the dimerization of oxidant alone, of reductant alone or of both, and also examples of the formation of addition complexes between oxidant and reductant. In cases where the dimer of oxidant or reductant is in reversible equilibrium with the monomer, the overall equation should contain terms involving total molar concentration as well as dimerization constants.

(*b*) *Formation of semiquinones* (*free radicals*)

In an oxidation–reduction involving two-electron transfer, experimental conditions may sometimes be devised to make apparent the formation of a free-radical intermediate containing an odd number of electrons. The existence of more or less short-lived intermediates should not affect the overall thermodynamic relation; but the accumulation of the intermediate may sometimes affect the titration curve sufficiently enough to necessitate special formulations in terms of the intermediate. Consider the scheme

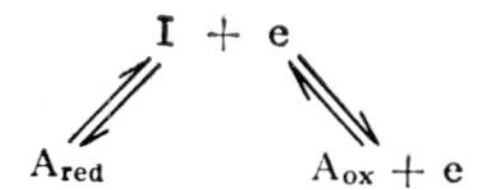

where I is the intermediate containing one exchangeable electron.

The overall system is here considered to be composed of two coupled oxidation–reduction systems one of which involves A_{red} and I (normal potential E_1) and the other I and A_{ox} (normal potential E_2). Since the systems are coupled, the E_h value obtained under given conditions should be linked to both E_1 and E_2 and the ratio of oxidized and reduced forms for each system:

$$E_h = E_1 + \frac{RT}{F} \ln \frac{(\mathrm{I})}{(\mathrm{A_{red}})} = E_2 + \frac{RT}{F} \ln \frac{(\mathrm{A_{ox}})}{(\mathrm{I})} \qquad (19)$$

One gets

$$E_2 - E_1 = \frac{RT}{F} \ln \frac{(\mathrm{I})^2}{(\mathrm{A_{red}})(\mathrm{A_{ox}})} = \frac{RT}{F} \ln K_i \qquad (20)$$

where K_i defined as equal to $(\mathrm{I})^2/(\mathrm{A_{red}})(\mathrm{A_{ox}})$ is the intermediate formation constant according to the relation $\mathrm{A_{red}} + \mathrm{A_{ox}} \rightleftharpoons 2\ \mathrm{I}$. The effect of intermediate formation on the shape of the titration curve thus depends on

References p. 88

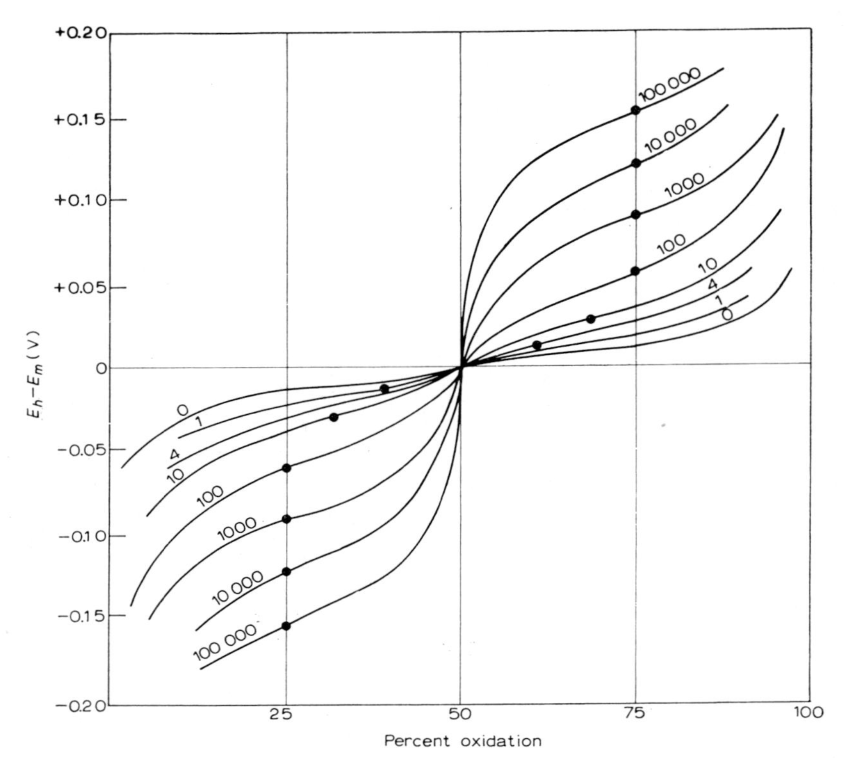

Fig. 4a. Expected forms of titration curves for systems having stable free-radical intermediate. The numbers on the curves are the values of intermediate formation constants K_i. The circles indicate the positions of E_1 and E_2. From Michaelis[1]. Courtesy of the *Journal of Biological Chemistry*.

the value of K_i as seen from Fig. 4a. As the value of K_i declines, the difference between E_2 and E_1 diminishes; at $K_i = 1$, the two potentials become identical and equal to the E_m of a simple system with no intermediates. The experimental titration curves of a real system showing stable intermediates, namely pyocyanine in acid solution, may be seen in Fig. 4b.

(c) *Complex formation*

The consequences of the coupling of an oxidation–reduction process with proton transfer, polymerization or hydrolysis have been briefly outlined in the preceding sections. It is desirable to mention another important aspect, namely the effect of adding a substance (ligand) that combines with one or

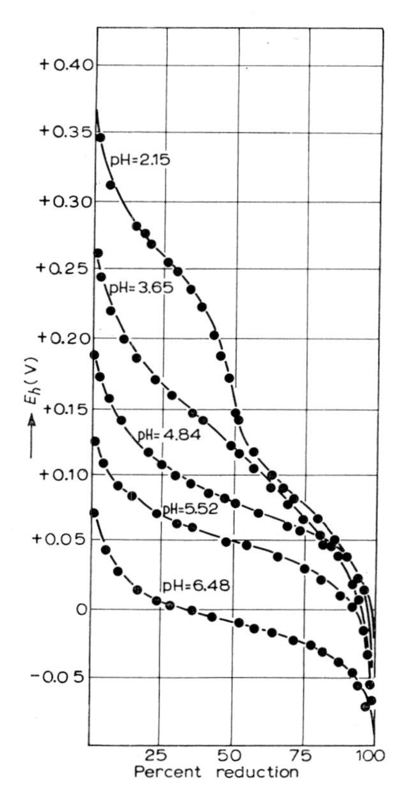

Fig. 4b. Titration curves of pyocyanine in solutions of different pH. From Elema[2]. Courtesy of *Recueil des Travaux Chimiques des Pays-Bas*.

both of the constituents of an oxidation–reduction system. Study of such systems is particularly interesting since they constitute useful models for many important oxidation–reduction enzymes.

The role of metals fixed to enzyme proteins is of interest in biochemistry. In many cases the metal ions which are themselves subject to oxidation–reduction are associated with enzymes that participate in specified biological oxidation–reductions. Of particular significance are the haematin enzymes; different protein moieties associated with the same haematin prosthetic group may constitute different haemoproteins or haematin enzymes having very dissimilar oxidation–reduction characteristics. Some of these are shown in Fig. 5a for purposes of illustration.

Admitting certain simplifications, all these systems might be considered to have been formed as a result of the addition of different ligands to both oxidant and reductant of the original oxidation–reduction system ferro-

References p. 88

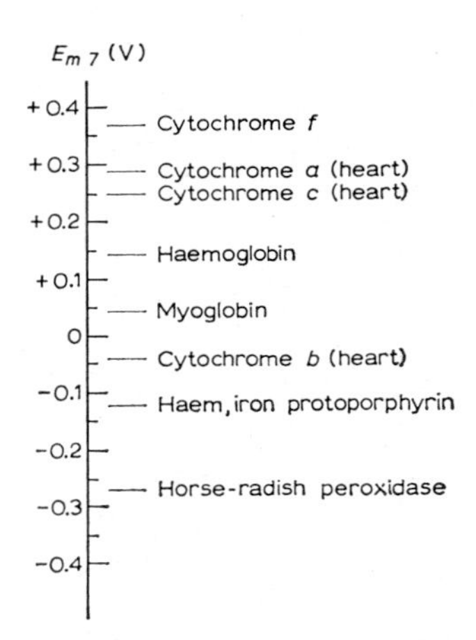

Fig. 5a. Half-reduction potentials of some haemoproteins.

porphyrin $\rightleftharpoons$ ferriporphyrin + e. The direction and extent of shifts of potential associated with the formation of complexes should naturally arouse interest.

Clark and collaborators have treated simple models where it is possible to predict such shifts in terms of dissociation constants of the oxidant–ligand and reductant–ligand complexes. In the case where a ligand L forms a complex OL_p with the oxidant, $K'_O = [O][L]^p/[OL_p]$, and a complex RL_q with the reductant, $K'_R = [R][L]^q/[RL_q]$, the potential of a half-cell containing the *primary* oxidation–reduction system ($R \rightleftharpoons O + e$) together with a total concentration S_L of the ligand may be shown to be, at constant pH, neglecting the activity coefficient terms and utilizing *apparent* equilibrium constants

$$E_h = E_1 + \frac{RT}{nF}\ln\frac{K'_O}{K'_R} + \frac{RT}{nF}\ln\frac{K'_R + S_{L_q}}{K'_O + S_{L_p}} + \frac{RT}{nF}\ln\frac{S_O}{S_R} \qquad (21)$$

where E_1 = half-reduction potential of the primary system, S_O = concentration of oxidant, combined and uncombined, S_R = total concentration of reductant, combined and uncombined.

It is easier to examine the significance of Eqn. 21 by assuming $p = q$, *i.e.* admitting that the ligand forms structurally analogous complexes with oxidant and reductant, assuming also that either S_L is very large or K'_O and K'_R are so small that practically all the oxidant and reductant exist in the form of complexes.

$$S_O \approx [OL_p] \qquad S_R \approx [RL_q]$$

These assumptions result in a simpler relation:

$$E_h = E_1 + \frac{RT}{nF} \ln \frac{K'_O}{K'_R} + \frac{RT}{nF} \ln \frac{[OL_p]}{[RL_q]} \tag{22}$$

At half-reduction of the complex ($[OL_p] = [RL_q]$)

$$E_m = E_1 + \frac{RT}{nF} \ln \frac{K'_O}{K'_R} \tag{22a}$$

This simplified relation permits a visualization of the relation between the half-reduction potential of the primary system (E_1) and that of the complex one (E_m). If $K'_O = K'_R$, one has $E_m = E_1$, in other words, no shift of potential should be observed even though complexes are formed. The condition $K'_O = K'_R$ is necessary and sufficient under given experimental conditions, the numerical value of the constants is without consequence.

When K'_O and K'_R are not equal, there will be a shift of potential; the direction and extent of the shift depends on the ratio K'_O/K'_R. If K'_O is greater than K'_R, that is if the ligand binds more firmly the reduced form

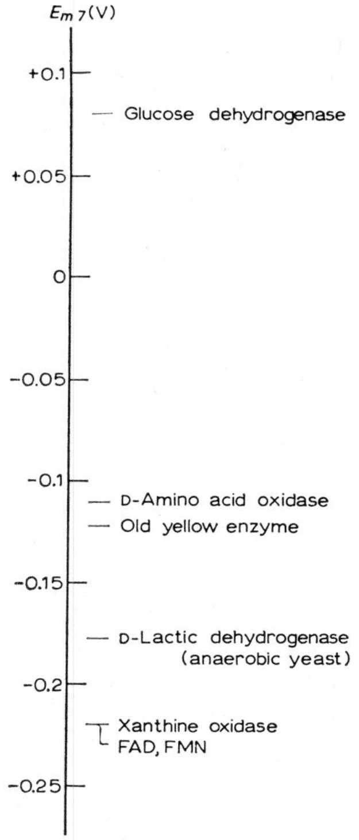

Fig. 5b. Half-reduction potentials of some flavo-enzymes.

References p. 88

R of the primary system, E_m—E_1 should be positive and the half-reduction potential of the complex should be higher in the scale of oxidation–reduction potentials. The reverse is true when K'_R is greater than K'_O. The magnitude of the shift depends on the ratio K'_O/K'_R and can be calculated from (22a). Note that these criteria can be applied only within the limit of conditions imposed by their derivation, *i.e.* when the transformation of the primary system into the complex one consists *only* in the formation of the complexes, with the exclusion of all other phenomena such as change of pH, change in states of aggregation, appearance of new ionizations, etc.

Direct experimental verification of the relation (22a) has been made[3] in the case of the system haem–pilocarpate. E_m—E_1 determined in aqueous buffer solutions accorded well with that calculated from observed K'_O and K'_R in similar conditions. E_m—E_1 was different in 4 *M* urea; the shift was satisfactorily accounted for by a change of the ratio K'_O/K'_R under these conditions, only K'_O being affected by a change of dielectric constant of the medium.

One may speculate on the relative firmness of binding of apoprotein moieties to ferri- and ferroporphyrin in different haemoproteins shown in Fig. 5a. According to existing knowledge, the same metalloporphyrin (iron protoporphyrin) is involved in the formation of most, if not all of these stable complexes. Such large differences of E_m undoubtedly reflect enormous differences in the firmness of bonds between the protein and the oxidized and reduced forms of the metalloporphyrin.

An estimate of this difference in bond strength in terms of free energy can be made from the relation:

$$\Delta G^0 = NF(E_m - E_1) = RT \ln \frac{K_O}{K_R}$$

where the standard free-energy change

$$\Delta G^0 = (\Delta G^0_{f_{OL_p}} - \Delta G^0_{f_O}) - (\Delta G^0_{f_{RL_q}} - \Delta G^0_{f_R})$$

is equal to the difference between the free energies of formation of the oxidized complex and the uncombined oxidant less the difference between the free energies of formation of the reduced complex and the uncombined reductant. This treatment, due to Clark, dissipates doubts that might be entertained on the physical significance of K_O and K_R for systems like cytochrome *c* (covalent linkage); since ΔG^0 can be derived from energies of formation each of which can theoretically be determined independently, it is immaterial whether the complexes OL_p and RL_q be formed reversibly or not, so far as thermodynamic relations are concerned. For metmyoglobin and methaemoglobin, the combination has been shown to be reversible; numerical values can be assigned to both K'_O and K'_R; knowing E_m—E_1

and either of the constants K'_O and K'_R, it is possible to calculate the other[4].

Available data on flavoenzymes (Fig. 5b) permit similar speculation on the differences of association energies between oxidized and reduced flavins on the one hand and the various enzymatic proteins on the other.

9. Oxidation–reduction enzymes

The energy requirements of heterotrophic organisms are met principally through oxidation of carbohydrates. Substantial amounts of energy should thus be released, since carbohydrates are good electron donors and oxygen one of the best electron acceptors known. Part of this energy is released as heat, a good part though in a form capable of being utilized for chemical synthesis, muscular, osmotic and other forms of work. The utilization of foodstuffs by the organism is accomplished through stepwise transformations catalyzed by specific enzymes. The enzymatic equipment involved in intermediary metabolism is described in detail elsewhere in this volume; we intend to confine ourselves to short observations on the sequence of some of these enzymes, namely those concerned with oxidation–reduction.

It is important to note that the oxidation–reduction enzymes in general carry prosthetic groups or coenzymes independently capable of functioning as oxidation–reduction systems. Combination with a protein moiety modifies the initial system (Fig. 5) so as to bring the E_0 value to a level suited to the specific enzymatic function: the role of intermediate between the given metabolite pair. The chain of reactions constituting the overall oxidative transformation of a metabolite, say succinate, to CO_2 is doubled by a parallel chain of linked oxidation–reduction enzymes, the first of which is near the substrate and the last near oxygen, the final acceptor. The energy of transferring electrons from the substrate to oxygen is thus nearly equal to the energy involved in transferring electrons from the reduced enzyme to oxygen. This energy is easily calculated since the redox potential of most oxidation–reduction enzymes as well as the O_2/H_2O system have been determined. The E_m values of the postulated members of a commonly accepted respiratory chain depicted below are given in Table I.

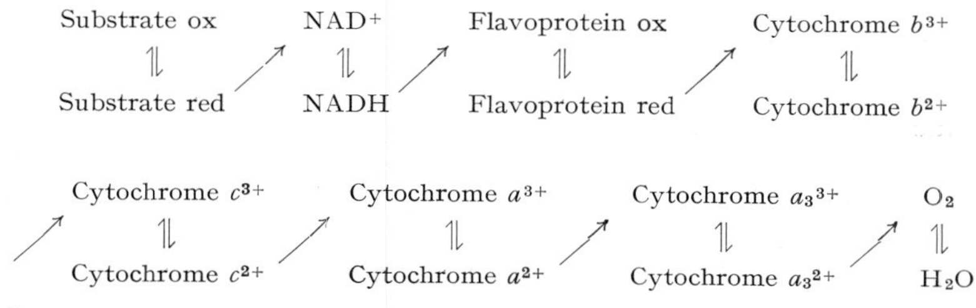

References p. 88

TABLE I

HALF-REDUCTION POTENTIALS OF RESPIRATORY CHAIN SYSTEMS

System	E_m *in V at pH 7*
Pyridine nucleotide	−0.32
Flavoprotein*	−0.06
Cytochrome *b*	−0.04
Cytochrome *c*	+0.25
Cytochrome *a*	+0.29
Cytochrome a_3	+0.285
Oxygen/H_2O	+0.82

* Arbitrarily chosen to be higher than E_{m7} of old yellow enzyme. See Chance and Williams[5].

The free energy derived from metabolism is thus liberated in successive steps, some of which are coupled to endergonic processes; this assures an economic utilization of energy and limits to a minimum its loss as heat.

A potential difference of 1 V corresponds to a free-energy change of about 46 kcal for 2 electron equivalents. The transfer of 1 pair of electrons from reduced pyridine nucleotide to oxygen thus releases about 52 kcal of free energy. Only a part of this energy is released in the form of heat, a good part is utilized for the synthesis of high-energy phosphate bonds necessary for oxidative phosphorylation. The difference of redox potential between adjacent carriers is also of interest, since this permits the location of the energy-yielding steps. For example, one may say that the one oxidative phosphorylation known to occur between cytochrome *c* and molecular oxygen must take place after cytochrome *a*; the very small amount of free energy evolved in the step between cytochrome *c* and cytochrome *a* precludes such energy-requiring synthesis.

10. Intracellular potentials

Many ingenuous experiments have been performed with a view to determine the redox potential of intracellular fluids in microorganisms or in tissues. Two types of experimental observations have been recorded: by injecting a series of non-toxic dyes of known and different E_m values into living cells, it has been possible to delimit a region of potential that can be supposed to exist inside the cell under given conditions. On the other hand, direct electrometric observations have been made, both on cell suspensions and on intracellular fluid under aerobic and anaerobic conditions. Many authors have simultaneously determined the intracellular pH either by micro-injection of pH indicators or by potentiometry with the help of specially devised electrodes.

It has been observed that the reduction of oxidation–reduction indicators by intracellular fluid takes place as if certain distinct potential levels existed therein. Two such levels have been distinguished; one is observable shortly after injection of the dye; a sufficiently long time after the injection, the potential seems to decrease until a limiting value is reached. Observations on numerous systems permit the conclusion that an intracellular potential of between −0.15 V and + 0.2 V at pH 7 is characteristic of a considerable number of organisms and living tissues under aerobic conditions. Some representative figures obtained by microinjection into eggs and tissues in aerobiosis are reproduced in Table II by way of illustration.

The cessation of oxygen supply results in all cases in a lowering of potential. In aerobic organisms, the potential limit is generally in the neighbourhood of −0.2 V at pH 7. It is significant that these potentials are near to what would be expected from the presence of considerable proportions of lactic acid in animal cells under anaerobiosis or alcohol in vegetable cells under the same conditions. In anaerobic organisms the potential may go down much further, and attain values not far from that of the hydrogen electrode in presence of H_2 under 1 atm pressure.

The cell interior is bathed by a multitude of redox systems composed of metabolite pairs and their associated enzymes. The observed potential of an electrode immersed in such a mixture should depend naturally not only on

TABLE II

INTRACELLULAR POTENTIALS

Material	*pH*	E_h	*Reference*
Eggs of *Paracentrotus lividus* (sea Urchins), fertilized or unfertilized	6.6	+0.21	Needham and Needham[6]
Oocytes of *Paracentrotus lividus* (sea Urchins), fertilized or unfertilized	7.2	+0.15	Rapkine and Wurmser[7]
Eggs of *Asterias glacialis*, fertilized or unfertilized	6.6	+0.21	Needham and Needham[6]
Eggs of *Ophiura lacertosa*, unfertilized	6.6	+0.25	Needham and Needham[6]
Eggs of *Sabellaria alveolata*, unfertilized	6.6	+0.24	Needham and Needham[6]
Amoeba proteus	7.6	+0.08	Rapkine and Wurmser[7]
Salivary gland cells of *Chironomus* larvae	7.2	+0.15	Rapkine and Wurmser[7]
Nyctotherus cordiformis	7.1	+0.16	Rapkine and Wurmser[7]

References p. 88

the intensity factor (E_0) but also on the capacity factor (concentration) of the systems involved. In addition, some of these systems should be faster than others, so that the overall "potential" becomes dependent on rate-limiting reactions. The latter are probably responsible for the existence of "potential levels".

Some recent work[16,17] confirms the notion put forward many years ago by one of us[18] that the degree of reduction of certain hydrogen transporters guides the metabolism to one of several alternative pathways; this may be brought forward through direct electrochemical equilibrium or through mediatory action on catalysts. According to this view, respiration and fermentation are only manifestations of the same function which consists in maintaining the redox level of cells to a value compatible with specific synthetic tasks. The latter, it may be recalled, are in a general way, reductions corresponding to an increase of free energy and should consequently be compensated for by being coupled with oxidations.

Certain empirical formulations made on the basis of observed intracellular potentials have been of use in microbiology, agriculture, and in clinical diagnosis.

11. Oxidation–reduction potentials and molecular electronic configurations

Attempts have recently been made[8] to understand the mechanism of functioning of oxidation–reduction coenzymes (NAD, NADP, FAD, FMN, haem) in terms of molecular electronic orbitals. In a reversible redox system, the standard potential E_0 depends both on the electron-donor capacity of the reduced form and the electron-acceptor capacity of the oxidized form. The energy implied in the transfer of an electron from one form to the other thus depends, in general, on the energies of the two orbitals involved in the transfer, *i.e.* the highest occupied molecular orbital (homo) for the reductant and the lowest empty molecular orbital (lemo) for the oxidant. Since $\Delta G = \Delta H - T\Delta S$ a simple relation between the total energy and free energy (hence E_0) can be obtained only if the entropy effects do not interfere. This happens to be the case in quinones, where a simple theoretical relation exists between ΔR and the orbitals involved in the electron transfer, so that E_0 is correlated both with the lemo and with the homo.

12. Table of oxidation–reduction potentials

Table III reproduces reported values of E_{m7} or $E_{R=1}$ at pH 7 of some systems of biological interest. Figures marked with an asterisk correspond to $R = 1$, where R is the ratio of activities or concentrations appearing in the electrode equation.

TABLE III

REPORTED VALUES OF OXIDATION–REDUCTION POTENTIALS AT pH 7 OF SOME SYSTEMS OF BIOLOGICAL INTEREST

System	*Temperature (°C)*	E_{m7} *or* $E_{R=1}$ *(Volts)*	*Ref.*[a]
Flavins			
Riboflavin	30	−0.208	
Riboflavin 5′-phosphate, FMN	30	−0.219	
Flavin-adenine dinucleotide, FAD	30	−0.219	
Flavoproteins			
Xanthine oxidase	30	−0.350	
		−0.220	9
D-Lactic dehydrogenase (anaerobic yeast)	30	−0.178	10
Old yellow enzyme	30	−0.123	
D-Amino oxidase		−0.110	11
NADH–cytochrome reductase (with Fe)		0	
Glucose dehydrogenase		+0.08	12
Butyryl coenzyme A dehydrogenase (with Cu)	25	+0.187	
Decarboxylase (lactic)		+0.19	
Haemoproteins and haem conjugates			
Horse radish peroxidase	30	−0.271	
Haem–(pilocarpate)$_2$	30	−0.230	3
Haem–$(CN)_2$	30	−0.190	
Haem, Fe protoporphyrin	30	−0.120	
Cytochrome b_6 (chloroplasts)	20	−0.06	
Cytochrome *b* (heart)	20	−0.04	
		+0.058	13
		+0.076	13a
		+0.068	13b
Cytochrome b_3 (pea leaves)		+0.04	
Cytochrome *b* (wheat root)		+0.15	
Metmyoglobin	30	+0.046	
Methaemoglobin	30	+0.144	
Cytochrome *c* (heart)	30	+0.250	
Cytochrome *a* (heart)	20	+0.29	
Cytochrome oxidase	25	+0.285	
Metabolites and miscellaneous			
Cysteine–cystine	37	−0.40*	
D-Glucose–gluconolactone	30	−0.362	
Thioglycollic acid	30	−0.340*	
NADH–NAD^+	25	−0.320	
NADPH–$NADP^+$	30	−0.316	
Propanol–acetone	25	−0.286	
L-β-Hydroxybutyrate–acetoacetate	25	−0.284	
Glutathione		−0.23*	
Formylcysteine		−0.23*	
Ethanol–acetaldehyde	30	−0.200	
D-Lactate–pyruvate	27	−0.190	14
L-Malate–oxaloacetate	25	−0.157	
Glycerate–hydroxypyruvate	25	−0.150	
D(—)Valine–NH_4^+-α-ketoisovalerate	30	−0.129*	15
D(—)Alanine–NH_4^+-pyruvate	30	−0.127*	15
Succinate–fumarate	25	+0.024	
Ascorbic acid	30	+0.058	

[a] References are given here only for those cases not cited or discussed by Clark (Bibliography, item 1).

References p. 88

BIBLIOGRAPHY

1 W. M. Clark, *Oxidation–Reduction Potentials of Organic Systems*, Williams and Wilkins, Baltimore, 1960.
2 R. Wurmser, *Oxydation et Réduction*, Presses Universitaires de France, Paris, 1930.
3 L. Michaelis, *Oxydations–Reduktions Potentiale*, Springer, Berlin, 1933.

REFERENCES

1 L. Michaelis, *J. Biol. Chem.*, 96 (1932) 703.
2 B. Elema, *Rec. Trav. Chim.*, 50 (1931) 807.
3 R. Banerjee, *J. Chim. Phys.*, 57 (1960) 615.
4 R. Banerjee, *Biochim. Biophys. Acta*, 64 (1962) 368.
5 B. Chance and G. R. Williams, *Adv. Enzymol.*, 17 (1956) 65.
6 J. Needham and D. M. Needham, *Proc. Roy. Soc. (London)*, *B*, 98 (1925) 259; 99 (1926) 173; 99 (1926) 383.
7 L. Rapkine and R. Wurmser, *Compt. Rend. Soc. Biol.*, 95 (1926) 604; *Proc. Roy. Soc. (London) B*, 102 (1927) 128.
8 A. Pullman, *J. Theor. Biol.*, 2 (1962) 259.
9 H. Niki, *Med. J. Osaka Univ.*, 9 (1957) 59.
10 M. Iwatsubo, *Biochim. Biophys. Acta*, 77 (1963) 568.
11 T. Yamano, Y. Miyake and K. Aki, *Tokushima J. Exptl. Med.*, 6 (1959) 137.
12 T. Yamano, Y. Miyake, K. Aki, K. Kusai and I. Sekuzu, *Tokushima J. Exptl. Med.*, 7 (1960) 169.
13 J. P. Straub and J. P. Colpa-Boonstra, *Biochim. Biophys. Acta*, 60 (1962) 650.
13a F. A. Holton and J. P. Colpa-Boonstra, *Biochem. J.*, 76 (1960) 179.
13b D. Feldman and W. W. Wainio, *J. Biol. Chem.*, 235 (1960) 3635.
14 F. Labeyrie, L. Naslin, A. Curdel and R. Wurmser, *Biochim. Biophys. Acta*, 41 (1960) 509.
15 R. Banerjee and R. Wurmser, *Biochim. Biophys. Acta*, 59 (1962) 216.
16 T. Bücher and M. Klingenberg, *Angew. Chem.*, 70 (1958) 552.
17 B. Chance and M. Baltscheffsky, *Biochem. J.*, 68 (1958) 283.
18 R. Wurmser, *Biol. Rev. Cambridge Phil. Soc.*, 7 (1932) 350.

Chapter IV

Enzyme Kinetics
(Optimum pH, Temperature and Activation Energy)

EDWIN A. DAWES

Department of Biochemistry, University of Hull (Great Britain)

1. Introduction

It is the purpose of the present Chapter to survey some general aspects of the effects of pH and temperature on enzyme-catalysed reactions. These effects may be quite complicated and are mainly attributable to the protein nature of enzymes, although the ionizing groups of other reactants must also be considered in connection with pH.

At the outset, it must be stressed that since a change of temperature usually affects ionization processes, the pH of an ionizing system will also undergo alteration in response to temperature variation. This interplay of temperature and pH has been emphasized by Levy and Benaglia[1] in their studies on protein denaturation. They pointed out that the intensity factors associated with pH and temperature are continuous and not mutually exclusive functions in aqueous solutions.

The effects of pH on enzymatic reactions may be manifest through some or all of the reactants, *e.g.* enzymes, substrates, coenzymes and co-factors, by virtue of ionizing groups. Moreover, pH affects the maximum velocity and the substrate affinity of an enzyme in different ways, so that the optimum pH can vary with substrate concentration. Perhaps the most striking example of this is encountered with alkaline phosphatase which at high concentrations of α-glycerophosphate has an optimum pH of about 9.1, but at lower, non-saturating concentrations[2] has an optimum at pH 7.4. The difference between artificial *in vitro* conditions and those encountered within the cell undoubtedly explain the apparent anomaly of an enzyme functioning optimally at a pH which is most unlikely to be found under physiological conditions.

When extrapolating *in vitro* results to *in vivo* conditions attention must also be paid to variation of pH at different localities within the cell. A

References p. 124

further factor is the difference in pH at surfaces compared with that in the bulk of the solution[3], a phenomenon illustrated by the well-known "protein error" of indicators, which is due in part to the adsorption of the indicator at an ionized surface where the pH is different from that in solution. Another problem to be considered under *in vivo* conditions is the occurrence of metabolic sequences of enzymes, which function as compact units. In these units the product of one enzyme may react so rapidly with the next enzyme in the sequence that it has not time to equilibrate with its surroundings, and hence may be unaffected by the pH of its immediate environment.

These examples serve to illustrate some of the differences between *in vitro* conditions and the living organism; the present paucity of information concerning such differences frequently makes the interpretation of *in vitro* experiments difficult.

Temperature has a profound effect on enzymatic activity and hence on overall metabolism. Mammalian organisms have efficient regulatory mechanisms which control the body temperature to within a range of a few degrees and therefore comparatively little variation in activity *in vivo* might be expected. However, some mammals and birds which are homoeothermic when active, are able to disengage the regulatory mechanism under certain conditions and become almost poikilothermic. The resulting reduction in metabolic rate produces torpidity and enables the animals to survive adverse environmental conditions for prolonged periods. This process of hibernation is not essentially different from the diurnal torpidity of bats and humming birds[4]. During recent years the technique of hypothermia has been the focus of considerable attention in surgery[5]. By suitable methods the patient's body temperature is lowered to 27°, or even 15°, to decrease the overall metabolic rate. Hypothermia presents certain problems associated with the reduced metabolic rate, such as respiratory acidosis and increased lactate production[5,6], which both lower the pH.

In contrast to mammals, poikilothermic animals undergo a marked daily variation of temperature, which may be as much as 25°, and therefore appreciable changes in enzymatic activity would be expected. While undoubtedly the variation of rates in cold-blooded animals is considerably greater than in mammals, nevertheless poikilothermic animals have evolved various homoeostatic mechanisms to compensate for these wide temperature differences and to maintain a certain level of metabolism which would otherwise be impossible. Various aspects of these problems have been reviewed by Bullock[7].

Further interesting examples of the adjustment of metabolic rates to environment are provided by the thermophilic bacteria and algae which live in hot springs at about 70°, a temperature which causes inactivation of most enzymes.

The topics considered in this Chapter have been the subject of reviews and extended treatments by Alberty[8,9], Dixon and Webb[10], Laidler[11], Reiner[12], Sizer[13], Stearn[14], Johnson *et al.*[51] and Bray and White[73].

2. Effect of pH

(*a*) *General considerations*

The activity of an enzyme is influenced by the pH of the medium. Generally activity is manifest over only a small range of pH, within which a definite optimum pH is discernible and outside which the activity falls rapidly to zero. The pH optimum varies widely from one enzyme to another, and examples are known of enzymes which function best in acid, alkaline and neutral solutions respectively.

The observed pH optimum may be due to one or more of the following reasons (*a*) the irreversible inactivation of the enzyme on one or both sides of the optimum, (*b*) an effect on the affinity of the enzyme for its substrate, the affinity decreasing on either side of the optimum with concomitant decrease of enzyme saturation, or (*c*) a reversible effect on the maximum velocity of the reaction, V.

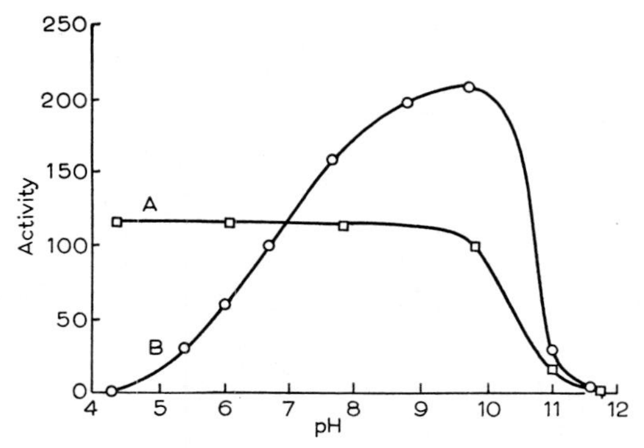

Fig. 1. Influence of pH on the activity of monoamine (tyramine) oxidase. Curve A shows the activity of the enzyme at pH 7.3 after being exposed for 5 min to the various pH values shown. Curve B is the activity when tested at the different pH values. The apparent optimum pH is clearly caused by irreversible inactivation of the enzyme. (Hare[74].)

The effect of pH on enzyme stability may be tested by holding the enzyme at a range of pH values for a given period and then readjusting the pH to some arbitrary value at which the activity can be measured, when irreversible inactivation will be revealed (Fig. 1). However, the extent of inactivation is dependent on the duration of exposure to the adverse pH and therefore the shape of the pH–activity curve and the apparent optimum pH are functions of time. In this respect the optimum pH may be compared with the "optimum temperature" (p. 104).

The effect of pH on the affinity of the enzyme is readily eliminated by the use of a substrate concentration high enough to saturate the enzyme at all pH values investigated. One of the major sources of error in this type of work has been the assumption, usually without experimental verification, that a substrate concentration adequate to saturate the enzyme at one particular pH also does so at other pH values. As the affinity may change considerably with alteration of pH, the assumption is often fallacious. The only safe method to define the pH effect is by determination of the maximum velocity of reaction, V, and the Michaelis constant, K_m, at each pH value by a suitable technique, *e.g.* that of Lineweaver and Burk[15]. However, most of the published pH curves are composite ones and do not distinguish between the effect of pH on V and K_m.

For an explanation of the effect of pH on enzymes we must look to their protein nature. Proteins behave as polyvalent electrolytes and, apart from the N-terminal and C-terminal groups, the polar side-chain groups of the amino acid residues are responsible for their electrolyte behaviour. The ionization of these groups, and consequently the resultant net charge on the protein, depends on their pK values and the pH of the medium. Typical side-chain groups of proteins and their approximate pK' values are compared in Table I. Hence every enzyme will behave in a characteristic manner, according to its amino acid composition, when the pH is changed. Various ionic species will be present but, since the activity is usually limited to a small range of pH, it is probable that only one of these species will be catalytically active. Furthermore, in the light of present knowledge concerning the role of the active centre in enzyme action, it might be expected that the primary effect of pH on activity would be on the charged groups of the active centre, or those in close proximity to it, whereas the ionization of groups further removed from the active centre would have relatively

TABLE I

pK' VALUES OF TERMINAL AND SIDE-CHAIN GROUPS OF PROTEINS

Group	*Amino acid residue*	*pK′ (25°)*
α-Carboxyl	C-terminal	3.0–3.2
Carboxyl	Aspartic acid	3.0–4.7
	Glutamic acid	~4.5
α-Amino	N-terminal	7.6–8.4
ε-Amino	Lysine	9.4–10.6
Imidazolyl	Histidine	5.6–7.0
Sulphydryl	Cysteine	9.1–10.8
Phenolic hydroxyl	Tyrosine	9.8–10.4
Guanidyl	Arginine	11.6–12.6

little effect. In recent years considerable attention has been directed to the elucidation of the amino acid sequence around the active centres of enzymes by methods which have included the use of irreversible inhibitors such as diisopropyl fluorophosphate, iodoacetate and bromoacetate, and by analysis of velocity–pH curves for enzymes[16,17]. This latter aspect is of paramount interest in the present context, since it emphasizes the importance of pH studies with enzymes as a means of linking kinetic investigations with those of the mechanism of action. The technique has been successfully applied in recent studies with bovine pancreatic ribonuclease[76] and with chymotrypsin[77].

Chymotrypsin may be cited as an example of an enzyme whose catalytic activity depends on at least three groups, two of which, belonging to a serine and a histidine residue respectively, have been thoroughly studied. More recently pH–rate studies have enabled the third catalytically reactive group to be identified as the amino group of the N-terminal isoleucine residue[77]. Activity of the enzyme parallels protonation of this group and loss of activity follows its acetylation.

Chymotrypsinogen can be acetylated by suitable treatment with acetic anhydride and, under the proper conditions, trypsin activation of this product yields an acetylated chymotrypsin which has only one amino group—that of the new N-terminal isoleucine. The pH–rate profile for the hydrolysis of acetyltryptophan ethyl ester by this acetylated enzyme is a bell-shaped curve (*cf.* Fig. 3) similar to that observed with many substrates of chymotrypsin. If the N-terminal isoleucine is amidinated by reaction with methylacetimidate the pK of its amino group shifts from 8.5–8.8 to more than 12; the resulting enzyme no longer displays a bell-shaped pH–rate profile for ester hydrolysis but an S-shaped curve with activity remaining constant from pH 8 to pH 11. As neither hydroxyl nor imidazolyl groups react with methylacetimidate it can be concluded that the right-hand side of the bell-shaped curve is associated with the deprotonization of the charged N-terminal amino group. Acetylation of this amino group is accompanied by loss of activity.

(*b*) *The Michaelis pH functions*

It may be reasoned that if an enzyme is active only in one particular ionic form then two charged groups of the active centre (or in close proximity to it) must be primarily involved in activity. These would correspond to the groups which ionize or lose their charge first when the pH is altered from the optimum in the acid and alkaline directions respectively; they are frequently referred to as the acidic and basic groups of the enzyme. Obviously as the pH becomes further removed from the optimum other ionizing

References p. 124

groups will be affected, but these correspond to changes in inactive forms of the enzyme and therefore are not relevant to the present discussion. This type of simplification makes it possible to treat the effect of pH on enzymes in terms of only two ionizing groups and hence to derive equations applicable to a dibasic acid or an ampholyte. In the following treatment the case of a symmetrical dibasic acid AH_2 is considered.

If a compound AH_2 ionizes in two successive stages, characterized by equilibrium (ionization) constants K_1 and K_2 respectively,

$$AH_2 \rightleftharpoons AH^- + H^+$$

$$AH^- \rightleftharpoons A^{2-} + H^+$$

then

$$K_1 = \frac{[AH^-][H^+]}{[AH_2]} \quad \text{and} \quad K_2 = \frac{[A^{2-}][H^+]}{[AH^-]}$$

The total compound, A_t, will be the sum of all the different forms of the compound present in the system, *i.e.*

$$A_t = [AH_2] + [AH^-] + [A^{2-}]$$

If the equilibrium equations are solved for each of these forms the following expressions are obtained

$$[AH_2] = \frac{A_t}{1 + \dfrac{K_1}{[H^+]} + \dfrac{K_1 K_2}{[H^+]^2}} = \frac{A_t}{f} \qquad (1)$$

$$[AH^-] = \frac{A_t}{1 + \dfrac{[H^+]}{K_1} + \dfrac{K_2}{[H^+]}} = \frac{A_t}{f^-} \qquad (2)$$

$$[A^{2-}] = \frac{A_t}{1 + \dfrac{[H^+]}{K_2} + \dfrac{[H^+]^2}{K_1 K_2}} = \frac{A_t}{f^{2-}} \qquad (3)$$

The denominators of these equations may be represented by f, f^- and f^{2-} respectively, as shown on the right-hand side above; these are known as the Michaelis *pH functions*[18]. Hence

$$A_t = f[AH_2] = f^-[AH^-] = f^{2-}[A^{2-}]$$

Thus the amount of any ionic form of a compound present in the system is obtained by dividing the total amount of the compound by the appropriate pH function.

The pH functions each contain three terms and when the pH is changed each term will in turn become dominant. For example, considering the intermediate form AH^-, at low pH (high $[H^+]$) the dominant term for f^- is $[H^+]/K_1$, whereas at high pH $K_2/[H^+]$ becomes dominant. For both these extremes

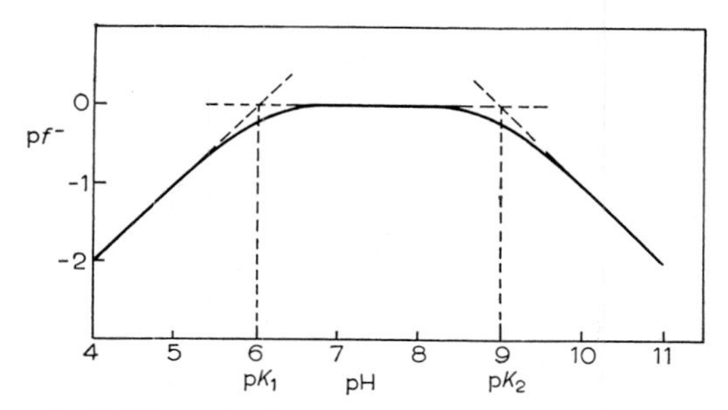

Fig. 2. Variation of pf^- (Eqn. 2) with pH, showing how the two pK values can be evaluated by extrapolation of the linear portions of the curve to their points of intersection.

the ratio A_t/f^- tends to zero, *i.e.* there is a negligible amount of AH^- present in the system. Between these two extremes, however, $[AH^-]$ must rise to a maximum at a particular pH value where these two terms are small in comparison with 1. This will occur when $[H^+]/K_1 = K_2/[H^+]$, that is when $[H^+] = \sqrt{(K_1K_2)}$, and the pH for the maximum is therefore given by

$$\text{pH} = \frac{\text{p}K_1 + \text{p}K_2}{2} \tag{4}$$

If the negative logarithm of f^-, denoted by $\text{p}f^-$, is plotted against pH, the resulting graph consists of three straight-line sections, each corresponding to a region of pH where only one term is important, joined by curved portions, corresponding to the regions where two terms are significant (Fig. 2). The gradient of the linear sections is equal to the power to which the hydrogen ion concentration is raised in the corresponding dominant term. Thus in Fig. 2, in the range of pH 4–5 the gradient is $+1$ corresponding to the region where $[H^+]/K_1$ is the dominant term, and $\text{p}f^- = -\log [H^+]/K_1 = \text{pH} - \text{p}K_1$. At pH 10–11 the dominant term is now $K_2/[H^+]$ and the gradient is -1; here $\text{p}f^- = \text{p}K_2 - \text{pH}$. Between pH 7 and 8, $\text{p}f^-$ is independent of pH and the curve has a zero slope. By producing the straight-line sections of the graph to their points of intersection the pK values may be ascertained; this is shown in Fig. 2. The general feature of such plots is that the gradient changes by one unit for each pK value. Graphs may be drawn in a similar manner for pf and $\text{p}f^{2-}$.

It should be noted with these plots that the pK values can be evaluated with reasonable accuracy only if they are fairly well separated, *e.g.* 3 units or more apart. The same consideration applies to the plot of maximum velocity against pH (Fig. 3), where $\text{p}K_1$ and $\text{p}K_2$ can be read off the curve as the pH values at which the velocity is one half of that at the optimum pH (compare with the determination of pK values from titration curves).

References p. 124

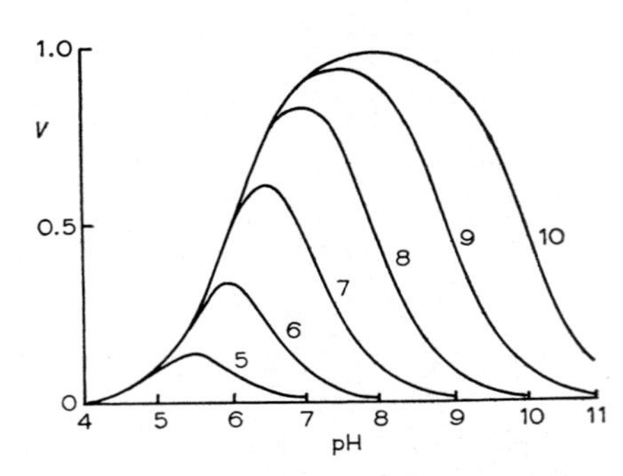

Fig. 3. Variation of the maximum initial velocity of reaction V with pH according to Eqn. 8, with $\bar{k}_{+2}\,e = 1$ and $pK_{es_1} = 6.00$ and the values of pK_{es_2} as shown on the graph. (Alberty and Massey[25].)

If the pK values are close together, however, this cannot be done accurately, as inspection of Fig. 3 will reveal. To calculate K values under these conditions, Alberty and Massey[25] showed that the following equations were applicable

$$K_{es_1} K_{es_2} = [H^+]_1 [H^+]_2 \tag{4a}$$

$$K_{es_1} = [H^+]_1 + [H^+]_2 - 4\sqrt{[H^+]_1 [H^+]_2} \tag{5}$$

where $[H^+]_1$ and $[H^+]_2$ are the hydrogen ion concentrations on the acidic and basic sides, respectively, at which the velocity is one half of that at the optimum pH. Here again, the closer together are the values of pH_1 and pH_2, the greater is the error in the calculated pK values.

The effects of pH on the equilibria of oxidation–reduction, and phosphorylation reactions[19], and on enzyme–substrate and enzyme–inhibitor combination have been treated in a similar fashion to ionization by Dixon and made the basis of a unified theory[20].

The foregoing treatment applies equally to any system undergoing two successive ionizations, *e.g.* an ampholyte, such as an amino acid, with positive and negative ion forms and having an intermediary dipolar ion form with no net charge. In general, any three ionic forms suffice provided that the one corresponding to AH_2 has the maximum number of protons. In the case of an enzyme, if the intermediate form were the active entity, then the pH at which its concentration is maximum would correspond to the pH of optimum activity; it might, under these conditions, correspond to the isoelectric form of the enzyme protein. This concept formed the basis of a theory propounded by Michaelis and Davidsohn[21] in 1911. However, investigation of the electrophoretic behaviour of various enzymes at their dotimum pH revealed that some migrated whereas others did not. The isoelectric species is therefore not always the active form of an enzyme.

Northrop[22] studied the action of pepsin and trypsin on a variety of proteins such as casein, edestin, gelatin, haemoglobin and globin, which have isoelectric points within the range 4.7 to 6.8. The pH–activity curves for these substrates coincided well with the titration curves of the proteins. He found that pepsin acted only on positively charged and trypsin only on negatively charged proteins; moreover pepsin combined most readily with its substrate in the region of its optimum pH. These and other data (see Haldane[23] for a summary) indicate that the active form of pepsin is negatively charged and that of trypsin is positively charged.

In the preceding derivations it should be noted that K_1 and K_2 refer to the first and second stages of the ionization and are not the ionization constants of particular groups (Adams[24]). Dixon and Webb[10] have emphasized this by pointing out that although the distinction is not very obvious when dealing with a symmetrical dicarboxylic acid such as succinic acid, since the same intermediate form is produced irrespective of which carboxyl group ionizes first, this is not true of an unsymmetrical molecule. For example, with the dibasic acid

$$\begin{array}{ll} R \cdot CH \cdot COOH & (a) \\ \quad\ \ | & \\ \quad\ CH_2 \cdot COOH & (b) \end{array}$$

two different intermediate forms of a singly-charged anion will be produced by the ionization of carboxyl groups *a* and *b* respectively. The unsymmetrical acid therefore has a total of four forms as opposed to the three of a symmetrical acid. While this distinction is unimportant for titration purposes since the two intermediate forms are equivalent and the amount of alkali required is the same, it may be of considerable importance for enzyme activity. The state of the ionizing groups of the active centre determines the activity of the enzyme and it is quite possible that only one of the intermediate forms will be active. The important terms in these circumstances are therefore K_a and K_b, the group-ionization constants, as opposed to the stages of ionization, K_1 and K_2, which are of interest for titration.

Dixon and Webb have considered the case of an unsymmetrical dibasic acid in detail and have derived the appropriate pH functions for the four states of ionization[10].

(c) *Effect of pH on the maximum velocity of reaction*

The state of ionization of the enzyme, substrate and enzyme–substrate complex may all be affected by pH. If the substrate concentration used is high enough to saturate the enzyme at all pH values tested, then the effect of pH on the maximum velocity of reaction, V, will be established. These

References p. 124

conditions ensure that all of the enzyme is present as the enzyme–substrate complex, the breakdown of which determines the overall rate of reaction. Consequently the effect of pH on the maximum velocity is influenced solely by the ionic state of the complex and is independent of the changes in the state of ionization of the free enzyme or substrate. The latter factors do, of course, influence K_m, but these effects are eliminated by the use of high substrate concentrations.

For the general enzyme reaction

$$\mathrm{E} + \mathrm{S} \underset{k_{-1}}{\overset{k_{+1}}{\rightleftharpoons}} \mathrm{ES} \overset{k_{+2}}{\rightarrow} \mathrm{E} + \mathrm{P}$$

the velocity of reaction is $v = k_{+2}\, c$, where c is the concentration of the enzyme–substrate complex. When the enzyme is saturated with substrate, c can be equated with e, the total concentration of enzyme, so that $V = k_{+2}\, e$. However, as only one ionic form of the complex is assumed to react, while c and k_{+2} refer to the total complex, *i.e.* all ionic forms present, k_{+2} will vary as the concentration of the reactive species varies with changes in pH. This means that k_{+2} is a composite term embracing the rate constant for the breakdown of the reactive species (denoted by $\tilde{k}_{+2}$) which is independent of pH, and the appropriate pH function which determines the concentration of this species at any pH.

The phenomenon of the pH optimum indicates that the reactive form of the complex is an intermediate state, so that the appropriate pH function will be f^- (Eqn. 2) and, using the terminology of Dixon and Webb[10],

$$k_{+2} = \frac{\tilde{k}_{+2}}{f^-_{es}} \tag{6}$$

where the subscript *es* refers to the ES complex. For convenience, the active form of the complex may be represented as ES^n, where n is the net negative charge; this does not presuppose that any particular ionizing groups are essential for activity nor any specified charged form. Then

$$v = \tilde{k}_{+2} \frac{c}{f^-_{es}} \tag{7}$$

where c/f^-_{es} is the concentration of ES^n and $\tilde{k}_{+2}$ the rate constant for its decomposition. The maximum velocity occurs when $c = e$, therefore

$$V = \frac{\tilde{k}_{+2}\, e}{f^-_{es}} = \frac{\tilde{k}_{+2}\, e}{1 + \dfrac{[\mathrm{H}^+]}{K_{es_1}} + \dfrac{K_{es_2}}{[\mathrm{H}^+]}} \tag{8}$$

The ionization constants K_{es_1} and K_{es_2} refer to the acid and alkaline sides respectively of the pH curve for the complex. Eqn. 8 represents the bell-shaped curve which is frequently obtained experimentally when V is plotted against pH. An example of this is shown in Fig. 3 for cases where pK_{es_1} is held constant at 6.0 and pK_{es_2} is varied from 5 to 10.

If it is assumed that the ionizations occur rapidly in comparison with the rate of formation and decomposition of ES, then the ionic forms will be in equilibrium with one another throughout and, using the formulation of Alberty and Massey[25], the system may be written as

$$\begin{array}{ccccc} E^{n-1} & & ES^{n-1} & & \\ \Updownarrow K_{e1} & & \Updownarrow K_{es1} & & \\ S + E^{n} & \underset{\tilde{k}_{-1}}{\overset{\tilde{k}_{+1}}{\rightleftharpoons}} & ES^{n} & \xrightarrow{\tilde{k}_{+2}} & E^{n} + P \\ \Updownarrow K_{e2} & & \Updownarrow K_{es2} & & \\ E^{n+1} & & ES^{n+1} & & \end{array} \qquad (I)$$

The rate constants are appropriate to the particular ionic species involved in the reaction. For the treatment of cases where the other ionic forms of the ES complex, *i.e.* ES^{n-1} and ES^{n+1}, might be decomposed to yield products the reader is referred to Dixon and Webb[10]. At present, however, there is no experimental evidence to suggest that two or more forms undergo simultaneous breakdown. If logarithms are taken of Eqn. 8, we may write

$$\log V = \log \tilde{k}_{+2}\, e + pf^{-}{}_{es} \qquad (9)$$

and, since $\log \tilde{k}_{+2}\, e$ does not vary with pH, a plot of $\log V$ against pH gives a graph similar to that shown in Fig. 2. This enables the pK values of the ionizing groups of the ES complex which will affect the activity to be ascertained from the points of intersection of the linear portions of the plot. These refer to the groups of the active centre or to those in its close proximity. If the pK values are close together, however, it is not possible to determine them with accuracy in plots of this type.

There are few reliable data at present available on the effect of pH on V; frequently there is uncertainty that the enzyme was saturated with substrate at all pH values tested. Fumarase was studied by Massey and Alberty[26], and Dixon and Webb[10] have presented $\log V$ *versus* pH plots for their data which reveal pK values of about 5.7 and 7.7 for the enzyme–fumarate complex, and 7 and possibly 9 for the enzyme–malate complex. Laidler[27] has made similar plots for the cholinesterase and xanthine oxidase data of Hase[28] and Lowry *et al.*[29] respectively, but in each case the data permitted only one pK to be evaluated.

(*d*) *Effect of pH on the Michaelis constant*

The effect of pH on the substrate constant and Michaelis constant has been

References p. 124

treated by Dixon[20] and Dixon and Webb[10] using equilibrium theory and by Waley[30] and Laidler[31] using steady state kinetics. The equilibrium theory approach[10] is adopted here for detailed derivation.

If an enzymatic reaction occurs as outlined in Scheme I on p. 99, where it is assumed that the substrate reacts in the unionized form, then the reaction may be written as

$$E^n + S \rightleftharpoons ES^n \rightarrow E^n + P \tag{10}$$

Further, provided that E^n and S remain in equilibrium throughout the reaction, the equation

$$\tilde{K}_s = \frac{[E^n][S]}{[ES^n]} \tag{11}$$

holds for the system. $\tilde{K}_s$ denotes that the equilibrium (substrate) constant applies to the ionic forms defined by Eqn. 10, and is therefore independent of pH. It is distinct from K_s which applies to the total enzyme, substrate and complex, *i.e.*

$$K_s = \frac{[E_t][S_t]}{[ES_t]} \tag{12}$$

where the subscript t denotes "total". If the respective pH functions are now substituted in this equation

$$K_s = \frac{f^-{}_e[E^n]f_s[S]}{f^-{}_{es}[ES^n]} = \tilde{K}_s \frac{f^-{}_e \cdot f_s}{f^-{}_{es}} \tag{13}$$

In an alternative form

$$pK_s = p\tilde{K}_s + pf_e{}^- + pf_s - pf^-{}_{es} \tag{14}$$

It should be noted that Eqn. 13 is obtained irrespective of the assumption made concerning the ionic forms involved in the combination; the pH functions used are determined solely by the way in which the equilibrium constant of Eqn. 14 is defined.

The derivation obtained may now be used to interpret the effect of pH on the system in the manner described by Dixon[20]. If pK_s is plotted against pH the slope of the curve will be dependent on the three pf terms of Eqn. 14, which will behave in a similar manner to that described for Fig. 2 except that since one term ($pf^-{}_{es}$) is of different sign to the others its effect will be inverted. (In Eqn. 14 the $p\tilde{K}_s$ term is a constant which only determines the vertical position of the graph.) The following "rules" have been enunciated by Dixon[20]. Provided that the pK values are sufficiently separated, the resulting graph consists of linear sections joined by short curved portions and the linear sections have integral gradients, *e.g.* −1, 0, +1 etc. The pH values at the points of intersection of the straight lines give the pK values of ionizing groups and each pK produces a unit change of gradient. From

Eqn. 14, each pK of an ionizing group in the ES complex produces an upward bend, *i.e.* the curve is concave upwards, whereas each ionizing group in the free enzyme or in the free substrate gives rise to downward bend. The line of curvature at the bends lies 0.3 pK units vertically below the point of intersection of the produced linear sections.

The gradient of the linear regions of the graphs is determined by the charges on those forms of the components that dominate in the given pH range: it is numerically equal to the change of charge occurring in that pH range when the enzyme–substrate complex dissociates into free enzyme and substrate. This may be illustrated as follows, where n is the number of negative charges

$$ES^{n-1} \rightarrow E^n + S, \quad \Delta \text{ charge} = -1, \quad \text{Gradient} = -1$$
$$ES^n \rightarrow E^n + S, \quad \Delta \text{ charge} = 0, \quad \text{Gradient} = 0$$
$$ES^{n+1} \rightarrow E^n + S^-, \quad \Delta \text{ charge} = 0, \quad \text{Gradient} = 0$$

As the net change in charge is the determining factor it is, of course, impossible to distinguish between ionizations of the free substrate and free enzyme. However, since pK values of substrates are generally known, or readily determined experimentally, the rule serves fairly well to identify each pK.

Should an ionizing group not be involved in the linkage between enzyme and substrate, change of pH will usually permit its ionization to occur in the complex in the normal way, although the combination might affect its pK value. Where this happens, it will be revealed in the plot of pK against pH as a vertical displacement of the horizontal section (see Fig. 4); the two levels are connected by a smooth curve and the vertical distance between them is equal to the change in pK produced by the combination (it is assumed that the pK and pH scales are identical, as in Fig. 4). Combination of the substrate with an ionizing group results in complete suppression of ionization and the gradient of the curve undergoes unit change from zero, as seen in Fig. 2.

It is possible to treat the effect of pH on the affinity of enzymes for inhibitors in precisely the same manner as for substrates, and in this way valuable information may be obtained concerning the mode of action of inhibitors.

The foregoing derivation of the effect of pH on the equilibrium constant of the enzyme–substrate complex, K_s, will, of course, apply equally to the Michaelis constant, K_m, provided that Michaelis–Menten kinetics hold for the system. Under conditions where Briggs–Haldane[41] kinetics apply, then K_m is equal to $(k_{-1} + k_{+2})/k_{+1}$ and change of pH might affect any or all of the three rate constants. However, it may be demonstrated that the effect of pH on K_m is exactly the same as its effect on K_s, by the following considerations[10]:

References p. 124

(*1*) The formation of the enzyme–substrate complex will depend solely on the state of ionization of the enzyme and the substrate, and not on that of the complex, whereas breakdown of the complex, by either the k_{-1} or k_{+2} reactions, will depend only on the ionization of the complex.

(*2*) The effect of pH on k_{+2} is compensated for by equating k_{+2} to $\tilde{k}_{+2}/f^{-}_{es}$ (Eqn. 6), where $\tilde{k}_{+2}$ and f^{-}_{es} are the rate constant and pH function appropriate to the ionic form of the enzyme–substrate complex involved in the reaction.

(*3*) If it is assumed that the same ionic form of the complex dissociates into enzyme and substrate, then $\tilde{k}_{-1}/f^{-}_{es}$ may be substituted for k_{-1}.

(*4*) The appropriate rate constant for the formation of the complex, which involves both free enzyme and substrate, will be $k_{+1} = \tilde{k}_{+1}/f_e^{-} \cdot f_s$ Hence

$$K_m = \frac{k_{-1} + k_{+2}}{k_{+1}} = \frac{\tilde{k}_{-1} + \tilde{k}_{+2}}{\tilde{k}_{+1}} \frac{f_e^{-} \cdot f_s}{f^{-}_{es}} \qquad (15)$$

and since $\tilde{k}_{+1}$, $\tilde{k}_{-1}$ and $\tilde{k}_{+2}$ are independent of pH, comparison with Eqn. 13 reveals that pH affects K_s and K_m in precisely the same manner.

Waley[30] has worked out the effect of pH on K_s for Briggs–Haldane steady-state kinetics in the following manner. If in Scheme I (p. 99) the concentrations of E^{n-1}, E^n and E^{n+1} are represented by e_1, e_2 and e_3, and those of ES^{n-1}, ES^n and ES^{n+1} by c_1, c_2 and c_3 respectively, the following relationships hold:

$$K_{e_1} = \frac{e_2[\mathrm{H}^+]}{e_1} \qquad K_{e_2} = \frac{e_3[\mathrm{H}^+]}{e_2}$$

$$K_{es_1} = \frac{c_2[\mathrm{H}^+]}{c_1} \qquad K_{es_2} = \frac{c_3[\mathrm{H}^+]}{c_2}$$

Also, the equilibrium relation for the steady state is

$$\tilde{K}_s = \frac{\tilde{k}_{-1} + \tilde{k}_{+2}}{\tilde{k}_{+1}} = \frac{e_2 s}{c_2} \qquad (16)$$

where s is the substrate concentration. e_1, e_3, c_1 and c_3 are then expressed in terms of e_2 and c_2, and e_2 is eliminated by means of Eqn. 16. The total enzyme E_t, given by

$$E_t = e_1 + e_2 + e_3 + c_1 + c_2 + c_3$$

can be expressed in terms of c_2 and, solving for c_2, the rate equation becomes

$$v = \tilde{k}_{+2}\, c_2 = \frac{\tilde{k}_{+2}\, s\, E_t}{\left[\tilde{K}_s\left(1 + \frac{[\mathrm{H}^+]}{K_{e_1}} + \frac{K_{e_2}}{[\mathrm{H}^+]}\right) + s\left(1 + \frac{[\mathrm{H}^+]}{K_{es_1}} + \frac{K_{es_2}}{[\mathrm{H}^+]}\right)\right]} \qquad (17)$$

$$v = \frac{\tilde{k}_{+2}\, s\, E_t}{\tilde{K}_s f_e^{-} + s f^{-}_{es}} \qquad (18)$$

$$v = \frac{\left(\frac{\bar{k}_{+2}}{f^{-}_{es}}\right) s\, E_t}{\bar{K}_s \left(\frac{f_e^{-}}{f^{-}_{es}}\right) + s} = \frac{\bar{k}'_{+2}\, s\, E_t}{\bar{K}'_s + s} \tag{19}$$

which is an equation of the Michaelis–Menten type. For low substrate concentrations the left-hand form of Eqn. 19 approximates to

$$v = \frac{\bar{k}_{+2}\, s\, E_t}{\bar{K}_s\, f_e^{-}} \tag{20}$$

while for high concentrations which saturate the enzyme

$$V = \frac{\bar{k}_{+2}\, E_t}{f^{-}_{es}} \tag{21}$$

These equations are of the same form as Eqn. 2 for $[AH^{-}]$ and therefore it follows that, in the same way as for $[AH^{-}]$, both rates must vary with pH and give rise to maxima. The maximum values of $[H^{+}]$ for v and V are, respectively, $\sqrt{K_{e_1} K_{e_2}}$ and $\sqrt{K_{es_1} K_{es_2}}$. Since these are not identical the pH optimum must vary with the substrate concentration. As previously mentioned, one of the most interesting examples of this variation is encountered with alkaline phosphatase[2].

Dixon[20] has examined the effect of pH on pK_m for published data on alkaline phosphatase, arginase, saccharase, cholinesterase, xanthine oxidase and urease. Dodgson *et al.*[32] have done likewise for the arylsulphatase of *Alcaligenes metalcaligenes* and the results obtained with three substrates are shown in Fig. 4. From these curves certain information may be derived by the use of Dixon's "rules". The enzyme has pK values of 8.2 and 9.4,

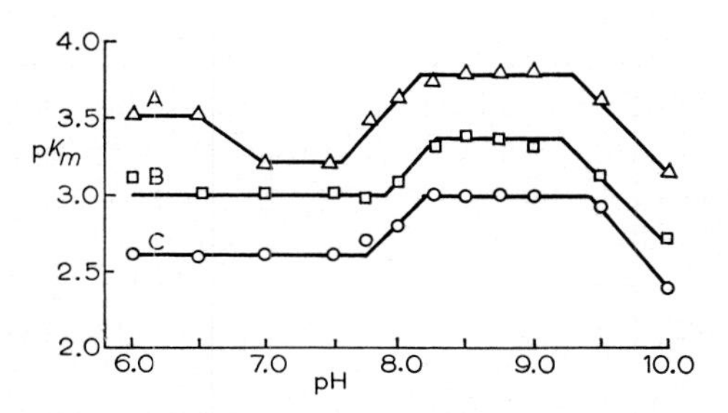

Fig. 4. Variation of pK_m with pH for the arylsulphatase of *Alcaligenes metalcaligenes*. The substrates are A, nitrocatechol sulphate; B, *p*-nitrophenyl sulphate and C, *p*-acetylphenyl sulphate. (Dodgson *et al.*[32].)

References p. 124

corresponding to the changes of gradient of the line, and the enzyme–substrate complex has one pK which varies from about 7.5 to 7.8, depending on the substrate. The further variations in the plot for nitrocatechol sulphate, observable at approximately pH 6.5 and 7.0, may be attributed to the extra hydroxyl group possessed by this substrate. Titration of the substrate revealed a pK of 6.5, indicating that the pK at 6.5 can be attributed to the free substrate and that at 7.0 to the enzyme–substrate complex. It may be deduced that the same group ionizes in the complex as in the free substrate, *i.e.* it is not involved in the enzyme–substrate linkage, but combination of substrate with the enzyme has raised its pK value.

3. Effect of temperature

(*a*) *Temperature coefficient*

The velocity of chemical reactions is generally increased by an increase in temperature, a rise of 10° producing a two- to threefold increase in rate. The magnitude of the temperature effect is frequently reported in terms of a *temperature coefficient*, which may be defined as the ratio of the reaction velocity at $t + 10°$ to that at $t°$, and denoted by Q_{10}. Thus

$$Q_{10} = \frac{k_{t+10}}{k_t}$$

where k_{t+10} and k_t are the rate constants at respective temperatures $t + 10$ and t. As the Q_{10} value does vary with temperature, the range of temperature for which the measurement was made should always be quoted.

The recognition that enzyme-catalysed reactions, unlike the majority of chemical reactions, are affected by temperature in two different ways, dates back to 1895, but for some time prior to this it was known that the velocity of enzymatic reactions increases with temperature until a certain "optimum temperature" is reached, above which the rate decreases rapidly. Tammann[33] suggested that an increase of temperature simultaneously accelerated two independent processes, namely the reaction catalysed and the thermal inactivation of the enzyme. Below the optimum temperature the main effect is on the reaction and above the optimum, inactivation of the enzyme becomes the predominant factor. However, it should be noted that significant inactivation may occur at temperatures below the optimum and attention should be paid to this factor when selecting a temperature for the assay of an enzyme.

Tammann's interpretation enables one to predict that the value of the optimum temperature should depend on the period of measurement used, higher values being obtained with experiments of shorter duration. This has been verified experimentally and emphasizes the fact that the "optimum temperature", being compounded of two variables, is itself a variable, and therefore has no particular significance.

The temperature coefficient for enzymatic reactions below the optimum temperature is similar to that for many chemical reactions and values between 1 and 2 are frequently encountered. Above the optimum temperature the Q_{10} decreases as a result of thermal inactivation. The temperature coefficients of catalysed reactions are generally lower than those for the corresponding uncatalysed reactions, although this is not readily demonstrable with enzymatic reactions since reaction does not usually occur in the absence of the enzyme.

(b) *The Arrhenius equation*

In 1889 Arrhenius[34] suggested that the available data on the effect of temperature on reaction rates could best be represented by the equation

$$\frac{\mathrm{d}\ln k}{\mathrm{d}T} = \frac{E}{RT^2} \quad \text{or} \quad \frac{\mathrm{d}\ln k}{\mathrm{d}(1/T)} = -\frac{E}{R} \tag{22}$$

where k is the rate constant, R the gas constant (1.987 cal/degree/mole), T the absolute temperature and E is a constant. The analogy with the Van 't Hoff[35] isochore relating to the change in equilibrium constant, K, with temperature, is apparent

$$\frac{\mathrm{d}\ln K}{\mathrm{d}T} = \frac{\Delta H}{RT^2} \tag{23}$$

Here ΔH is the change in enthalpy when 1 mole of reactants forms 1 mole of products. K is, of course, equal to k_{+1}/k_{-1} where k_{+1} and k_{-1} are the rate constants for the forward and reverse reactions of the equilibrium, and hence the relationship of the Arrhenius and Van 't Hoff equations follows.

Arrhenius suggested that when reaction occurs an equilibrium exists between the reactants and an intermediate collision complex, or *activated complex*, which has an energy content higher than that of the reactants. The energy required in order to pass from the initial state to the activated state is termed the *energy of activation* and is given by the term E in Eqn. 22. Although there may be many collision complexes existing in a reaction system at a given time, only those possessing the minimum amount of energy E can progress to the final state.

Eqn. 22 can be integrated to yield

$$\ln k = -\frac{E}{RT} + \text{constant} \tag{24}$$

References p. 124

which may be written in the alternative form of

$$k = A\,e^{-E/RT} \tag{25}$$

where A is a constant known as the *frequency factor*. The factor $e^{-E/RT}$ is the Boltzmann expression for the fraction of the systems that have energy E in excess of the average thermal energy, *i.e.* the fraction of the collision complexes that are activated and have sufficient energy to react.

The activation energy of a reaction may be obtained by determining the rate constant k at a series of different temperatures and then plotting ln k (or log k) against the reciprocal of the absolute temperature. The Arrhenius equation indicates that a straight line will be obtained of gradient $-E/R$ (or $-E/2.303R$) and this has been experimentally verified for all types of chemical reactions including enzymatic reactions. Fig. 5 illustrates the evaluation of E by an Arrhenius plot of this type for the hydrolysis of adenosine triphosphate by myosin.

It should be noted that since temperature affects ionization it will also affect the activities of the ionized molecules. This means that measurement of the velocity of reaction at different temperatures, but at the same pH, does not give correct results for the activation energy, because the activities (or concentrations) of the reactive ionic species have been altered by the change in temperature[71,72]. Accurate values for the activation energy can only be obtained if the heats of dissociation of all the ionizing processes leading to the formation of the activated complex are subtracted from the overall value (see p. 121).

The activation energy of biological reactions is frequently denoted by μ,

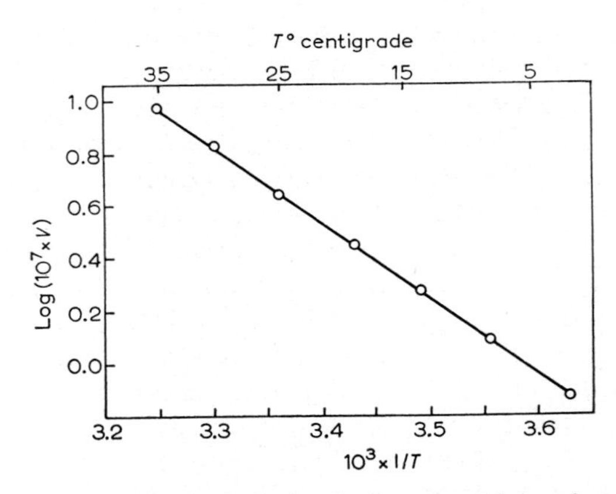

Fig. 5. Arrhenius plot for the hydrolysis of adenosine triphosphate by myosin, *i.e.* adenosine triphosphatase activity. The ATP concentration was 1 mM and the enzyme concentration 0.09 g/l. $\Delta H^{\neq}$ was evaluated as 12.4 kcal/mole. (Ouellet *et al.*[75].)

rather than E, and is termed the *critical increment of temperature*. Huennekens[36] suggests that the main purpose of this alternative formulation is to avoid any connotation of physical meaning which might attach to the phrase "energy of activation" when, for example, the Arrhenius equation is applied to overall physiological processes rather than individual enzyme reactions.

(c) *The collision theory of reaction rates*

The frequency factor of the Arrhenius equation (Eqn. 25) can in the case of simple gas reactions, and also some reactions in solution, be equated with Z, the collision number of the Lewis[37] theory of reaction rates, *e.g.* for a bimolecular reaction

$$k = Z\,e^{-E/RT} \tag{26}$$

This expression gives the rate as the number of molecules colliding per second per unit volume (Z) which have a joint energy E in excess of the mean thermal energy. However, with more complex reactions considerable deviations from this equation are encountered, and the observed frequency factors are often lower by powers of ten than the simple collision theory would predict. These discrepancies are attributable to the application of the kinetic theory of gases to non-gaseous reactions; clearly if reaction is to occur, molecules must not only collide with sufficient mutual energy but must also be orientated with respect to one another in such a manner that reaction is favoured, *i.e.* so that the requisite bonds may be broken and formed. Thus not every collision of molecules possessing sufficient mutual energy is effective, and only that fraction of them which is properly orientated will react. To take this aspect into account while still retaining the kinetic theory of gases, an empirical *probability* or *steric factor* P (for which there is no theory) was introduced into Eqn. 26

$$k = PZ\,e^{-E/RT} \tag{27}$$

This is still unsatisfactory for some reactions, however, since correct orientation is not the only factor involved and other factors such as electrostriction may be of importance. Furthermore, although P would be expected to have a value between zero and unity, in the case of protein denaturation, such as thermal inactivation of enzymes, P may have an astronomical value. The reason for this discrepancy is discussed on p. 113. Thus the collision theory of reaction rates does not provide an entirely satisfactory explanation of the frequency factor of the Arrhenius equation and for this we must turn to the theory of absolute reaction rates.

References p. 124

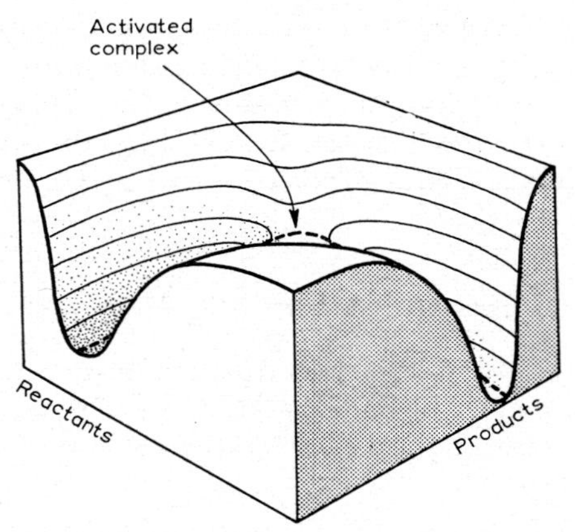

Fig. 6a. Three-dimensional "landscape" model of potential energy relationships for a simple reaction of the type

$$AB + C \rightleftharpoons ABC \rightleftharpoons A + BC$$

The "pass" separating the valleys corresponds to the activated complex ABC.

(*d*) *The theory of absolute reaction rates*

The frequency factor of the Arrhenius equation may be determined by the theory of absolute reaction rates developed by Eyring and his collaborators[38]. This treatment of reactions is based on the concept that before molecules can react they must combine to form an intermediate complex, the transition state or activated complex, which has an energy content greater than either

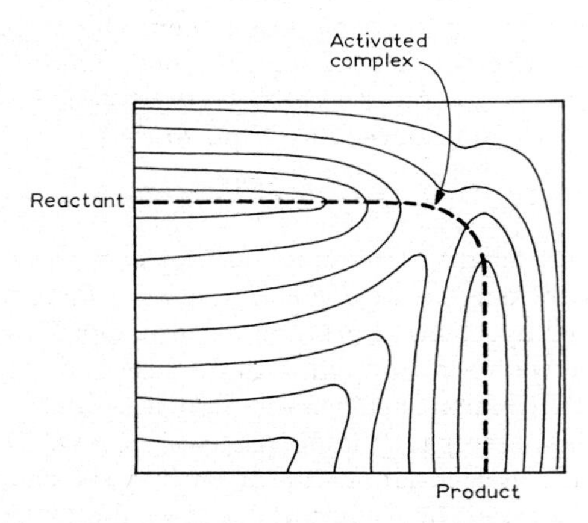

Fig. 6b. Contour map of Fig. 6a showing reaction path (dotted line) from the reactants, via the activated complex, to the products.

the reactants or products and which are, in consequence, separated by an energy barrier. The height of this barrier is the energy of activation.

The situation is best visualized in terms of an energy contour map. If all of the distances which must be specified to determine the potential energy of the activated complex are plotted on independent co-ordinates, and the corresponding potential energy is plotted in an independent direction, then a three-dimensional "landscape" is obtained. The valleys correspond to compounds, and the "saddles", or lowest points of the passes separating the valleys, correspond to the activated complexes. The reaction path leading from reactant to product will follow the lowest energy surface common to both, that is will progress to the head of the "reactant valley", traverse the lowest point of the pass and descend into the "product valley". Fig. 6 illustrates the potential energy contours for a simple reaction of the type

$$AB + C \rightleftharpoons \underset{\text{activated complex}}{ABC} \rightleftharpoons A + BC$$

and Fig. 7 shows the potential energy for the reaction as a function of the reaction co-ordinate, *i.e.* the reaction pathway along the lowest common energy surface.

The formation of the activated complex is treated in the same manner as ordinary equilibria. The complex itself is regarded as an ordinary molecule possessing all the usual thermodynamic properties with the exception that motion in one particular direction, namely along the reaction co-ordinate, leads to decomposition at a given rate, *i.e.* one of the degrees of vibrational freedom is replaced by translational motion along the reaction co-ordinate.

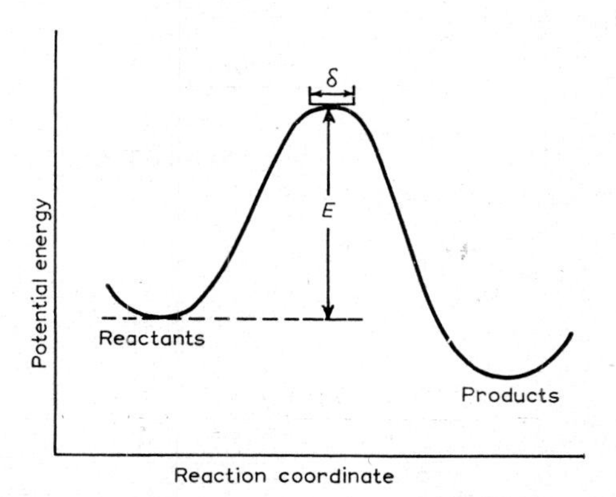

Fig. 7. Potential energy for the reaction of Figs. 6a and b as a function of the reaction coordinate, *i.e.* the reaction pathway along the lowest common energy surface, as indicated by the dotted line of Fig. 6b.

References p. 124

Consider a reaction of the type

$$\text{A} + \text{B} \rightarrow \text{Activated complex} \rightarrow \text{Products}$$

The equilibrium constant $K^{\neq}$ for the reaction leading to the formation of the activated complex is related to the standard free energy, enthalpy and entropy changes in the following way†

$$\begin{aligned} \Delta G^{\circ\neq} &= -RT \ln K^{\neq} \\ &= \Delta H^{\circ\neq} - T\Delta S^{\circ\neq} \end{aligned} \tag{28}$$

For convenience, in the subsequent discussion the °superscripts to denote the standard state will be omitted.

Now the rate of reaction will be equal to the concentration of activated complex at the top of the energy barrier multiplied by the frequency of crossing the barrier. Thus if C^* is the number of activated complexes in unit volume lying along a length δ of the reaction co-ordinate at the top of the barrier (Fig. 7), and v is the mean velocity of traversing this length, then v/δ is the frequency of crossing the barrier. However, since only half of the activated complexes will be moving in the forward direction leading to reaction, the reaction rate is given by

$$\text{Reaction rate} = \tfrac{1}{2}\, C^* \frac{v}{\delta}\, \varkappa$$

where $\varkappa$ is the transmission coefficient. This coefficient represents the quantum mechanical chance that a system having crossed the barrier will continue through to yield products. By use of the partition function for the activated complex, which is equal to $(2\pi m^{\neq} kT)^{\frac{1}{2}}/h$, where $m^{\neq}$ is the effective mass of the activated complex in the co-ordinate of reaction, k is the Boltzmann constant and h is Planck's constant

$$C^* = \frac{C^{\neq}(2\pi m^{\neq} kT)^{\frac{1}{2}}\, \delta}{h}$$

Further, it can be shown that the mean velocity of crossing the energy barrier in the direction of decomposition is

$$v = \left(\frac{2kT}{\pi m^{\neq}}\right)^{\frac{1}{2}}$$

Hence,

$$\begin{aligned} \text{Reaction rate} &= \tfrac{1}{2}\, \frac{C^{\neq}(2\pi m^{\neq} kT)^{\frac{1}{2}}\, \delta}{h} \cdot \left(\frac{2kT}{\pi m^{\neq}}\right)^{\frac{1}{2}} \cdot \frac{1}{\delta} \cdot \varkappa \\ &= \varkappa C^{\neq} \frac{kT}{h} \end{aligned} \tag{29}$$

---

† The symbol $\neq$ is used to denote functions associated with the activated complex.

This result demonstrates that the effective rate of crossing the barrier is equal to a universal frequency, kT/h, which is completely independent of the nature of the reactants and type of reaction and depends solely on the absolute temperature.

Now if it is assumed that the activated complex is in equilibrium with reactants A and B, the thermodynamic equilibrium constant $K^{\neq}$ for the formation of the activated complex may be obtained, as for any ordinary reaction, and is

$$K^{\neq} = \frac{a^{\neq}}{a_{\mathrm{A}} a_{\mathrm{B}}} \tag{30}$$

The activity coefficients for the various species may be included in the equilibrium constant, which then becomes $K_c^{\neq}$, and

$$K_c^{\neq} = \frac{C^{\neq}}{C_{\mathrm{A}} C_{\mathrm{B}}} \tag{31}$$

If the rate constant is k_r, the rate of reaction will be

$$\text{Reaction rate} = k_r C_{\mathrm{A}} C_{\mathrm{B}}$$

Therefore

$$\varkappa C^{\neq} \frac{kT}{h} = k_r C_{\mathrm{A}} C_{\mathrm{B}}$$

and

$$k_r = \varkappa \frac{kT}{h} \cdot \frac{C^{\neq}}{C_{\mathrm{A}} C_{\mathrm{B}}} = \varkappa \frac{kT}{h} K_c^{\neq} \tag{32}$$

For reactions in homogeneous media which involve simple bond rearrangement the transmission coefficient may be taken as unity, and this is probably true also of enzymatic reactions of this type. Thus hydrolysis, hydration and group-transfer reactions would fall in this category. However, it is possible that other enzymatic reactions may have transmission coefficients appreciably less than unity on account of changes of electronic states during reaction or because the reactions proceed via quantum mechanical tunnelling through the potential energy barrier. If the transmission coefficient is taken as unity then, by paying proper regard to the activity coefficients, *i.e.* using $K^{\neq}$ rather than $K_c^{\neq}$, the equilibrium constant can be related to the standard free energy change and we obtain

$$\Delta G^{\neq} = -RT \ln \frac{k_r h}{kT} = \Delta H^{\neq} - T\Delta S^{\neq} \tag{33}$$

This equation may be written in exponential form as

$$k_r = \frac{kT}{h} \mathrm{e}^{-\Delta G^{\neq}/RT} = \frac{kT}{h} \mathrm{e}^{\Delta S^{\neq}/R} \mathrm{e}^{-\Delta H^{\neq}/RT} \tag{34}$$

References p. 124

and assuming that $\Delta S^{\neq}$ is independent of temperature then, by taking logarithms of Eqn. 34 and differentiating

$$\frac{\mathrm{d}\ln k_r}{\mathrm{d}T} = \frac{\Delta H^{\neq}}{RT^2} + \frac{1}{T} = \frac{\Delta H^{\neq} + RT}{RT^2} \tag{35}$$

A comparison of Eqn. 35 with one form of the Arrhenius equation (Eqn. 22) reveals that

$$E = \Delta H^{\neq} + RT \tag{36}$$

This demonstrates that the difference between the observed change in enthalpy and the activation energy is dependent on temperature. It has been fairly common practice to equate E and $\Delta H^{\neq}$ at physiological temperatures, but the difference of some 600 cal is frequently significant.

When E and $\Delta H^{\neq}$ are equated, then

$$k_r = \frac{kT}{h}\,\mathrm{e}^{\Delta S^{\neq}/R}\,\mathrm{e}^{-E/RT} \tag{37}$$

and comparing this with Eqns. 25 and 27 we obtain

$$\frac{kT}{h}\,\mathrm{e}^{\Delta S^{\neq}/R} = PZ = A \tag{38}$$

Since for a given temperature kT/h is constant it is clear that the frequency factor is controlled by the magnitude of the entropy of activation. Laidler[11] has pointed out that since it is extremely difficult to evaluate partition functions for substances in the liquid phase, the entropy of activation approach is a most useful one for such reactions. If the frequency factor of a reaction has been evaluated experimentally by determining k_r at a series of temperatures, the entropy of activation can be readily obtained.

It follows from Eqn. 38 that wide variations in the empirically derived probability factor P are related to large changes in entropy involved in the activation reaction. Entropy changes may be correlated with values of P, in an approximate fashion, as follows

If $P = 1$, $\Delta S^{\neq} = 0$

$P < 1$, $\Delta S^{\neq}$ is negative and the reaction is "slow"

$P > 1$, $\Delta S^{\neq}$ is large and positive and the reaction is "fast"

The entropy change is a measure of the probability of a reaction taking place and the smaller the decrease in entropy involved the faster will the reaction occur. Consequently if the formation of the activated complex does not demand a decrease in entropy the reaction may be considered as a very probable one which will proceed at a fast rate. In the case of protein denaturation many hydrogen bonds are broken and the highly organized α-helix structure is disorganized with resultant very large increases in entropy, both for the activation and for the overall step. This explains the abnormally high values of the probability factor in the collision rate expression (Eqn. 27).

The theory of absolute reaction rates, unlike the kinetic theory, thus takes into account the entropy changes involved in the reactions. It interprets the orientation and electrostriction effects in terms of entropy changes and also recognizes that since the ratio of the rate constants of forward and reverse reactions is an equilibrium constant, it must involve an entropy term.

It must be pointed out that the activated complex of the theory of absolute reaction rates is not identical with the enzyme–substrate complex of the Michaelis–Menten theory. The present concept of enzyme reaction is as follows. When substrate and enzyme react they must first pass through an activated complex before the enzyme–substrate complex is formed. The latter compound then undergoes further activation leading via a second activated complex to an enzyme–product complex, and the latter dissociates to enzyme and product after passing through a third activated complex. For a reversible reaction it is clear that the formation of an enzyme–product complex must be postulated since, for reaction in the reverse direction, this becomes the enzyme–substrate complex. The overall reaction and the changes in enthalpy for the various activation and reaction steps may be written as given in Scheme II (p. 114).

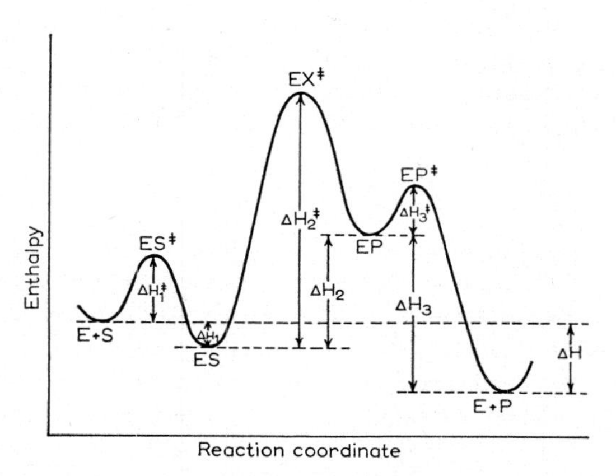

Fig. 8. Reaction profile of the changes in enthalpy for the forward direction of the enzymatic reaction of Scheme II. $ES^{\neq}$, $EX^{\neq}$ and $EP^{\neq}$ are the activated complexes and ES and EP are Michaelis–Menten complexes.

References p. 124

$$\underbrace{E + S \rightleftharpoons ES^{\neq}}_{\Delta H_1^{\neq}} \rightleftharpoons \underbrace{ES \rightleftharpoons EX^{\neq}}_{\Delta H_2^{\neq}} \rightleftharpoons \underbrace{EP \rightleftharpoons EP^{\neq}}_{\Delta H_3^{\neq}} \rightleftharpoons E + P \qquad \text{(II)}$$

$$\Delta H_1 \qquad \Delta H_2 \qquad \Delta H_3$$

$$\Delta H$$

where ΔH is the change in enthalpy for the overall reaction. The reaction profile for the forward reaction is illustrated in Fig. 8. In the reverse reaction the values of $\Delta H^{\neq}$ for the activation steps will be different, but the others including ΔH for the overall reaction, will remain the same but with opposite sign.

There are six stages to the reaction as formulated and therefore to define the reaction completely with respect to ΔG, ΔH and ΔS, eighteen thermodynamic parameters will be required. Such extensive information is not yet available for any enzymatic reaction. Various aspects of this problem are discussed by Dixon and Webb[10]. An enthalpy profile for fumarate hydratase was obtained by Massey[39] from the determined activation energies by the use of the equation ($\Delta H^{\neq} = E - RT$). These results are shown in Fig. 9 for the reaction at pH 6.35.

(e) *Energy of activation of enzymatic reactions*

The Michaelis–Menten[40] and Briggs–Haldane[41] kinetic treatments of enzyme-catalysed reactions of the general type

$$E + S \underset{k_{-1}}{\overset{k_{+1}}{\rightleftharpoons}} E{-}S \overset{k_{+2}}{\rightarrow} E + \text{products}$$

are based on the postulate that the reaction occurs in two stages, namely the formation of an enzyme–substrate complex followed by its breakdown to products of the reaction, and that the velocity of reaction v is determined by the second stage. These treatments lead to the expression

$$v = k_{+2}\, c = \frac{k_{+2}\, e\, s}{K_m + s} \qquad (39)$$

where e and s are the total concentrations of enzyme and substrate respectively, c is the concentration of enzyme–substrate complex and K_m the Michaelis constant. Under these conditions, a plot of log k_{+2} against $1/T$ permits the energy of activation of this process to be determined. Now, if c is kept constant while the temperature is varied, v will be proportional to k_{+2} and

$$\frac{d \ln v}{d(1/T)} = \frac{d \ln k_{+2}}{d(1/T)} = -\frac{E}{R} \qquad (40)$$

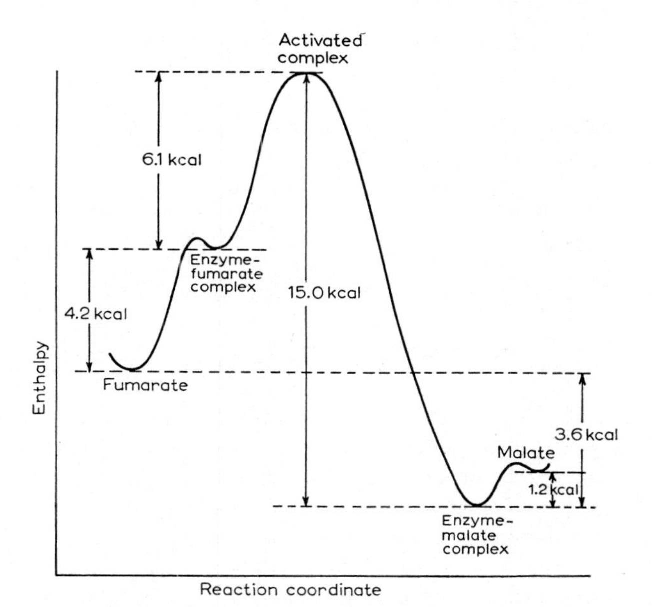

Fig. 9. Enthalpy profile for fumarate hydratase (fumarase) (Massey[39]).

To hold c constant the simplest procedure is to have a high substrate concentration so that the enzyme is saturated and displays zero-order kinetics with respect to substrate; c then tends to e, the total concentration of the enzyme. Consequently, an Arrhenius plot of the logarithm of the maximum velocity of reaction V against $1/T$ enables E to be evaluated (Eqn. 40 with V replacing v).

When the substrate concentration is not high enough to saturate the enzyme the concentration of enzyme–substrate complex is

$$c = \frac{e\,s}{K_m + s}$$

Gibson[42] has pointed out that if c could be kept constant by varying the concentration of substrate, at all temperatures Eqn. 40 would still be valid, but if e and s are held constant while T is varied then

$$\frac{\mathrm{d} \ln v}{\mathrm{d}(1/T)} = \frac{\mathrm{d}}{\mathrm{d}(1/T)}\left[\ln\left(\frac{k_{+2}\,e\,s}{K_m + s}\right)\right]$$

$$= \frac{\mathrm{d} \ln k_{+2}}{\mathrm{d}(1/T)} - \frac{\dfrac{\mathrm{d}K_m}{\mathrm{d}(1/T)}}{K_m + s}$$

References p. 124

$$= \frac{\mathrm{d} \ln k_{+2}}{\mathrm{d}(1/T)} - \left(\frac{K_m}{K_m + s}\right) \frac{\mathrm{d} \ln K_m}{\mathrm{d}(1/T)} \tag{41}$$

If the apparent activation energy derived from an Arrhenius plot under these conditions is denoted by μ, then

$$\frac{\mathrm{d} \ln v}{\mathrm{d}(1/T)} = -\frac{\mu}{R} = -\frac{E}{R} - \left(\frac{K_m}{K_m + s}\right) \frac{\mathrm{d} \ln K_m}{\mathrm{d}(1/T)}$$

and

$$\mu = E + \left(\frac{K_m}{K_m + s}\right) R \frac{\mathrm{d} \ln K_m}{\mathrm{d}(1/T)} \tag{42}$$

Therefore μ differs from E to an extent which depends on the concentration of substrate, and the discrepancy will be greatest at low concentrations and negligible at very high concentrations. As K_m is not, in general, independent of temperature, $(\mu - E)$ would be expected to vary slightly with temperature.

Where Michaelis–Menten kinetics are operative and K_m is equal to the dissociation constant of the enzyme–substrate complex (or the reciprocal of the equilibrium constant for the formation of this complex), the Van 't Hoff relationship leads to the expression

$$\frac{\mathrm{d} \ln K_m}{\mathrm{d}(1/T)} = -\frac{\Delta H}{R} \tag{43}$$

where ΔH is the change in enthalpy associated with the formation of the enzyme–substrate complex. Eqn. 42 may then be written as

$$\mu = E + \left(\frac{K_m}{K_m + s}\right) \Delta H \tag{44}$$

which holds for all conditions where K_m is an equilibrium constant.

Gibson has thus focused attention on two quantities that must be considered in enzymatic activation; these are (*1*) the heat of formation of the enzyme–substrate complex and (*2*) the energy of activation of the complex. The significance of these quantities is made clear by Fig. 10, where ΔH_f is the change in enthalpy for the formation of the enzyme–substrate complex via an activated complex, in the forward direction, and E_f is the energy of activation of the complex leading to reaction, *i.e.* product formation. ΔH_r and E_r are the corresponding values for the reverse reaction.

Some of the literature on activation energies of enzyme reactions available up to 1953 was surveyed by Gibson and he concluded that the majority of values reported were open to criticism because they were compounded of the two quantities, enthalpy change and activation energy. Notable ex-

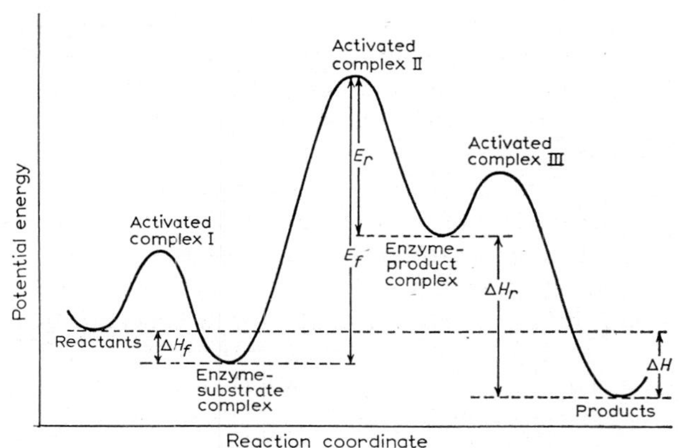

Fig. 10. Enthalpy and energy of activation relationships for the forward and reverse directions of an enzyme reaction.

ceptions included the work of Dann[43] on the citric dehydrogenase of peas, Kiese[44] on carbonic anhydrase, Kaufman *et al.*[45] on chymotrypsin and Lumry *et al.*[46] on carboxypeptidase. Some of the recorded activation energies appear to be in error to the extent of several kilocalories. To determine the activation energy of an enzymatic reaction it is essential, therefore, that the maximum initial velocity be measured at a series of

TABLE II

ENERGIES OF ACTIVATION FOR VARIOUS ENZYMES AND SUBSTRATES

Enzyme	*Source*	*Substrate*	*E (cal/mole)*
Dihydropyrimidinase (EC 3.5.2.2) (formerly known as hydantoinase)	Liver	Hydantoin	5 300[a]
Dihydropyrimidinase	Jack bean	Hydantoin	11 600[a]
β-Fructofuranosidase (EC 3.2.1.26)	Malt	Sucrose	13 000[b]
β-Fructofuranosidase	Yeast	Sucrose	11 000[b]
β-Fructofuranosidase	Yeast	Raffinose	11 000[b]
(Hydrogen ion)	—	Sucrose	25 700[b]

[a] Eadie *et al.*[62].

[b] These values are quoted from Sizer[13] where references to the original literature will be found.

References p. 124

temperatures. It must be ascertained that the substrate concentration employed *at each temperature* is sufficient to saturate the enzyme. To define the reaction, ΔH must also be determined and this can be done by ascertaining the effect of temperature on K_m and plotting log K_m against $1/T$, when the slope is $-\Delta H/2.303\ R$. Alternatively, if the velocity of the reaction is measured at very low substrate concentrations, a plot of log v against $1/T$ enables ΔH to be evaluated since under these conditions $K_m/(K_m + s)$ tends to unity and μ tends to $E + \Delta H$ (Eqn. 44). Gibson also suggests that E and ΔH could be calculated from Lineweaver–Burk[15] plots at different temperatures, using constant enzyme concentration. V and K_m would then be obtained for each of the temperatures and, from the series of these, E and ΔH could be evaluated by means of Eqns. 40 and 43.

Some values for the activation energy of various enzymatic reactions are presented in Table II and from these data an interesting feature is apparent. If a reaction is catalysed by two or more enzymes, a different activation energy is found for each enzyme, but where a given enzyme acts on several substrates the activation energy is frequently the same for all, suggesting that the enzyme rather than the substrate determines the observed activation energy.

Activation energies have been recorded in the literature for complex reactions, such as protein hydrolysis and haemolysis, but these are usually devoid of significance because the mechanism and rate-determining step of the overall process are unknown. Gibson[42] has pointed out that in reactions such as these the enzyme combines with many degradation products of the original substrate, having a different affinity for each, so that no value can be assigned to K_m.

(*f*) *The Crozier concept*

There have been a number of studies of the effect of temperature on various biological activities and Crozier and his colleagues[47–49], in the course of publishing further work on this topic, endeavoured to interpret all the available data in terms of a generalized theory[50]. The main points of this theory were as follows: (*1*) every physiological process consists of a catenary series of reactions, each with a characteristic μ value; (*2*) the rate of the overall process, within a given range of temperature, is controlled by a master reaction, which corresponds to the slowest step in the series; (*3*) as the temperature is changed, at a certain critical temperature the rate determining step may be shifted from one reaction to another, resulting in a sharp discontinuity in the gradient of an Arrhenius plot of the data; and (*4*) on the basis of measured μ values it might prove possible to identify corresponding controlling reactions in different physiological processes.

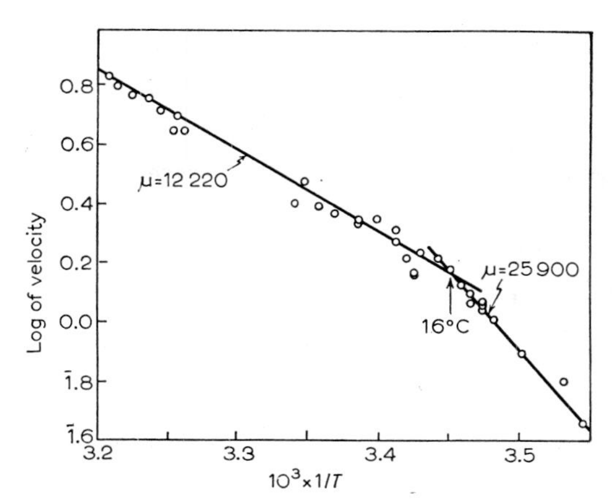

Fig. 11. Arrhenius plot for the velocity of creeping of the ant *Liometopum apiculatum* (Crozier[47], based on the data of Shapley[52]).

The first feature of interest is the surprising number of biological processes which conform to the Arrhenius equation, at least over certain ranges of temperature. These include such diverse phenomena as ciliary activity, creeping of ants, chirping of crickets, flashing of fireflies, oxygen consumption, carbon dioxide production and bacterial growth. In many of these cases there is an apparent transition or critical temperature (frequently around 15°), as indicated by the intersection of two lines of different gradient corresponding to different μ values. Fig. 11 shows Crozier's[47] plot of the data of Shapley[52] for the effect of temperature on the velocity of creeping of the ant. However, criticisms have been levelled at the validity of these plots; it would, for instance, be equally possible to draw a smooth curve rather than two discontinuous straight lines through the data of Fig. 11. Buchanan and Fulmer[53] have illustrated how contraction of the ordinate makes it possible to misconstrue a continuous variation in μ as successive linear relations.

The concept of the "master" reaction, while undoubtedly possessing certain attractive features, has been the subject of much criticism. Morales[54] has indicated that for one of two consecutive reactions to assume control, within 10%, at a critical temperature, its activation energy would have to be 2.7 times that of the other, and Booij and Wolvekamp[55] concluded that the idea of a master reaction is untenable. On the premise that the proper understanding of *in vivo* reactions must depend on steady-state formulations rather than on *in vitro* reactions, Stearn[14] has considered theoretical aspects of consecutive and simultaneous reactions in the steady state. He concluded that, in general, any agreement between μ for the overall reaction and μ for

References p. 124

an individual step is fortuitous. Monod[56] has pointed out that for a complex activity such as exponential bacterial growth, comprised of a vast network rather than a chain of reactions, the operation of a master reaction is extremely improbable. However, an important point was established by Sizer[57,58] when he demonstrated that the sucrase (invertase) of yeast had the same activation energy for sucrose hydrolysis whether the measurement be made with living or dead yeast cells or with the isolated and partially purified enzyme. The same was shown to be true of urease[58,60], thus indicating for simple reactions that the observed *in vivo* activation energy is also characteristic of that for the isolated enzyme.

Discontinuities in Arrhenius plots have been observed for individual enzyme reactions in addition to those of overall physiological processes involving complex sequences or networks of enzyme reactions. The interpretation of these plots displaying apparently two different activation energies is not straightforward and various explanations have been offered: a brief consideration of these follows, more detailed information being presented by Dixon and Webb[10].

(*1*) A phase change in the solvent has been postulated since at about 0° the activation energy of lipase changes from 37 000 cal below to 7 600 cal above this temperature. It is not, however, due simply to the freezing of water because the addition of glycerol did not influence the results[13].

(*2*) A change of the rate-determining step from one enzyme in a reaction sequence to another. The reaction with the largest temperature coefficient will become the faster reaction as the temperature is raised, the other reaction then becomes rate-limiting and its activation energy will be characteristic of that for the overall process. This reaction will have the lowest activation energy, giving the more usual type of discontinuous Arrhenius plot with downward concavity[14].

(*3*) Two simultaneous reactions with different temperature coefficients, *e.g.* different active centres. As before, the reaction with the higher coefficient accelerates more rapidly with increase of temperature than does the other, and hence predominates at higher temperatures. In this case the activation energy will be greatest at the elevated temperature, giving rise to a less usual type of Arrhenius plot with an upward concavity.

(*4*) The enzyme exists in two forms of differing activities. If the two forms (both active) are in equilibrium with each other and have different activation energies, and the conversion of one form to the other is markedly affected by temperature, then an abrupt discontinuity will be seen. This type of behaviour has been noted with fumarate hydratase in alkaline solution[39] and it has been suggested that this is caused by dissociation of the enzyme into units of smaller molecular weight, the sub-units having a higher activation energy.

(5) Reversible inactivation of the enzyme. In this case the Arrhenius plot gives straight lines when the majority of the enzyme is either in the active or inactive form; the slopes are E and $E - \Delta H_c$ respectively, where ΔH_c is the enthalpy change of the conversion of one form to the other (Kistiakowsky and Lumry[61]).

(g) *Effect of temperature on ionization*

There is a further and extremely important consideration to be taken into account when studying the effect of temperature on enzymatic reactions and inactivation. Steinhardt[71] and La Mer[72] first drew attention to the necessity for comparing reaction rates at constant concentration of reactive ionized species instead of at different temperatures and the same pH. When this factor is taken into consideration, many of the reported high values for ΔH in denaturation turn out to be illusory. Steinhardt has illustrated this by the following example. If a protein P_0 undergoes n ionization steps to yield P_n, and P_n is the form which is activated to give the activated complex $P_n^{\neq}$, then increasing the temperature promotes ionization to form P_n as well as the transition to the activated complex. Consequently, the usual method of determining the activation energy, *e.g.* at constant pH and different temperature, leads to a composite value of E which includes the heats of dissociation of the n steps as well as the true heat of activation. From measurements of the rate at different pH, the value of n and the dissociation constant (assuming the value to be identical for each step) may be determined and this permits calculation of the heat of dissociation (ΔH_i) of each group. The energy of activation is then the observed E minus $n\Delta H_i$.

In the case of the alkaline inactivation of pepsin, correction for five dissociations each with a ΔH of 9 040 cal, reduced the apparent activation energy[71] from 63 500 to 18 300 cal, a value which is within the normal range for most chemical reactions.

Subsequently Levy and Benaglia[1] carried out an extensive study of the thermal denaturation of crystalline ricin over a wide range of pH. They made a fundamental modification to Steinhardt's concept in that each of the prototropic steps, and not simply the final one, leads to a change in the stability of the protein; furthermore the stability may be increased or decreased by the dissociation reactions. These modifications naturally result in a much more complex treatment of the process.

The effect of temperature on the ionization of both enzyme and substrate in enzymatic reactions will depend on the magnitude of the heats of ionization of the particular ionizing groups concerned. It will manifest itself by changes in both the affinity of enzyme for substrate (K_m), and the maximum velocity of reaction, V. The pH curves therefore change with temperature.

References p. 124

(*h*) *Thermal inactivation of enzymes*

The thermal inactivation of enzymes is now known to derive from their protein nature. It is largely due to the pioneer work of Northrop and his collaborators[63] that the identity of the mechanism of protein denaturation with that of enzyme inactivation was established. These workers demonstrated an exact proportionality between denaturation and the loss of enzymatic activity for both pepsin[64] and trypsin[65]. Their work is of particular interest because some of the conditions employed permitted reversal of denaturation, and catalytic activity was then regained in parallel with renaturation. Chymotrypsinogen[66] also displays reversible inactivation of this type.

Anson and Mirsky[67] studied the equilibrium between the active and inactive forms of trypsin in 0.1 *N* hydrochloric acid and found that raising the temperature from 40° to 50° effected a change from virtually complete activity to complete inactivity, 50% inactivation occurring at 44°. From these data the change in enthalpy was computed to be 67 600 cal/mole; the corresponding entropy change is 213 entropy units (cal/mole/degree). Stearn[14] quotes values of 40 200 cal/mole and 44.7 entropy units respectively for the changes in enthalpy and entropy for the activation process of denaturation and this emphasizes the unusual feature that in denaturation, unlike most other reactions, the activation step involves smaller changes in these quantities than does the overall reaction.

For both trypsin and chymotrypsinogen the heat of activation of the reactivation reaction is negative and there is a large loss of entropy in going from the denatured protein to the activated complex. The explanation of these phenomena must be sought in the mechanism of protein denaturation.

The fact that $\Delta S^{\neq}$ is smaller than ΔS indicates that formation of the activated complex does not involve such an extensive "opening up" or disorganization of the native protein structure as does the subsequent conversion of the complex to denatured protein. The very large entropy changes involved offer an explanation for the difficult reversibility of denaturation and why it is usually an irreversible reaction. Some workers have sought to explain the process in terms of the number of bonds broken in activation and in denaturation, *e.g.* Mirsky and Pauling[68], attributing denaturation to the rupture of hydrogen bonds, calculated the number of bonds broken by dividing the activation energy E by 5 000 calories, the average value assigned to a hydrogen bond. The knowledge that other bonds must also be involved led Eyring and Stearn to attempt further assessments[14,69,70]. Stearn[70] estimated that the activation process in trypsin denaturation involved the rupture of 8 bonds while 14 were broken in the overall reaction. The calculated entropy change per bond broken in activation was 5.5 e.u. as compared with 28 e.u. for the remaining 6 bonds broken after activation. This is not interpreted as involving bonds of a different type, but rather that the changes leading to activation do not substantially alter the overall configuration of the protein molecule, whereas after activation critical bonds are broken which result in the complete collapse of the molecule.

Now the changes in enthalpy and entropy are related to the free energy change by the equation

$$\Delta G = \Delta H - T\Delta S$$

and it must always be borne in mind that ΔG is the term which determines the feasibility of reaction. Thus the relative magnitudes of ΔH (which is approximately equal to E, the activation energy, as discussed on p. 112) and ΔS can influence the value of ΔG, and high values of ΔH will make a reaction more difficult to accomplish while high values of ΔS will have the opposite effect. However, in the case of trypsin, when the free energy profile for the activation and overall reaction is considered, it is found to resemble that for any other type of reaction, with the free energy of the activated complex at a maximum (*e.g.* Fig. 7). Thus, although the activated complex has enthalpy and entropy values intermediate between those of the native and denatured states, its free energy is greater.

NOTE ADDED IN PROOF

Evidence for sharp temperature breaks in Arrhenius plots associated with protein conformational changes has now been obtained for three enzymes by Dr. V. Massey (personal communication). The D-amino acid oxidase of pig kidney shows marked changes in physical properties, *e.g.* sedimentation coefficient, ultraviolet difference spectra and protein fluorescence, around 12–15°. The change in configuration involves a different environment for tryptophan residues and the plot of log V against $1/T$ has a sharp break at 14°. Lipoyl dehydrogenase exhibits a pronounced change in ultraviolet difference spectrum around 24°. The Arrhenius plot (V) displays a break at 13–15°. The difference in physical and kinetic results is explicable in terms of the different oxidation states of the enzyme (spectral studies, oxidized form; kinetic work, mainly reduced). Studies with fumarase suggest that changes in both protein fluorescence and ultraviolet difference spectra can be correlated with the phenomena previously described[39].

ACKNOWLEDGEMENTS

It is a pleasure to thank the following authors and publishers for their permission to reproduce certain diagrams: Fig. 1, M. L. C. Bernheim (née Hare) and *The Biochemical Journal*; Fig. 3, R. A. Alberty, V. Massey and Elsevier Publishing Company; Fig. 4, K. S. Dodgson and *the Biochemical*

References p. 124

Journal; Fig. 5, K. J. Laidler and Academic Press Inc.; Fig. 9, V. Massey and *The Biochemical Journal*; Fig. 11, The Rockefeller Institute Press, from *The Journal of General Physiology*, 7 (1925) 123.

REFERENCES

1 M. Levy and A. E. Benaglia, *J. Biol. Chem.*, 186 (1950) 829.
2 M. H. Ross, J. O. Ely and J. G. Archer, *J. Biol. Chem.*, 192 (1951) 561.
3 J. F. Danielli and J. T. Davies, *Advan. Enzymol.*, 11 (1951) 35.
4 L. H. Matthews, *Brit. Med. Bull.*, 17 (1961) 9.
5 Hypothermia and the Effects of Cold, *Brit. Med. Bull.*, 17 (1961).
6 E. Neil, in C. P. Stewart and Th. Strengers (Eds.), *Symposium on Water and Electrolyte Metabolism* (*West-European Symposia on Clinical Chemistry*, Vol. I), Elsevier, Amsterdam, 1961, p. 143.
7 T. H. Bullock, *Biol. Rev. Cambridge Phil. Soc.*, 30 (1955) 311.
8 R. A. Alberty, *Advan. Enzymol.*, 17 (1956) 1.
9 R. A. Alberty, *J. Cellular Comp. Physiol.*, Suppl., 47 (1956) 245.
10 M. Dixon and E. C. Webb, *The Enzymes*, 2nd ed., Longmans, Green & Co., London, 1964, Chapter IV.
11 K. J. Laidler, *The Chemical Kinetics of Enzyme Action*, Clarendon, Oxford, 1958, Chapters II, V, VII and XIII.
12 J. M. Reiner, *Behaviour of Enzyme Systems*, Burgess, Minneapolis, 1959, Chapters XII and XIII.
13 I. W. Sizer, *Advan. Enzymol.*, 3 (1943) 35.
14 A. E. Stearn, *Advan. Enzymol.*, 9 (1949) 25.
15 H. Lineweaver and D. Burk, *J. Am. Chem. Soc.*, 56 (1934) 658.
16 E. L. Smith, A. Light and J. R. Kimmel, *Biochem. Soc. Symp. (Cambridge, Engl.)*, 21 (1962) 88.
17 D. E. Koshland Jr., *The Enzymes*, Vol. I, 2nd ed., Academic Press, New York, 1959, p. 305.
18 L. Michaelis, *Die Wasserstoffionenkonzentration*, Springer, Berlin, 1922, p. 48.
19 M. Dixon, *Multi-Enzyme Systems*, University Press, Cambridge, 1949.
20 M. Dixon, *Biochem. J.*, 55 (1953) 161.
21 L. Michaelis and H. Davidsohn, *Biochem. Z.*, 35 (1911) 386.
22 J. H. Northrop, *J. Gen. Physiol.*, 5 (1922) 263.
23 J. B. S. Haldane, *The Enzymes*, Longmans, Green & Co., London, 1930, p. 22.
24 E. Q. Adams, *J. Am. Chem. Soc.*, 38 (1916) 1503.
25 R. A. Alberty and V. Massey, *Biochim. Biophys. Acta*, 13 (1954) 347.
26 V. Massey and R. A. Alberty, *Biochim. Biophys. Acta*, 13 (1954) 354.
27 K. J. Laidler, *Trans. Faraday Soc.*, 51 (1955) 550.
28 E. Hase, *J. Biochem. (Tokyo)*, 39 (1952) 259.
29 O. H. Lowry, O. A. Bessey and E. J. Crawford, *J. Biol. Chem.*, 180 (1949) 399.
30 S. G. Waley, *Biochim. Biophys. Acta*, 10 (1953) 27.
31 K. J. Laidler, *Trans. Faraday Soc.*, 51 (1955) 528.
32 K. Dodgson, B. Spencer and K. Williams, *Biochem. J.*, 61 (1955) 374.
33 G. Tammann, *Z. Physik. Chem.*, 18 (1895) 426.
34 S. Arrhenius, *Z. Physik. Chem.*, 4 (1889) 226.
35 J. H. van 't Hoff, *Études de dynamique chimique*, Muller, Amsterdam, 1884.
36 F. M. Huennekens, *Techniques of Organic Chemistry*, Vol. VIII, Interscience, New York, 1953, p. 597.
37 W. C. McC. Lewis, *J. Chem. Soc.*, 113 (1918) 471.
38 S. Glasstone, K. J. Laidler and H. Eyring, *The Theory of Rate Processes*, McGraw-Hill, New York, 1941.
39 V. Massey, *Biochem. J.*, 53 (1953) 72.

[40] L. Michaelis and M. L. Menten, *Biochem. Z.*, 49 (1913) 333.
[41] G. E. Briggs and J. S. B. Haldane, *Biochem. J.*, 19 (1925) 338.
[42] K. D. Gibson, *Biochim. Biophys. Acta*, 10 (1953) 221.
[43] W. J. Dann, *Biochem. J.*, 25 (1931) 177.
[44] M. Kiese, *Biochem. Z.*, 307 (1941) 400.
[45] S. Kaufman, H. Neurath and G. W. Schwert, *J. Biol. Chem.*, 177 (1949) 793.
[46] R. Lumry, E. L. Smith and R. R. Glantz, *J. Am. Chem. Soc.*, 73 (1951) 4330.
[47] W. J. Crozier, *J. Gen. Physiol.*, 7 (1925) 123.
[48] W. J. Crozier and H. Federighi, *J. Gen Physiol.*, 7 (1925) 137, 151, 565.
[49] W. J. Crozier and T. B. Stier, *J. Gen. Physiol.*, 7 (1925) 429, 571, 699, 705.
[50] W. J. Crozier, *J. Gen. Physiol.*, 7 (1925) 189.
[51] F. H. Johnson, H. Eyring and M. J. Polissar, *The Kinetic Basis of Molecular Biology*, John Wiley & Sons, New York, 1954, Chapters 1 and 8.
[52] H. Shapley, *Proc. Natl. Acad. Sci. U.S.*, 6 (1920) 204.
[53] R. E. Buchanan and E. I. Fulmer, *Physiology and Biochemistry of Bacteria*, Vol. II, Williams & Wilkins, Baltimore, 1930, p. 47.
[54] M. F. Morales, *J. Cellular Comp. Physiol.*, 30 (1947) 303.
[55] H. L. Booij and H. P. Wolvekamp, *Rec. Trav. Chim.*, 64 (1945) 316.
[56] J. Monod, *Ann. Rev. Microbiol.*, 3 (1949) 371.
[57] I. W. Sizer, *Enzymologia*, 4 (1938) 215.
[58] I. W. Sizer, *J. Gen. Physiol.*, 21 (1938) 695.
[59] I. W. Sizer, *J. Biol. Chem.*, 132 (1940) 209.
[60] I. W. Sizer, *J. Gen. Physiol.*, 22 (1939) 719.
[61] G. B. Kistiakowsky and R. Lumry, *J. Am. Chem Soc.*, 71 (1949) 2006.
[62] G. S. Eadie, F. Bernheim and M. L. C. Bernheim, *J. Biol. Chem.*, 181 (1949) 449.
[63] J. H. Northrop, *Crystalline Enzymes*, Columbia University Press, New York, 1939.
[64] J. H. Northrop, *Ergeb. Enzymforsch.*, 1 (1932) 302.
[65] J. H. Northrop, *Ergeb. Enzymforsch.*, 2 (1933) 104.
[66] M. A. Eisenberg and G. W. Schwert, *J. Gen. Physiol.*, 34 (1951) 583.
[67] M. L. Anson and A. E. Mirsky, *J. Gen. Physiol.*, 17 (1934) 393.
[68] A. E. Mirsky and L. Pauling, *Proc. Natl. Acad. Sci. U.S.*, 22 (1936) 439.
[69] H. Eyring and A. E. Stearn, *Chem. Rev.*, 24 (1939) 253.
[70] A. E. Stearn, *Ergeb. Enzymforsch.*, 7 (1938) 1.
[71] J. Steinhardt, *Kgl. Danske Videnskab. Selskab, Mat. fys. Medd.*, 14 (1937) No. 11.
[72] V. K. La Mer, *Science*, 86 (1937) 614.
[73] H. G. Bray and K. White, *Kinetics and Thermodynamics in Biochemistry*, Churchill, London, 1957, pp. 138, 228.
[74] M. L. C. Hare, *Biochem. J.*, 22 (1928) 968.
[75] L. Ouellet, K. J. Laidler and M. F. Morales, *Arch. Biochem. Biophys.*, 39 (1952) 37.
[76] A. P. Mathias and B. R. Rabin, *Federation of European Biochem. Socs., 1st Meeting, Abstract D3*, 1964.
[77] B. Labouesse, H. L. Oppenheimer and G. P. Hess, *Federation of European Biochem. Socs., 1st Meeting, Abstract D7*, 1964.

Chapter V

*Quantitative Aspects of Enzymes and Enzyme Systems**

JOHN M. REINER

Committee on Biophysics and Department of Microbiology, Division of Basic Health Sciences, Emory University, Atlanta, Ga. (U.S.A.)

1. Introduction

The purpose of this chapter is to survey and summarize the quantitative relations exhibited by enzymes and systems of enzymes. These relations are largely kinetic: they are concerned with the rates of enzyme-catalyzed reactions, as they depend on the variables and parameters of the enzymatic environment, such as substrate concentrations, activator and inhibitor concentrations, pH, temperature, and ionic strength. Quantitative energy relations for isolated enzyme systems are dealt with in another chapter, and will be ignored here; such relations for *in vivo* systems, which are open, demand the application of the thermodynamics of irreversible systems[1], and present special problems which space considerations forbid us to go into. Theories of enzymatic catalysis, also dealt with elsewhere, are for the most part qualitative or semiquantitative at present; they are primarily concerned with elucidating mechanisms of activation rather than with *e.g.*, the prediction of numerical values of rate constants.

Certain points are assumed in the development of quantitative theories of enzyme behavior:

(*1*) Enzymes are perfect catalysts. Whatever may be their stability in the environment in which they work, they are not consumed or transformed by virtue of their catalytic activity.

(*2*) Enzymes possess varying degrees of specificity towards the compounds with which they react; some enzymes act upon large groups of chemically similar compounds, some appear (in nature) to act only upon one compound. But the specificity is never perfect; hence the possibility that chemical (or electronic) analogues of the natural substrate may inhibit enzymes, protect

* Contribution No. 627 from the Division of Basic Health Sciences.

them against the effects of physical changes or against other enzymes, or otherwise interact with them in specific ways.

(3) All enzymes known in nature are proteins, simple or conjugated. The function of each enzyme depends on its primary structure and on its conformation. Hence, any environmental factor that can modify protein conformation may modify enzyme activity, and any factor that can affect the stability of protein conformation to the extent of denaturation may destroy enzyme activity.

2. The basis of enzyme kinetics

In the early days of enzymology, enzymatic catalysis was shrouded in the same fog as catalysis in general. Some theories of enzyme action attempted to adapt the theory of chain reactions involving free radicals[2]. The attempt to understand the properties of proteins through a theory of colloids suitable almost exclusively for hydrophobic compounds helped not at all.

Perhaps the greatest contribution of Jacques Loeb to modern biology was his emphasis on proteins as multivalent electrolytes, and his insistence that the so-called colloidal properties of proteins were to be understood in terms of chemically orthodox stoichiometry[3]. The only picture of enzyme action that has survived the test of experiment is closely related to this view of Loeb's. The support for this picture is now so overwhelming that discussion of the once-popular alternatives would be a waste of time. We state it as a postulate that is fundamental for all enzyme kinetics:

In every enzymatic reaction, the interaction of the participants (enzyme, substrate, activator, inhibitor) takes place through the formation of, and transformation of well-defined stoichiometric compounds. The compounds need not be (and usually do not seem to be) primary valence compounds. The enzyme may have more than one site (active site) capable of reacting with the substrate (although evidence for such multivalency is scarce).

It follows that enzyme kinetics is a sub-division of ordinary chemical kinetics[4]. The procedure for setting up a kinetic theory of any enzymatic reaction or set of reactions will be: (*a*) to write down the postulated reactions in stoichiometric form; and (*b*) to write down the rate equations which these represent. For every molecular species postulated in the model (set of stoichiometric reactions), the rate of change of its concentration X, namely dX/dt, is given by one of the rate equations; this rate is a function of the concentrations of X and the concentrations of all compounds that are converted into it in the scheme, the form of the function being dictated by the mass action law. Given the system of differential equations for each dX/dt of the system, and the initial conditions (total enzyme in the system, substrate initially added, etc.), the future of the system is in principle

References p. 164

determined. The solution of the equations would give each concentration X as a function of time t after mixing the components of the system; the functions $X(t)$ will also depend on a set of parameters, the velocity constants for the various elementary reactions postulated in the model.

To illustrate the point, we consider the simplest valid model of an enzymatic reaction, that of Briggs and Haldane[5]. The postulated model, stated verbally, is this: A single substrate combines reversibly with free enzyme to form an intermediate compound, which reacts irreversibly to give a molecule of product and the free enzyme once again. We may write the reaction scheme, denoting free enzyme by E, substrate by S, the intermediate compound by C, and the product by P.

$$\mathrm{E} + \mathrm{S} \underset{-1}{\overset{1}{\rightleftharpoons}} \mathrm{C} \overset{2}{\longrightarrow} \mathrm{P} + \mathrm{E} \qquad (1)$$

The reactions are numbered, the numbers being written over the reaction arrows, back reactions being denoted by a minus (—) sign before the number. The reaction velocity constants will be indicated by corresponding subscripts, as k_1, k_{-1}, and k_2.

The differential equations (rate equations) which follow immediately from this scheme are:

$$\begin{aligned} \mathrm{d}S/\mathrm{d}t &= -k_1SE + k_{-1}C \\ \mathrm{d}C/\mathrm{d}t &= k_1SE - k_{-1}C - k_2C \\ \mathrm{d}P/\mathrm{d}t &= k_2C \\ \mathrm{d}E/\mathrm{d}t &= -k_1SE + k_{-1}C + k_2C \end{aligned} \qquad (2)$$

Obviously, not all the equations are independent. For instance, it is evident that

$$\mathrm{d}E/\mathrm{d}t + \mathrm{d}C/\mathrm{d}t = 0$$

This calls our attention to the fact that, if enzyme is not made or destroyed in the system, the total amount of enzyme in the system must be constant, and the free and bound forms of enzyme, E and C, must add up to this total. From $\mathrm{d}E/\mathrm{d}t + \mathrm{d}C/\mathrm{d}t = 0$, however, it follows that $E + C =$ constant. Writing this constant as E_t, we have:

$$E + C = E_t \qquad (3)$$

which we will refer to as the conservation equation for enzyme. By means of this relation, we can eliminate one of E and C. Eliminating E, and dropping the superfluous equation for $\mathrm{d}E/\mathrm{d}t$:

$$\begin{aligned} \mathrm{d}S/\mathrm{d}t &= -k_1S(E_t - C) + k_{-1}C \\ \mathrm{d}P/\mathrm{d}t &= k_2C \\ \mathrm{d}C/\mathrm{d}t &= k_1S(E_t - C) - k_{-1}C - k_2C \end{aligned} \qquad (4)$$

The expressions for dS/dt and dC/dt are independent of P, as would be expected from the irreversibility of reaction 2. If these two equations could be solved, we would have dP/dt given as an explicit function of t, and a simple quadrature would complete the solution for the system.

The mathematical difficulties of solving the two non-linear differential equations for S and C have never been overcome. Approximate solutions are possible; and numerical solutions (for assumed numerical values of the rate constants) have been obtained with the aid of computers (*e.g.*, by Chance[6]). Numerical solutions may be useful for special problems; but they really are not what is wanted. At best, if one tries enough combinations of assumed values of the rate constants and of E_t, one will get a family of curves, and the experimental curve one obtains may be fitted by one of them. For purposes of theoretical analysis and prediction of enzyme behavior, one wants an explicit formula giving the dependent variables as functions of t and of the parameters. The need for such a solution can be met by an approximate treatment[5].

(*a*) *Steady-state approximation*

It is possible to analyze the set of eqns. (4) and to infer some of their properties without solving them[7]. Such analysis shows that the curve of S against t decreases monotonically toward zero, and that the $C-t$ curve rises from zero to a maximum value and then decreases again to zero.

At the maximum $dC/dt = 0$, and from (4) this gives a relation between C and S:

$$C = SE_t/(K + S) \tag{5}$$

(dC/dt also vanishes when C and S both vanish—the tail-end of the time curves, of no consequence to us.)

It also follows, if $dC/dt = 0$, that $dS/dt + dP/dt = 0$, as is evident from (4). That is, the maximum of C is attained when product is formed just as fast as substrate disappears. Under these conditions the enzyme-catalyzed reaction has a uniquely defined velocity, $-dS/dt = dP/dt$. From (4) ($dP/dt = k_2C$) and (5), this velocity is:

$$v = k_2SE_t/(K + S) \tag{6}$$

where we use the abbreviation

$$K = (k_{-1} + k_2)/k_1$$

Inasmuch as the condition $dC/dt = 0$ and its corollary (5) define a *point* on the time curve of the reaction, rather than a region, the practical application of the velocity formula (6) rests on the validity of two fuither assumptions:

References p. 164

(*1*) The time curve of C rises towards the maximum level very rapidly when the enzyme and substrate are mixed; and

(*2*) the $C-t$ curve is relatively flat near the maximum; in other words, the curve declines toward its eventual zero level quite slowly.

If these conditions are fulfilled, one can take the velocity formula to be approximately correct throughout the time period of an experiment. This is the sense in which one speaks of a steady state. A true steady state for C—a condition in which C has and *maintains* a certain value independent of time—cannot subsist for a system described by eqns. (4).

The validity of the assumptions for many if not all enzymes is attested indirectly by the effectiveness of the velocity equation (6) in describing enzymatic catalysis, and directly by such evidence as that of Chance[6], who was able to follow rapid reactions by means of special spectrophotometric methods. Theoretical analysis of the assumption is somewhat rewarding. From (4), the initial slope of the $C-t$ curve is k_1SE_t. If we approximate the rise of the curve by the linear relation $C = k_1SE_t\, t$, this intersects the steady-state level $C = SE_t/(K + S)$ at $t = 1/k_1(K + S)$. We may ask whether this relation may be realized for reasonable values of t and of the constants. Since the relation may be rewritten as $S = 1/k_1t - K$, and since S must be positive, $1/k_1t$ must exceed K. Many known K values lie in the range from 10^{-1} to 10^{-3}; let us take 10^{-2} for the sake of example. Suppose t must be about 10 sec in order that the rise or induction period of C should not be too great a fraction of the experimental time. Then the condition for S to be positive means that $10k_1$ must be less than 10^2. In view of the wide range of values of rate constants in solution (4), this may certainly be fulfilled, but need not always hold. When it does hold, one can obviously choose a value for S (the initial substrate concentration is implied under our conditions) such that the relation $S = 1/k_1t - K$ will be approximately satisfied.

The flatness of the $C-t$ curve near the maximum would be expressed by the condition that d^2C/dt^2 is small in the neighborhood of the point specified by $dC/dt = 0$. The second derivative is easily calculated with the help of (4) and (5); for $dC/dt = 0$, it is $-k_1k_2KSE_t^2/(K + S)^2$. If K and S differ appreciably, then either $K/(K + S)$ approaches 1 and $S/(K + S)$ approaches 0, or conversely. Thus, if S and K differ, for instance, by a factor of 5, the second derivative is approximately $(5/36)k_1k_2E_t^2$. With $k_1t < 10^2$, hence $k_1 < 10$, the expression is approximately equal to (or less than) $k_2E_t^2$. If $K \sim S$, the second derivative is $k_1k_2E_t^2/4$, and again is approximately $k_2E_t^2$. To get an estimate of what this might be like in order of magnitude, consider an enzyme of molecular weight 70 000, with turnover number $k_2 \sim 10^6$ sec^{-1}, used at a concentration of 1 mg/ml. Then $k_2E_t^2 \sim 2 \cdot 10^{-4}$. To see whether this small value obtains in the neighborbood of the maximum as well, we can make a rough calculation, using the numerical values given above, of C and its derivatives when S has dropped to half its value at the maximum. We take $dS/dt = -k_2C$, and $C = E_t/2$ (from (5) when $S = K$). The time required for S to drop to one-half is 10^{-3} sec. We then write

$$dC/dt = k_1[S(E_t - C) - KC]$$

(from the definition of K), and put S equal to 3/4 of the original value at the maximum (3/4 as a mean between 1 and 1/2), but let C remain at $E_t/2$, thus getting a maximum approximation to the (negative) slope of the $C-t$ curve. In 10^{-3} sec, C drops by about 10^{-10}, or about 0.001%. Similarly, recalculating d^2C/dt^2 to take into account the non-vanishing of dC/dt and the changes in S and in dS/dt on this part of the curve, we find that it has increased in magnitude from our previous estimate of $2 \cdot 10^{-4}$ to about $2.5 \cdot 10^{-4}$. Thus, for at least one not implausible example, we can show that the curve of C against t remains appreciably flat while S decreases by one-half. The calculation seems a conservative one: a turnover number of 10^6 is high, and so is an enzyme concentration of 1 mg/ml. We assumed $S \sim 10^{-2}$ M, which is a fairly common value in practice. If we assume that S and K are not equal, but that S exceeds K by a factor of 5, S drops to one-half in half the time, the concomitant drop in C is about $2.5 \cdot 10^{-11}$ or 0.0001%, and the second derivative becomes about $1.4 \cdot 10^{-4}$.

While it is apparently not possible to give a general proof for the closely approximate validity of the steady state, the significance of the foregoing calculations is emphasized by a simple consideration. From (4)

$$dS/dt = -dC/dt - k_2C$$

Then,

$$dC/dS = (dC/dt)/(dS/dt) = -(dC/dt)/(dC/dt + k_2C)$$

When dC/dt is small compared with k_2C, as of course it is in the neighborhood of the maximum of the $C-t$ curve, dC/dS will be small. That is, although C cannot remain strictly constant (since dC/dt depends on the changing quantity S), C will be relatively little affected by an appreciable consumption of S.

Throughout most of this chapter, therefore, we will take it for granted that, in addition to our assumptions, we maintain the validity of the steady-state approximation, and assume that this approach can be used to treat kinetic problems in general. That is, whatever compounds of enzyme with other components of the system may be postulated in a kinetic mechanism, we shall assume that each such compound is in an approximate steady state. Accordingly, we set the corresponding time derivatives equal to zero, and solve the resulting algebraic equations in order to get the relations between the concentrations of the intermediates and the other variables and parameters of the system.

References p. 164

(b) *Interpretation of kinetic equations*

The velocity equation (6) has certain obvious properties. As a function of E_t, v is linear; hence (neglecting certain complications to be considered later) we would expect, when crude enzyme preparations are used, that v will be linear in the volume of extract, volume of homogenate, or other measure of the amount of enzyme-containing material added to the incubation mixture.

As a function of S, v is a hyperbola, with horizontal asymptote k_2E_t. Abbreviating this expression by V, we can rewrite (6) as:

$$v = VS/(K + S) \tag{6'}$$

The constants are readily evaluated from data in which rate of reaction is measured at various substrate concentrations, and linearizing the relation[8] by taking reciprocals:

$$1/v = (K/V)(1/S) + (1/V) \tag{7}$$

Thus, in a plot of $1/v$ against $1/S$, a system satisfying (6′) and therefore (7) will give a straight line. The intercept on the $1/v$ axis will be $1/V$, the slope will be K/V, and the intercept on the (negative side of the) $1/S$ axis will be $-1/K$.

The parameter V is the maximal velocity, corresponding to the situation when every substrate-binding site of the enzyme is in fact occupied (if $C = E_t$, $v = k_2C = k_2E_t = V$). Further interpretation meets with the difficulty that V is the product of an intrinsic factor (the turnover number k_2) and an accidental one (the concentration of enzyme used, E_t). Thus estimating V does not give k_2 unless the enzyme is pure and its molecular weight is known, so that E_t can be expressed in moles/litre.

Similarly, K is by virtue of its definition not the dissociation constant of the compound C. If we call this dissociation constant K_m (defined as k_{-1}/k_1), $K = K_m + k_2/k_1$. Hence, the estimation of K gives no measure of the relative affinity of enzyme for substrate unless a way can be found to estimate k_2/k_1.

We shall consider some approaches to the approximate evaluation of the separate rate constants. It is important to stress another limitation of such numerical estimates, however. Until a physico-chemical theory of the mechanism of enzyme action is sufficiently advanced to propose theoretical estimates of the constants, any numbers which are obtained from experimental data will have at most relative value in the comparison of different enzymes. As absolute magnitudes, they will have no significance.

Nevertheless, graphical methods like those derived from the relation (7) are of the utmost value in theoretical enzymology, not because they make it easy to evaluate parameters numerically, but because they make it easy to get at stoichiometric mechanisms. There are many useful kinetic models which do not fit (7), and many which appear to, but in which the parameters do not have the form of those in (7). The departure of experimental data from the simple pattern of eqn. (7) indicates a stoichiometric mechanism different from that of eqn. (1); and it may point to the alternative model that should be adopted. We shall see some examples; for others, consult ref. 7.

We can get the S–t curve for the steady-state approximation by integrating the equation:

$$-\mathrm{d}S/\mathrm{d}t = v = VS/(K + S) \tag{8}$$

The solution is:

$$K \ln (S/S_0) + S - S_0 = -Vt \tag{9}$$

where ln stands, as usual for the natural logarithm, and S_0 is the initial value of S. There is nothing in this solution that is not implicit in (6) or (7). But it is interesting to note the characteristics of the curve in passing. For small values of t, when S is close to S_0, we may write a simple approximation. Writing the argument of the logarithm, S/S_0, as

$$1 + (S - S_0)/S_0$$

and noting that the second term is quite small, we use the expansion of the logarithm

$$\ln (1 + x) = 1 + x + \ldots$$

and keep only the first two terms of the series. Then,

$$S - S_0 = -VS_0t/(K + S_0) \tag{9'}$$

The relation of S to t is linear, as one would expect for a reaction of zero order. The apparent reaction rate is $-VS_0/(K + S_0)$, that is to say, the value of v for S maintained constant at $S = S_0$. If S_0 is large compared to K, (9′) reduces to the simpler form $S - S_0 = -Vt$.

For later times, when S becomes small compared to S_0, the logarithmic term becomes large in magnitude compared to the linear term in S (the logarithm of a fraction is negative, and the negative value increases rapidly as the fraction becomes smaller). Thus we have nearly:

$$S/S_0 = \mathrm{e}^{-Vt/K} \tag{9''}$$

This is the expected solution for a first-order reaction. It is obvious that (6) is of the correct form when S becomes small compared to K, when v has the approximate form VS/K.

The time curve of S predicted by (9) thus starts like that of a zero-order reaction, and melts, as it were, into that of a first-order reaction—a result obtained in some of the earliest careful studies in quantitative enzymology[9].

(c) *Estimation of rate constants*

If the nature of the enzyme is such that one can detect the intermediate C, and follow its time course (*e.g.*, by rapid-flow spectrophotometry), then eqns. (4) permit a fairly direct approach to the rate constants. The initial slope of the $C-t$ curve, for instance, is k_1SE_t, S being estimated at its initial value (amount added to incubation mixture). From this and $V = k_2E_t$ we can calculate k_2/k_1, and hence from $K = K_m + k_2/k_1$ we get $K_m = k_{-1}/k_1$, the dissociation constant of the compound C. To get k_1 independently, we first get k_2 by observing that $dP/dt = k_2C$. We can either get k_2 as $(dP/dt)/C$, from the curves for C and for product formed; or we can integrate the equation over the entire range of the experiment (to exhaustion of substrate), giving

$$P_{total} = S_0 = k_2 \int_0^\infty C\, dt$$

The integral is the area under the $C-t$ curve, hence k_2 is S_0 divided by this area. From k_2 and the ratio k_2/k_1 we get k_1. From k_1 and $K_m = k_{-1}/k_1$ we get k_{-1}.

Another approach[10] is to integrate the equations for C and P treating S as constant ($S \sim S_0$) on the grounds that the data used will be those of the very short induction period before the steady state is attained. That is, instead of the non-linear system (4) we deal with the approximate linear system:

$$\begin{aligned} dC/dt &= k_1[S_0E_t - (S_0 + K)C] \\ dP/dt &= k_2C \end{aligned} \qquad (4')$$

The solutions are:

$$\begin{aligned} C &= (1 - e^{-\beta t})/\alpha \\ P &= k_2t/\alpha + k_2(e^{-\beta t} - 1)/\alpha\beta \end{aligned} \qquad (10)$$

with the abbreviations

$$\alpha = (S_0 + K)/S_0E_t \qquad \beta = k_1(S_0 + K)$$

Expanding in P the exponential

$$e^{-\beta t} = 1 - \beta t + \tfrac{1}{2}\beta^2t^2 - \ldots$$

we have approximately, for small values of t, $\frac{1}{2}k_1k_2S_0E_tt^2$. If we plot the pre-steady-state data for P against t^2, we get a straight line with slope $k_1k_2S_0E_t/2$. Since $V = k_2E_t$, we have an estimate of k_1 from this slope. Moreover, the initial slope of the $C-t$ curve is again $k_1S_0E_t$, from which, knowing k_1 and S_0, we can get E_t. Hence, from $V = k_2E_t$, we have k_2. Thus all the constants are obtainable as before.

A method proposed by Slater and Bonner[11] is of more dubious value. It rests on the relation $K = K_m + k_2/k_1$, which can be rewritten

$$K = K_m + k_2E_t/k_1E_t = K_m + V/k_1E_t$$

A plot of K against V has a slope of $1/k_1E_t$, and intercepts K_m and $-k_{-1}E_t$ on the K and V axes respectively. However, this makes sense only if it is possible to vary V without varying either E_t or k_1, that is, if it is possible to vary k_2 experimentally. Whether this is truly possible is highly questionable; and it is not easy to see how one would demonstrate it within the framework of the relation used. The approach has been to work with systems involving more than one substrate, say a group donor and a group acceptor. Then it is argued that k_2 is actually proportional to the concentration of acceptor, say $k_2'A$, and can be varied by varying A. The trouble with this argument is that, as we shall see when we consider bimolecular enzyme-catalyzed reactions, throwing the velocity equation into the form (6) or (7) gives an apparent K that is a complex function of numerous constants and of the acceptor concentration (for example see ref. 7, p. 105, eqn. VI.9′). The apparent K_m depends on acceptor concentration, and the apparent k_2 is a hyperbolic rather than a linear function of acceptor concentration. Only in a very special case will the trick work.

(*d*) *Summary*

We have stated three assumptions basic to the development of enzyme kinetic theory: the limited specificity of enzymes, the protein nature of enzymes, and the formation of stoichiometric compounds between enzyme and other components as the key to the mechanism of action of enzymes. We developed the consequences of the third assumption; the first two will play their part subsequently. To these three we added a fourth: Intermediate compounds, not found among the reactants or products, are in a practical though approximate steady state throughout the course of a usual experiment. The principles have been illustrated with the help of a simple system—the irreversible conversion of a single substrate, with the formation of a single enzyme–substrate compound.

3. Reversible and bimolecular reactions

(*a*) *Reversible reactions*

Enzymatic reactions are known to be reversible, though to varying degrees. The system of the preceding section must be considered as at best an approximation to the actual situation, possibly valid during the early stage

References p. 164

of a reaction, when the amount of product is relatively insignificant, or for enzymes (*e.g.*, hydrolases) whose equilibrium is far to one side.

The problem was first treated by Haldane[12]; the technique is a simple extension of that of the previous section. One important difference must be noted, however. When one considers a reversible reaction, it seems clear that one intermediate compound is not sufficient. On chemical grounds one would suppose that the compound formed by E and S would differ from the compound formed by E and P; indeed, the catalytic function of the enzyme would consist precisely in the transition from one of these compounds to the other. Hence the stoichiometric scheme is written

$$\mathrm{E} + \mathrm{S} \underset{-1}{\overset{1}{\rightleftharpoons}} \mathrm{C_1} \underset{-2}{\overset{2}{\rightleftharpoons}} \mathrm{C_2} \underset{-3}{\overset{3}{\rightleftharpoons}} \mathrm{E} + \mathrm{P} \tag{11}$$

The kinetic equations are written from inspection of (11), and the steady-state assumption is applied to C_1 and C_2. Adding the conservation equation for enzyme:

$$E_t = E + C_1 + C_2 \tag{12}$$

one can solve the system. The net reaction rate from left to right is

$$v = -\mathrm{d}S/\mathrm{d}t = \mathrm{d}P/\mathrm{d}t = (VK'S - V'KP)/(K'S + KP + KK') \tag{13}$$

with the abbreviations:

$$\begin{aligned} V &= k_2k_3E\,/(k_2 + k_{-2} + k_3) \\ V' &= k_{-1}k_{-2}E_t/(k_{-1} + k_2 + k_{-2}) \\ K &= (k_{-1}k_{-2} + k_{-1}k_3 + k_2k_3)/k_1(k_2 + k_{-2} + k_3) \\ K' &= (k_{-1}k_{-2} + k_{-1}k_3 + k_2k_3)/k_{-3}(k_{-1} + k_2 + k_{-2}) \end{aligned} \tag{14}$$

The net rate from right to left is simply the negative of (13).

In a system containing both S and P, the reaction will go from left to right when $VK'S$ exceeds $V'KP$, from right to left when the reverse is true. The reaction will be at equilibrium when these quantities are equal. The equilibrium ratio is:

$$(P/S)_{\mathrm{equil.}} = VK'/V'K = (k_2/k_{-2})[(k_1/k_{-1})/(k_{-3}/k_3)] \tag{15}$$

The bracketed expression is obviously the ratio of the affinities of S and P for the enzyme, while k_2/k_{-2} is the ratio of the turnover numbers for the two key intermediates, from left to right and from right to left respectively. (Affinity is to be understood as the reciprocal of dissociation constant.)

Suppose that $P \sim 0$. Then (13) takes the familiar form (6). But the constants V and K are now given by (14). Since the argument in favor of two intermediate compounds is just as applicable to the system of the preceding section as to the present one, it is clear that the correct form of

K and V is in all cases that of (14). It follows that the devices described earlier for getting numerical values of the rate constants are fundamentally irrelevant, since they obviously can not apply here. This furnishes further support to our preceding emphasis on the use of special graphical methods, not for numerical evaluation of constants, but for detection of mechanisms.

We may inquire about the case where the enzyme system is practically irreversible because of the values of the constants. First, suppose we set $k_{-3} = 0$; this implies that the enzyme does not combine with P at all. In that case, $K' \to \infty$, and we again get eqn. (6), with the constants given by (14). On the other hand, we may set $k_{-2} = 0$, which implies that E can combine with P but fails to convert it to S. Then $V' = 0$, and (13) becomes:

$$v = VS/(S + K + KP/K') \tag{16}$$

with the constants given by (14), where $k_{-2} = 0$.

This relation describes the well-known phenomenon of the inhibition of an enzyme by its product. For if $P \neq 0$, the rate given by (16) is lower than for $P = 0$, even though the enzyme cannot convert P to S. This is not a matter of a back reaction, but of a true inhibition, in which enzyme is put out of the running by combination with P, the combination being non-functional.

The same argument applies to the complete equation (13). If we begin with $P = 0$, the consumption of S and production of P are initiated. When P reaches a finite level, the rate from left to right decreases, not only because of the back reaction, which is roughly described by the numerator of (13), but also because of the term containing P in the denominator, which results from the binding of enzyme by P. That is, while some of the molecules of C_2 are decreasing the effective rate from S to P, because they are turning over and making S (back reaction), those molecules of C_2 which are not turning over at any given moment are still lowering the rate because they are unavailable for S.

(b) *Bimolecular reactions*

Most enzymatic reactions are in fact bimolecular; that is, they require the enzyme-mediated interaction of two molecules of substrate, generally belonging to distinct molecular species.

Ruling out ternary collisions of enzyme and two substrate molecules as unlikely, we have two principal possibilities for bimolecular reactions to occur in reasonable stages. The first involves the assumption that only one intermediate is formed, by the reaction of enzyme and one of the substrates. The second substrate reacts with this intermediate without combining with it, releasing enzyme and products. This, which might be called the hit-and-

References p. 164

run mechanism, is represented schematically by:

$$\begin{aligned} E + S_1 &\underset{-1}{\overset{1}{\rightleftharpoons}} C \\ C + S_2 &\xrightarrow{2} E + P_1 + P_2 \end{aligned} \tag{17}$$

We have written the last step as irreversible for the sake of simplicity. The solution of the system for the steady state is:

$$v = k_2 S_2 C = k_2 E_t S_1 S_2 / (S_1 + K_1 + g S_2) \tag{18}$$

with

$$K_1 = k_{-1}/k_1, \quad g = k_2/k_1$$

With two substrates, one may saturate the enzyme with either one while maintaining the other at a non-saturating level. We will thus speak of partial saturation with respect to one or the other substrate, and denote the partially saturated rates by V with appropriate numerical subscripts. In this case:

$$\begin{aligned} V_1 &= k_2 E_t S_2 \\ V_2 &= k_1 E_t S_1 \end{aligned} \tag{19}$$

The prediction that saturating the enzyme with respect to one substrate would permit the rate to increase indefinitely in proportion to the concentration of the other substrate is both implausible and contrary to experience.

The situation is readily improved if we once again take cognizance of the extra step required for the activation process. Let S_2 hit and run as before; but let the result be another intermediate, which now breaks up and releases the product:

$$\begin{aligned} E + S_1 &\underset{-1}{\overset{1}{\rightleftharpoons}} C_1 \\ C_1 + S_2 &\underset{-2}{\overset{2}{\rightleftharpoons}} C_2 + P_2 \\ C_2 &\xrightarrow{3} E + P_1 \end{aligned} \tag{20}$$

The solution is

$$v = k_3 E_t S_1 S_2 / [K K_m + g S_2 + S_1 (K + S_2)] \tag{21}$$

with

$$\begin{aligned} K &= (k_{-2} P_2 + k_3)/k_2 \\ K_m &= k_{-1}/k_1 \\ g &= k_3/k_1 \end{aligned}$$

Now we find

$$\begin{aligned} V_1 &= k_3 E_t S_2 / (K + S_2) \\ V_2 &= k_3 E_t S_1 / (g + S_1) \end{aligned} \tag{22}$$

This is the plausible and observable result for a two-substrate system: when one substrate ceases to be limiting, the other gives behavior formally like that one of the one-substrate equation (6).

The dependence of K on P_2 (the conversion product of the hit-and-run substrate) gives an instance of inhibition by product, since K occurs only in the denominator of v. Note from (22) that this effect, if it occurs, will show up in the partially saturated case V_1, but not in V_2.

If we remove the hit-and-run character of (20), thus:

$$\begin{aligned} E + S_1 &\underset{-1}{\overset{1}{\rightleftharpoons}} C_1 \\ C_1 + S_2 &\underset{-2}{\overset{2}{\rightleftharpoons}} C_2 \\ C_2 &\xrightarrow{3} E + P_1 + P_2 \end{aligned} \qquad (23)$$

we get a solution formally identical with (21) and (22), except that the term $k_{-2}P_2$ in K is replaced by k_{-2}, so that neither product inhibits any longer (at least, in the early stages of the reaction, when the irreversibility of step 3 is not too unreasonable). If $k_{-2} = 0$, the two cases will be identical.

This is an interesting and significant result. Since (20) and (23) are formally identical in their consequences, one must ask why the consequences of (17) are different from either, and implausible. The hit-and-run function of S_2 cannot be responsible, for it is common to (17) and (20). The important feature must be the extra intermediate, missing in (17) and present in (20) and (23), whether or not S_2 is included in that intermediate. The latter is clear if we think about the formal properties of a step like 2 in any of these schemes: if A and B react to give C, the rate of formation of C will be proportional to AB, whether the product of the reaction is bound B or not; if there is a back reaction, its rate will depend on C, and on the conversion product of B if it occurs (*e.g.*, P_2 in eqn. 20), but not on B.

Why should the extra step be important? This is obvious if we look at the schemes. In (17), if we saturate the enzyme with S_1, the rate of reaction is simply proportional to S_2 times the total enzyme. In (20) and (23), if we saturate the enzyme with S_1 the rate of reaction is proportional to that fraction of the total enzyme that is in the form C_2. The rate of formation of that fraction is proportional to S_2, but the amount of the fraction is proportional to $S_2/(K + S_2)$. Hence the rate will be limited as S_2 increases, which one would expect from common experience with such systems.

In the preceding cases, we have implicitly assumed that the reaction steps are ordered—that S_1 necessarily combines with E before S_2. Let us briefly consider the alternative—that the two substrates may combine with E in

References p. 164

either order. We begin with the most general case, in which the system is reversible:

$$\begin{aligned}
E + S_1 &\underset{-1}{\overset{1}{\rightleftharpoons}} C_1 \\
C_1 + S_2 &\underset{-2}{\overset{2}{\rightleftharpoons}} C_3 \\
E + S_2 &\underset{-3}{\overset{3}{\rightleftharpoons}} C_2 \\
C_2 + S_1 &\underset{-4}{\overset{4}{\rightleftharpoons}} C_3 \\
C_3 &\underset{-5}{\overset{5}{\rightleftharpoons}} C_4 \\
C_4 &\underset{-6}{\overset{6}{\rightleftharpoons}} C_5 + P_1 \\
C_5 &\underset{-7}{\overset{7}{\rightleftharpoons}} E + P_2
\end{aligned} \tag{24}$$

The solution is:

$$v = (k_7 S_1 S_2 A - k_{-7} r_5 r_6 P_1 P_2 B) E_t / \{(B + k_5) D (1 + S_1/K_1 + S_2/K_3) + (1 + g_1/K_1 + g_3/K_3)(ADS_1S_2 + k_{-5}M) + (M + N)(B + k_5)\} \tag{25}$$

with the abbreviations

$$\begin{aligned}
K_1 &= (k_{-1} + k_2 S_2/k_1) \\
K_3 &= (k_{-3} + k_4 S_1/k_3) \\
g_1 &= k_{-2}/k_1 \\
g_3 &= k_{-4}/k_3 \\
r_5 &= k_{-5}/k_5 \\
r_6 &= k_{-6}/k_6 \\
A &= k_2/K_1 + k_4/K_3 \\
B &= k_{-1} g_1/K_1 + k_{-3} g_3/K_3 \\
D &= k_7/k_5 + r_5(k_7/k_6 + r_6 P_1) B/(B + k_5) \\
M &= K_6 A/(B + k_5) + g_5 g_6 P_1 P_2 \\
N &= A/(B + k_5) + g_6 P_2 [k_6/k_5 + r_5 B/(B + k_5)] \\
g_5 &= k_{-6}/k_5 \\
g_6 &= k_{-7}/k_6 \\
K_5 &= (k_{-5} + k_6)/k_5 \\
K_6 &= (k_{-6} P_1 + k_7)/k_6
\end{aligned}$$

It should be noted that we have not randomized the steps 6 and 7, simply in order to keep the already considerable complexity of this system within limits. Thus the dependence of v on P_1 and P_2 is relatively simple. The rate is inhibited by both products (if present) if step 5 is made irreversible, by P_2 if step 6 is irreversible, and by P_1 if step 7 is irreversible.

The dependence of v on substrate, for instance on S_1, is complicated. If we attempt to simplify it by omitting steps 6 and 7, and making step 5 irreversible, v becomes a quotient of two cubic polynomials in S_1. If we now form the reciprocal, by analogy with eqn. (7), we get, writing x for $1/S_1$, an expression of the form

$$(a + bx + cx^2 + dx^3)/(A + Bx + Cx^2)$$

This approaches the asymptote $(c + dx)/C$ as x becomes large. The earlier part of the graph is curved, and in principle might have a minimum. The initial slope is $(Ab - aB)/A^2$. If it is less than the final slope d/C, the curve bends upwards; if greater, downwards. If it is negative, the curve has a minimum. Unfortunately, when one writes out the conditions in full (substituting appropriate expressions for a, b, etc.), they are complicated functions of S_2 and of the various constants of the system; and they cannot be shown to be satisfied, one way or another, by any simple relationship. We can show that

$$Ab - aB = (k_4/k_3)^3\{k_2^2(g_1 + K_1)k_4/k_3 + k_2k_{-3}g_3K_1 + (k_{-1}g_1 + k_5K_1)k_4K_1(k_2/k_3 - 1)\}$$

One can make out a plausible argument for the supposition that $k_2 > k_3$, which would mean that S_2 combines with the enzyme more readily after S_1 has combined; for if one is dealing with a group-transfer reaction, one might expect the presence of the donor to attract the acceptor and conversely. If this argument is acceptable, the entire expression is necessarily positive, and the reciprocal plot has no minimum.

No such straightforward argument permits the comparison of the initial slope $(Ab - aB)/A^2$ with the final slope d/C. If we assume that the constants of reaction 1 equal the corresponding constants of step 4, and likewise for steps 2 and 3 (that is, if we assume that the equilibrium of each substrate with the enzyme is independent of the binding of the other substrate), one can readily show that the initial slope is less than the final slope, and that the reciprocal plot therefore bends upward to its asymptote. If this not altogether convincing simplification is not adopted, inspection of the expressions suggests that the relation may still hold. But this cannot be demonstrated, and in particular it cannot be shown to hold independent of the value of S_2.

The reversible form of the ordered bimolecular reaction (S_1 goes on ahead of S_2 always) is obtained if we eliminate reactions 3 and 4 from (24). The

References p. 164

result of this is to eliminate the terms S_2/K_3 and g_3/K_3 from (25), the term k_4/K_3 from the constant A, and the term $k_{-3}g_3/K_3$ from the constant B. With these modifications, the case is represented by eqn. (25). Since the constants A, B, M, and N are now independent of S_1, the dependence of v on S_1 is now formally the same as that of eqn. (21). The difference lies in the effects of the products.

The cases of partial saturation and of practical irreversibility (one thinks for example of hexokinase as an example of the latter situation) are interesting because they help in identifying the actual substrates and products with their numbered representatives in the equations, and in localizing the irreversibility. Thus, finding V_1 by letting S_1 become infinitely large, we observe that the denominator is a function of P_1 and not of P_2. Calculating V_2 in a similar fashion (remembering that K_1 is a linear function of S_2), we find that the denominator contains both P_1 and P_2. Thus we may saturate an enzyme first with one substrate and then with the other: if only one product is inhibitory in one of the cases, the saturating substrate is S_1 and the inhibitory product P_1. This pattern also indicates the ordered character of the bimolecular reaction; for the random case is symmetrical with respect to S_1 and S_2.

The argument about irreversibility, immediately following eqn. (25), still holds, and helps us to locate the irreversible step by studying product inhibition in the unsaturated system. In order to decide which product is P_1 and which P_2, a preliminary study under conditions of partial saturation is carried out. In the S_1-saturated system, P_1 is still inhibitory if step 7 is the irreversible one, but not if 5 or 6 is the site. In the S_2-saturated system, P_2 inhibits if step 5 is irreversible or if step 6 is irreversible, but not if step 7 is irreversible; and P_1 inhibits if step 5 is irreversible. The possible results of studying product inhibition of V_1, V_2, and v are then: (*a*) no inhibition by either product for one substrate saturating, inhibition by both products with the other saturating substrate, and inhibition by both products for v (no saturation); (*b*) no inhibition by either product for one saturation case, inhibition by the same product both for the other case of saturation and for v. In case (*a*), the products cannot be ordered, but the irreversible step is 5. In case (*b*), the product is either P_2 and the step 6, or P_1 and the step 7; and again the products cannot be ordered. In the irreversible case, then, product-inhibition studies can distinguish between irreversibility at step 5 as against irreversibility at either step 6 or step 7; no more information is yielded unless one can infer the identity of the two products (*i.e.*, which is P_1 and which P_2) independently.

One way to get at the problem depends on the fact that V_1 as a function of S_2 is more complex than V_2 as a function of S_1. The latter is in fact formally identical with (6), and would give a reciprocal plot like (7). But the former is quadratic with respect to S_2 in both numerator and denominator; and the reciprocal plot will curve downwards and approach a straight line for larger values of $1/S_2$. This distinction makes it possible to identify S_1 and S_2. Once this is done, the product-inhibition studies yield the rest of the information. The product that inhibits with S_1 saturation is P_1, provided the irreversible step is 7; otherwise there is no product inhibition. The product that inhibits with S_2 saturation is P_2 if the irreversible step is 6; there is no inhibition if step 7 is irreversible, and both products inhibit in case of step 5.

4. Activation and inhibition

Returning to our initial assumptions about the behaviour of enzymes, we can reason that the limited specificity of enzymes implies the possibility of combination with chemical analogues of the substrate, presumably through the same binding sites as the substrate. Whether such analogues are or are not turned over by the enzyme, they will compete with substrate for the supply of enzyme molecules. The net effect of adding such an analogue to the system will be inhibition, a decrease of the rate below that expected in the absence of the intruder. Depending on the relative efficacy of binding of substrate and analogue, one would expect that an increase of the substrate concentration would lower the extent of inhibition. We leave open the nature and extent of the analogy required to produce inhibition; the minimum requirement is that it must suffice to permit the analogue to occupy substrate-binding sites.

The assumption that enzyme activity depends on the conformation of the enzyme protein opens up other possibilities. Evidently, a compound that can combine with the enzyme at a site other than the substrate-binding site may modify the conformation in such a way as to inhibit the enzymatic reaction, either by decreasing the capacity of the enzyme to combine with substrate, or by lowering its ability to convert substrate to product, or both. Such inhibition would not be decreased by increasing substrate.

We can go a step further. If, as has been proposed[13], the combination of substrate with enzyme induces a conformational change in the enzyme, the result might be a change in the combining power of the enzyme for other compounds. Thus an inhibitor of the kind just discussed (conformation-changing inhibitor) might be unable to combine with the enzyme after the substrate is bound when it could combine before, or the reverse situation might obtain.

Obviously, a conformation-changing compound need not decrease the enzyme activity, but may increase it instead. The increase may be relative to an initial non-zero level of activity, or even relative to an initial zero level

References p. 164

of activity. In either case, we may speak of activation, and term the compound an activator.

Having considered the possibility of altering (specifically, of increasing) the activity of an enzyme by combination with a non-substrate, we may complete the picture by contemplating a form of activation which takes place at the site eventually occupied by substrate. In this case, activation before substrate binding is compulsory. This is still a special case of the more general considerations advanced in the last paragraph, however; for an activator might be required to permit substrate binding by inducing a change of conformation, rather than by acting as a ligand.

Obviously, activation and inhibition have some rather strong formal and actual resemblances. This is most readily seen if we begin by setting up a stoichiometric scheme in which we do not commit ourselves, as yet, about the eventual effects:

$$\begin{aligned}
\mathrm{E} + \mathrm{S} &\underset{-1}{\overset{1}{\rightleftharpoons}} \mathrm{C} \\
\mathrm{C} &\overset{2}{\longrightarrow} \mathrm{E} + \mathrm{P} \\
\mathrm{E} + \mathrm{X} &\underset{-3}{\overset{3}{\rightleftharpoons}} \mathrm{E}_x \\
\mathrm{C} + \mathrm{X} &\underset{-4}{\overset{4}{\rightleftharpoons}} \mathrm{C}_x \\
\mathrm{E}_x + \mathrm{S} &\underset{-5}{\overset{5}{\rightleftharpoons}} \mathrm{C}_x' \\
\mathrm{C}_x &\overset{6}{\longrightarrow} \mathrm{E}_x + \mathrm{P} \\
\mathrm{C}_x' &\overset{7}{\longrightarrow} \mathrm{E}_x + \mathrm{P}
\end{aligned} \tag{26}$$

where X is the activating or inhibiting compound. The solution will be simpler if we treat step 3 as being in equilibrium. Doing this for the moment, we get:

$$v = VS(1 + k_6'X/K_4 + k_7'zX/K_3)/[K_1(1 + X/K_3) + S(1 + X/K_4 + zX/K_3)] \tag{27}$$

where

$$V = k_2E_t, \quad k_6' = k_6/k_2, \quad k_7' = k_7/k_2, \quad z = K_1/K_5$$

$$K_1 = (k_{-1} + k_2)/k_1, \quad K_3 = k_{-3}/k_3$$

$$K_4 = (k_{-4} + k_6)/k_4, \quad K_5 = (k_{-5} + k_7)/k_5$$

The result will perhaps be more perspicuous if it is put into the reciprocal form:

$$\begin{aligned}
1/v = {} & (K_1/V)[(1 + X/K_3)/(1 + k_6'X/K_4 + k_7'zX/K_3)](1/S) \\
& + (1/V)[(1 + X/K_4 + zX/K_3)/(1 + k_6'X/K_4 + k_7'zX/K_3)]
\end{aligned} \tag{28}$$

This expression differs from eqn. (7) in the two factors in square brackets. Consider the second one (the intercept of the graph) first, as being simplest. Obviously, the expression will be greater or less than one according as k_6' and k_7' are less or greater than one. That is, the intercept of the reciprocal plot will be increased by inhibition and decreased by activation.

The slope factor in brackets leads to a similar though not quite so simple conclusion. If $k_7'z$ is greater than one, this factor will be less than one, irrespective of the value of k_6'. That is, activation of the free enzyme will decrease the slope of the reciprocal plot, even if the bound enzyme is simultaneously inhibited. But note that the critical constant is not k_7', but $k_7'z$. It is possible that $k_7' < 1$ (inhibition), but that $K_5 < K_1$ (hence $z > 1$) in such a way as to more than compensate. Hence the slope may be decreased by an inhibitor, provided only that $k_7' \neq 0$.

The slope may be decreased by an inhibitor even if $k_7' = 0$ or $z = 0$, provided $k_6' > K_4/K_3$. This may be the case even if $k_6' < 1$ (inhibition), provided that K_4/K_3 is sufficiently small—that is, provided that E binds X more strongly than C does.

The case $k_6' = 0$, $k_7' = 0$ corresponds to complete inhibition. In this case (no other conditions being imposed), both the slope and the intercept of the reciprocal plot will be increased.

(a) *Inhibition*

Consider *complete inhibition*, in which X combines only with E and not with C. Then $1/K_4 = 0$. It will still be true that both slope and intercept are increased by the inhibition. But suppose also that E_x cannot bind S, so that $1/K_5 = 0$. Then $z = 0$, and the intercept will be unchanged while the slope is increased. This special case corresponds to the classical notion of competitive inhibition: only free enzyme is bound, and it is bound in such a way as to exclude binding of substrate. Note, in the light of our introductory discussion, that X need not bind E at the S site; it need only modify the conformation so that S cannot bind, or interfere sterically. The term competitive is therefore somewhat misleading; the binding site of X is not decided simply by the kinetic relations. We have therefore[7] proposed to call this situation *exclusive E inhibition*.

The converse case, where $1/K_3 = 0$ (X does not bind to E), gives an increased intercept and no effect on the slope. For the sake of keeping the terminology parallel with the preceding case, we call this *exclusive C inhibition* (sometimes called un-competitive in the older literature).

To see how the value of S affects these results, we can recast the equations in terms of the fractional inhibition

$$i = (v_{\text{un.}} - v_{\text{in.}})/v_{\text{un.}}$$

References p. 164

where $v_{un.}$ and $v_{in.}$ stand for uninhibited and inhibited rates respectively. After some elementary manipulations we get

$$X = Mi/(1 - i) \tag{29}$$

with

$$M = (K_1 + S)/(K_1/K_3 + S/K_4 + zS/K_3)$$

Consider the value of X required to give some particular fractional inhibition, say 0.5. X as function of S is a hyperbola. At $S = 0$, $X = K_3$. At large values of S, X approaches $K_3K_4/(K_3 + K_4z)$. This curve rises, falls, or remains unchanged with increasing S according as $K_4(1 - z)$ is greater than, less than, or equal to K_3. These cases have been termed[7] *substrate-promoted*, *substrate-antagonized*, and *substrate-indifferent*. Exclusive E inhibition is a special case of the second category; exclusive C inhibition is a special case of the first category. The third category is what is often called non-competitive in the older literature.

Note that the plot of X against $i/(1 - i)$ is a straight line passing through the origin. This type of graph is extremely useful in the analysis of inhibition. In the case of complete inhibition, the graph is no longer linear if we are using X in a limited amount, so that the amount of X bound to various forms of enzyme must be considered. The conservation equation for X is (X_t being total X added)

$$X_t = X + E_x + C_x + C_x' \tag{30}$$

The inhibition relation becomes, instead of (29):

$$X_t = iE_t + Mi/(1 - i) \tag{31}$$

If this is plotted against $i/(1 - i)$, it gives a curve that bends downwards, approaching a linear asymptote. The slope of the asymptote is M, as in (29), and the intercept is E_t; the initial slope is $E_t + M$. Observe that this plot furnishes an estimate of E_t, as compared with (7), which gives only $V = k_2E_t$.

An interesting and useful result is also obtained from inhibitors that bind tightly (more or less irreversibly). Suppose $K_3 \sim 0$ or $K_4 \sim 0$ (or both); then $M \sim 0$. Note that i (fractional inhibition) must lie between 0 and 1. If $i < 1$, the second term of (31) vanishes, and $X_t = iE_t$. Since

$$i = 1 - v_{in.}/v_{un.}$$

we have, recalling that $v_{un.} = k_2E_tS/(K_1 + S)$:

$$v = [k_2S/(K_1 + S)](E_t - I_t) \tag{32}$$

That is, if we plot v against I_t, we get a straight line with a negative slope, which intersects the I_t axis at $I_t = E_t$. The rate v of course remains zero when $I_t > E_t$. Thus the inhibitor may be said to *titrate* the enzyme, giving maximal inhibition when all enzyme has been bound.

(b) Activation

Most of what one might say about activation is obvious from eqn. (27). *Complete activation* will be the case where $k_2 = 0$ (no activity of unactivated enzyme). Considering v as a function of X, the relation is the same as that of v to S in (6). The reciprocal plot ($1/v$ against $1/X$) is linear. The slope of the graph varies as $(1 + K_1/S)$. If we assume that the enzyme does not combine with substrate at all before activation, the slope varies simply as $1/S$, so that this case of *compulsory activation* may be distinguished from the more general case by the fact that the plot of the slope against $1/S$ passes through the origin.

If $k_2 \neq 0$, the reciprocal plot against $1/X$ is non-linear (a hyperbola), approaching asymptotically, as $1/X$ increases, a horizontal line, with height

$$(K_1 + S)/k_2 E_t S$$

An interesting case arises, as in the case of inhibition, if bound activator cannot be neglected compared with free activator. For the sake of simplicity, let us discuss complete and compulsory activation, and add the conservation equation

$$X_t = X + E_x + C_x \tag{33}$$

The stoichiometric scheme is

$$\begin{aligned} &\mathrm{X + E} \underset{-1}{\overset{1}{\rightleftharpoons}} \mathrm{E}_x \\ &\mathrm{E}_x + \mathrm{S} \underset{-2}{\overset{2}{\rightleftharpoons}} \mathrm{C}_x \\ &\mathrm{C}_x \xrightarrow{3} \mathrm{E}_x + \mathrm{P} \end{aligned} \tag{34}$$

The solution is

$$v = \tfrac{1}{2}k_3 \Big\{X_t + E_t + K_1K_2/(K_2 + S) - [(X_t + E_t + K_1K_2/(K_2 + S))^2 - 4X_tE_t]^{\frac{1}{2}}\Big\} S \Big/ (K_2 + S) \tag{35}$$

with

$$K_1 = k_{-1}/k_1, \quad K_2 = (k_{-2} + k_3)/k_2$$

Consider partial saturation with respect to X_t and to E_t, the latter being a new feature

$$\begin{aligned} V_x &= k_3E_tS/(K_2 + S) \\ V_e &= k_3X_tS/(K_2 + S) \end{aligned} \tag{36}$$

Note the symmetry between X_t and E_t in these relations, as in (35). The curve of v against X_t and that of v against E_t are formally identical, and will be superimposable provided that we express E_t and X_t in the same units.

References p. 164

Note also the novel conclusion: it is possible to saturate the activator with enzyme as well as to saturate the enzyme with activator.

Saturation with S gives another interesting result:

$$\begin{aligned} V_s &= k_3 X_t \quad \text{if} \quad X_t < E_t \\ V_s &= k_3 E_t \quad \text{if} \quad X_t \geqslant E_t \end{aligned} \tag{37}$$

We have another *titration curve*: a straight line with slope k_3, when V_s is plotted against X_t, breaking off to a horizontal line at $X_t = E_t$. The same result will be obtained if the activator is strongly bound ($K_1 \sim 0$). If experimental error makes it difficult to be sure that a broken-line plot has been obtained, the reciprocal plot ($1/V_s$ against $1/X_t$) is useful, since it will consist of a horizontal part followed by a straight line with slope $1/k_3$; the linear portion, if extrapolated, will pass through the origin of the graph.

(*c*) *Competitive interactions*

If a substrate analogue is also a substrate for the enzyme, the significance of the constants in the inhibitor equations is modified. Consider as an example:

$$\begin{aligned} E + S_1 &\underset{-1}{\overset{1}{\rightleftharpoons}} C_1 \\ C_1 &\xrightarrow{2} E + P_1 \\ E + S_2 &\underset{-3}{\overset{3}{\rightleftharpoons}} C_2 \\ C_2 &\xrightarrow{4} E + P_2 \end{aligned} \tag{38}$$

where S_2 is an analogue of S_1. We express the solution in terms of the reciprocal plot:

$$1/v = (1/V)[(1 + S_2/K_2)K_1(1/S_1) + 1] \Big/ [1 + g(S_2/K_2)K_1(1/S_1)] \tag{38a}$$

where

$$V = k_2 E_t, \quad K_1 = (k_{-1} + k_2)/k_1, \quad K_2 = (k_{-3} + k_4)/k_3,$$
$$g = k_4/k_2$$

Considered as a function of $1/S_1$, (38a) is non-linear; it is a hyperbola with initial slope

$$(K_1/V)[1 + (1 - g)(S_2/K_2)]$$

and horizontal asymptote

$$(1/V)(K_2 + S_2)/gS_2$$

For quite small values of g, the curve will tend toward the conventional linear form.

If we were to analyze experimental data by comparing the slope of the initial portion with the slope of the conventional curve for complete exclusive E inhibition, writing K_i for the dissociation constant of the E–X compound, we would get:

$$K_i = K_2(1 - g) \tag{39}$$

Thus the measurements would not give a dissociation constant at all, and the result would also depend on the ratio of turnover numbers g.

The result (38a) follows if we measure a common product resulting from the action of E on substrate and analogue (*e.g.*, inorganic phosphate if both are phosphate esters). If we measure specifically only the product of S_1, then the turnover of S_2, k_4, drops out and g becomes zero. The graph is now linear all the way. But the resulting comparison $K_i = K_2$ still invalidates any attempt to treat the data as measures of affinity of analogue for enzyme, since the expression for K_2 will be unaltered, and will still contain the turnover number k_4.

Competitive interactions may arise among activators, and indeed seem quite common[14,15]. Consider for example the scheme:

$$\begin{aligned}
E + X_1 &\underset{-1}{\overset{1}{\rightleftharpoons}} E_{x1} \\
E_{x1} + S &\underset{-2}{\overset{2}{\rightleftharpoons}} C_{x1} \overset{3}{\longrightarrow} E_{x1} + P \\
E + X_2 &\underset{-4}{\overset{4}{\rightleftharpoons}} E_{x2} \\
E_{x2} + S &\underset{-5}{\overset{5}{\rightleftharpoons}} C_{x2} \overset{6}{\longrightarrow} E_{x2} + P
\end{aligned} \tag{40}$$

For the sake of simplicity, let us calculate the rate at saturation with S. This is:

$$V_s = (k_3X_1/K_1K_2 + k_6X_2/K_4K_5)E_t \Big/ (X_1/K_1K_2 + X_2/K_4K_5) \tag{41}$$

where

$$K_1 = k_{-1}/k_1, \quad K_4 = k_{-4}/k_4, \quad K_2 = (k_{-2} + k_3)/k_2,$$
$$K_5 = (k_{-5} + k_6)/k_5$$

Comparing this with the saturation value obtained if only X_1 is present, $V_{s1} = k_3E_t$, we may ask under what conditions $V_s < V_{s1}$; and we find immediately the answer: $k_6 < k_3$. In short, as perhaps common sense would have warned us, a second activator of low efficiency will act as an inhibitor. Other activation models give similar results. It seems probable that many mutual antagonisms of similar ions, such as Ca^{2+} and Mg^{2+}, may have as their basis this kind of competitive activation accompanied by unequal activation efficiency.

References p. 164

If substrates and activators can compete, so can inhibitors. Consider, as one example which yields specially interesting results, a complete and a partial inhibitor:

$$
\begin{array}{c}
\mathrm{E + S} \underset{-1}{\overset{1}{\rightleftharpoons}} \mathrm{C} \overset{2}{\longrightarrow} \mathrm{E + P} \\
\mathrm{E + X_1} \underset{-3}{\overset{3}{\rightleftharpoons}} \mathrm{E_{x1}} \\
\mathrm{E + X_2} \underset{-4}{\overset{4}{\rightleftharpoons}} \mathrm{E_{x2}} \\
\mathrm{E_{x2} + S} \underset{-5}{\overset{5}{\rightleftharpoons}} \mathrm{C_x} \overset{6}{\longrightarrow} \mathrm{E_{x2} + P}
\end{array}
\tag{42}
$$

The solution is:

$$v = k_2 S E_t(1 + gK_1X_2/K_4K_5) \Big/ [K_1(1 + X_1/K_3 + X_2/K_4) + S(1 + K_1X_2/K_4K_5)] \tag{43}$$

with $g = k_6/k_2$, and the other constants are obvious from the scheme. It is obvious that v may be an increasing as well as a decreasing function of X_2. In fact, if

$$gK_1(1 + X_1/K_3) > K_5 + S(1 - g)$$

X_2 will increase the rate found in the presence of inhibitor X_1; and if also

$$gK_1 < K_5 + S(1 - g)$$

X_2 will still inhibit the enzyme if it is present alone. Thus an inhibitor may act as an anti-inhibitor.

With a slightly different mechanism of partial inhibition, v may have a maximum with respect to X_2, after which it eventually drops to zero. This occurs if we replace the steps 5 and 6 by

$$\mathrm{E_{x2} + S} \underset{-5}{\overset{5}{\rightleftharpoons}} \mathrm{C + X_2}$$

that is, if substrate does not merely combine with the E_x form, but displaces the inhibitor from it. For details, see ref. 7, where many other cases are considered.

The predicted type of behavior is often observed, Inhibitors which raise rates to a maximum at low concentrations and then inhibit at higher concentrations have frequently been met (*e.g.*, refs. 16, 17). Such a result is not necessarily due to mutual competition of two inhibitors; it might also be due to such a mechanism as protection against denaturation[7], a phenomenon for which there is ample evidence (*e.g.*, from the work of London[18]). Without such a maximum, reversals of inhibitor effects by other inhibitors have been observed (*e.g.*, reversal of fluoride inhibition by oxalate as well as by citrate[19]); and the data have been successfully fitted to the theory.

(*d*) *Non-enzymatic interactions*

It is obvious that activation and inhibition need not involve direct action upon the enzyme. Compounds of either type may also react with substrate, which then either reacts with enzyme when it would not do so before, or acts as an inhibitor for enzyme; inhibition by mere tying up of substrate may occur, but is trivial. Moreover, an inhibitor may act by combining with an activator, and either removing it from reaction or converting it into an inhibitor of the enzyme.

For an instance of *substrate-mediated activation*, consider the simple scheme:

$$\begin{aligned} E + S_x \underset{-1}{\overset{1}{\rightleftharpoons}} C_x \overset{2}{\longrightarrow} E + X + P \\ S + X \underset{-3}{\overset{3}{\rightleftharpoons}} S_x \end{aligned} \tag{44}$$

with the conservation relations:

$$E_t = E + C_x \qquad S_t = S + S_x \qquad X_t = X + S_x \tag{45}$$

The last two of these are approximate; we take account of substrate and activator tied up in S_x, but not of the amount in C_x. The solution is:

$$\begin{aligned} v &= VS_x/(K_1 + S_x) \\ S_x &= \tfrac{1}{2}\{(S_t + X_t + K_3) - [(S_t + X_t + K_3)^2 - 4S_tX_t]^{\frac{1}{2}}\} \end{aligned} \tag{46}$$

where

$$K_1 = (k_{-1} + k_2)/k_1, \quad K_3 = k_{-3}/k_3, \quad V = k_2E_t$$

As one would expect from looking at step 3, S_x, and therefore v, is symmetrical in S_t and X_t; the graph with respect to either will be formally identical with that against the other. Considering X_t as the variable for the sake of example, S_x rises from 0 when $X_t = 0$ to S_t when X_t approaches infinity. Since v is a monotonic increasing function of S_x, it behaves in the same way.

If $K_3 \sim 0$, we get something like a titration curve. For $X_t < S_t, S_x = X_t$; for $X_t \geqslant S_t$, $S_x = S_t$. Since v is hyperbolic in S_x, this feature will not show up in v. But the plot of $1/v$ against $1/X_t$ is of the broken-line type. When $1/X_t \leqslant 1/S_t$, the plot is a horizontal line

$$1/v = (K_1 + S_t)/VS_t$$

When $1/X_t > 1/S_t$, the plot is a line of the conventional type

$$1/v = (1/V)(1 + K_1/X_t)$$

with slope K_1/V and intercept $1/V$.

References p. 164

It seems likely that this kind of activation plays at least a large if not the exclusive rôle in divalent cation activation of phosphotransferases[20,21]. The symmetry with respect to S_t and X_t, which is the key to the detection of a substrate–activator reaction, has been demonstrated.

Let us proceed to *substrate-mediated inhibition*. If the inhibition consists merely in tying up substrate, as in our previous treatments of inhibition in which it consisted merely of tying up enzyme, we would expect similarities in the kinetics. Consider for example:

$$\mathrm{E + S} \underset{-1}{\overset{1}{\rightleftharpoons}} \mathrm{C} \overset{2}{\longrightarrow} \mathrm{E + P}$$

$$\mathrm{S + X} \underset{-3}{\overset{3}{\rightleftharpoons}} \mathrm{S}_x$$

and

$$\begin{aligned} E_t &= E + C \\ S_t &= S + S_x \\ X_t &= X + S_x \end{aligned} \tag{48}$$

We include conservation of S and X with respect to the free forms and the combined forms, since the supply of each is crucial here. The solution, expressed as the diagnostic plot of X_t against $i/(1 - i)$, is:

$$X_t = Ru[K_3 + S_t/(1 + Ru)] \tag{49}$$

where

$$R = 1 + S_t/K_1, \quad u = i/(1 - i), \quad K_3 = k_{-3}/k_3,$$
$$K_1 = (k_{-1} + k_2)/k_1$$

As we expect, the plot of X_t against u curves downward towards an asymptote with slope K_3R, while the initial slope is $(K_3 + S_t)R$. The important difference between this and the graph of eqn. (31) is that the intercept of the asymptote is now S_t instead of E_t. This makes it easy, as a rule, to distinguish the cases.

A more interesting case is one in which the compound of S and X is an inhibitor. In this case, the supply of S is not crucial; a small amount of S may be used to form a powerful inhibitor. We can therefore simplify the mathematical treatment somewhat. We add to (48) the reaction $\mathrm{E + S}_x \rightleftharpoons \mathrm{C}_x$, drop out the conservation condition for S, and add C_x to that for E. We get:

$$X_t = [(K_1 + S)(K_3 + S)K_4/K_1S]u \tag{50}$$

where

$$K_4 = k_{-4}/k_4$$

This is a straight line passing through the origin. The slope as a function of S_t may be helpful in pinning things down: it is very large as S_t approaches 0, descends to a minimum value at $S_t = (K_1K_3)^{\frac{1}{2}}$, and then rises, approaching an asymptote with slope K_4/K_1.

If we combine the mechanisms of the last two cases (*i.e.*, put back the conservation equation for S into the last case), we get:

$$X_t = Ru[K_3/Q + S_t/(Q + Ru)] \tag{51}$$

where

$$Q = 1 + S_t/K_4$$

This relation formally resembles (49). But the presence of Q, involving S_t, changes the character of the initial slope, which is now

$$K_4R(K_3 + S_t)/(K_4 + S_t)$$

This equals K_3 at $S_t = 0$. It increases with S_t, and bends down or up or is a straight line according as

$$K_4(K_1 + K_3) - K_1K_3$$

is greater, less than, or equal to K_4^2.

Activator-mediated inhibition gives similar results. If we take as a model compulsory activation together with the interaction of X and the activator (let us call it A to distinguish it from X):

$$X_t = wu[K_4 + A_t/(1 + wu)] \tag{52}$$

where

$$w = 1 + RA_t/K_1$$

and K_4 is the dissociation constant of the X–A compound. The plot is like that of (49); but now the intercept is A_t instead of S_t. Inhibition by the X–A compound gives:

$$X_t = (1 + K_4/A_t)K_5uw \tag{53}$$

where K_5 is the dissociation constant of the inhibited triple X–A–E compound, and the other symbols are as before. Again the initial slope of this straight line, considered as a function of A_t, has a minimum.

The classical example of inhibition of enzyme by an activator–inhibitor complex is the fluoride inhibition of enolase, found by Warburg to be due to a magnesium fluorophosphate.

5. Structural relations

Up to this point, we have ignored the nature of the bond or bonds formed between the enzyme and the various components of the enzyme system. In point of fact, we know or have reason to believe, in many if not in all cases, that substrate, for example, forms two or three bonds with the enzyme, rather than one. This offers new kinetic possibilities.

References p. 164

Suppose that the substrate-binding site of an enzyme is twofold, and that there are two corresponding sites on the substrate. Let us assume that the first bond can be formed, giving compound C_1, and then the second to give C; or the second bond can be formed, giving compound C_2, and then the first to give C. If the final closing of both bonds is not fast enough, suppose that a second molecule of S can sometimes unite with C_1 or C_2 by way of the open bond, giving compound C′, which is enzymatically inactive. The scheme is:

$$\begin{aligned}
E + S &\underset{-1}{\overset{1}{\rightleftharpoons}} C_1 \\
E + S &\underset{-2}{\overset{2}{\rightleftharpoons}} C_2 \\
C_1 &\underset{-3}{\overset{3}{\rightleftharpoons}} C \\
C_2 &\underset{-4}{\overset{4}{\rightleftharpoons}} C \\
C &\overset{5}{\longrightarrow} E + P \\
C_1 + S &\underset{-6}{\overset{6}{\rightleftharpoons}} C' \\
C_2 + S &\underset{-7}{\overset{7}{\rightleftharpoons}} C'
\end{aligned} \tag{54}$$

The solution is:

$$v = VAS/[1 + (A + B)S + DS^2] \tag{55}$$

where

$$\begin{aligned}
V &= k_5 E_t \\
K_1 &= (k_{-1} + k_3)/k_1, \quad g_1 = k_{-3}/k_1 \\
K_2 &= (k_{-2} + k_4)/k_2, \quad g_2 = k_{-4}/k_2 \qquad K_6 = k_{-6}/k_6 \\
A &= (k_3 K_2 + k_4 K_1 + k_5 K_1 K_2)/(k_{-1} g_1 K_2 + k_{-2} g_2 K_1) \\
D &= (1 + g_1 A)/K_1 K_6 \\
B &= (1 + g_1 A)/K_1 + (1 + g_2 A)/K_2
\end{aligned}$$

The graph of v against S has a maximum at $S = 1/D^{\frac{1}{2}}$, and with further increase of S drops to zero. This is therefore a model for *auto-inhibition*—inhibition of enzyme by excess of substrate. This model is readily extended in various directions, although the algebraic manipulations become increasingly tedious. (Examples are found in ref. 7.) For instance, one might suppose, in a *quasi-symmetrical* system like fumarase, that fumarate (or malate) binds through the two carboxyls. Presumably either carboxyl might bind at either site. But it is obvious from inspection of the substrates that the enzyme region that operates on the two non-carboxyl carbons cannot be symmetrical, as is also clear from Massey's model[22] of the reaction. Thus each substrate can bind at each site in a right way (suitable for further reaction) and a wrong way. The principle of the treatment can also be extended to bimolecular systems.

It should be obvious that the preceding line of reasoning should extend readily to activators. This is so, and the method is quite obvious; we refer the reader either to paper and pencil or to ref. 7. Examples of well-marked peaks for enzyme activity as a function of activator concentration are not hard to find[23,24].

6. Multivalent enzymes

There are some indications[25,26] that certain enzymes may be multivalent—that is, that the same protein may contain more than one set of sites capable of binding and turning over the substrate. It is therefore worth considering how such systems would behave.

The problem is somewhat analogous to that of bimolecular reactions, in that one is forced to consider the possibility of random order of filling and reaction at the sites. Consider for example an enzyme with two sites; we will call the E–S compound formed at the first site C_1, at the second C_2, and with both sites filled C. We begin by assuming that the kinetic constants for the sites are not the same.

$$\begin{aligned}
E + S &\underset{-1}{\overset{1}{\rightleftharpoons}} C_1 \\
C_1 + S &\underset{-2}{\overset{2}{\rightleftharpoons}} C \\
E + S &\underset{-3}{\overset{3}{\rightleftharpoons}} C_2 \\
C_2 + S &\underset{-4}{\overset{4}{\rightleftharpoons}} C \\
C_1 &\xrightarrow{5} E + P \\
C_2 &\xrightarrow{6} E + P \\
C &\xrightarrow{7} C_1 + P \\
C &\xrightarrow{8} C_2 + P
\end{aligned} \tag{56}$$

The solution is:

References p. 164

$$v = [k_5S(1 + g_1AS)/K_1 + k_6S(1 + g_3AS)/K_3 + (k_7 + k_8)AS^2]E_t \Big/ [1 + S(1 + g_1AS)/K_1 + S(1 + g_3AS)/K_3 + AS^2] \quad (57)$$

where

$$K_1 = (k_{-1} + k_5 + k_2S)/k_1, \quad g_1 = (k_{-2} + k_7)/k_1$$

$$K_3 = (k_{-3} + k_6 + k_4S)/k_3, \quad g_3 = (k_{-4} + k_8)/k_3$$

$$A = (k_2/K_1 + k_4/K_3) \Big/ [g_1(k_{-1} + k_5)/K_1 + g_3(k_{-3} + k_6)/K_3]$$

The occurrence of S^2 in the numerator and denominator of v suggests the possibility that a maximum may occur in the v–S curve. The conditions for the maximum are complex; and we shall defer consideration of this question for a somewhat simpler model. We can, however, ask a simple question: How would this system behave if the sites were identical and independent, so that rate constants for binding or releasing or turning over substrate would be the same for both single complexes and for the double complex?

This implies that the rate constants for steps 1, 2, 3, and 4 are identical, and that the turnover constants of steps 5, 6, 7, and 8 are identical. If we introduce these conditions, we get:

$$v = 2k_5E_tS/(g + S) \quad (58)$$

where k_5 is the common turnover constant,

$$g = (k_{-1} + k_5)/k_1$$

and k_1 and k_{-1} are the common binding and release constants for the combination of S with the various forms of enzyme.

Eqn. (58) is formally identical with eqn. (6), except for the factor 2. The system behaves like a system of enzyme molecules with single sites, but at a concentration $2E_t$ instead of E_t.

In the foregoing model, we included the most general assumptions. We not only assumed that steps 1 and 2 were distinct, and steps 3 and 4 distinct, but also that 1 is distinct from 3 and 2 from 4, etc. This implies not merely that a second site behaves differently if the first site is already occupied, which would be consistent with a mutual influence of the sites, but also that the sites are in some respects different *a priori*, as might be the case if they were surrounded by different (relevant) neighboring groups. Consider instead of this the simpler model which merely assumes that the presence of bound S on one site affects the kinetics at the other, the sites being otherwise equivalent:

$$\begin{aligned} E + S &\underset{-1}{\overset{1}{\rightleftharpoons}} C_1 \\ C_1 &\xrightarrow{1a} E + P \\ C_1 + S &\underset{-2}{\overset{2}{\rightleftharpoons}} C_2 \\ C_2 &\xrightarrow{2a} C_1 + P \end{aligned} \quad (59)$$

The solution now becomes:

$$v = (k_{1a}S/K_1 + k_{2a}S^2/K_1K_2)E_t/(1 + S/K_1 + S^2/K_1K_2) \tag{60}$$

with

$$K_1 = (k_{-1} + k_{1a})/k_1$$

$$K_2 = (k_{-2} + k_{2a})/k_2$$

We can now ask about a maximum. Calculating dv/dS, and setting it equal to zero, we get the condition:

$$k_{1a}K_1K_2 + 2k_{2a}K_1S + (k_{2a} - k_{1a})S^2 = 0 \tag{61}$$

This quadratic has a real solution only if $k_{2a} < k_{1a}$, since the sum of positive terms cannot possibly equal zero. The discriminant of (61) is positive if

$$k_{2a} < k_{1a}[K_2 + (K_2^2 - 4K_1K_2)^{\frac{1}{2}}]/2K_1$$

and this is the precise relation between k_{2a} and k_{1a} that is required for a maximum to occur. The common sense behind this result is obvious: As S increases, doubly-occupied enzyme molecules will begin to predominate over singly-occupied molecules; and, if the former turn over more slowly than the latter, the net rate will decrease. It is obvious from (60) that the limiting rate for large S will be $k_{2a}E_t$.

If we collapse this model into one of two independent sites, taking into account the fact that free enzyme has two sites available for filling and hence must react with S twice as fast as singly-bound enzyme, and so forth, we get the same result as (58).

The two-site case of model (59) is readily generalized to n sites:

$$v = \left(\sum_j k_{ja}E_tS^j/p_j\right) \Big/ \left(1 + \sum_j S^j/p_j\right) \tag{62}$$

where k_{ja} is the turnover number of j-filled enzyme

$$p_j = \prod_1^j K_i$$

and Σ and Π are the conventional mathematical symbols for sum and product. If the sites are independent, and we allow for the statistical factors as before (number of ways an S can be added to a complex with a certain number of free places, etc.), we retrieve the simple formula of type (58), but with n in place of the factor 2.

It may be of some interest to consider activation in the light of the theory of multiple binding. If we take a model with compulsory activation, and let n molecules of activator X be bound on kinetically independent sites, we get:

$$v = kE_tS(X/M)^n \Big/ [K(1 + X/M)^n + S(X/M)^n] \tag{63}$$

where k is the turnover number of the activated enzyme, K is the usual

References p. 164

substrate constant, and M is the dissociation constant for activator–enzyme binding. For sufficiently large values of X, this of course approaches the form $kE_tS/(K + S)$, the partial saturation value V_x.

The most noteworthy feature of this system is its behaviour as a function of X. When $X/M < 1$, $(X/M)^n$ is very small. When $X/M > 1$, $(X/M)^n$ soon becomes quite large. Thus the curve tends to hug the X axis for $X/M < 1$, and to rise rapidly to its maximum value for $X/M > 1$. The curve will be S-shaped, with an inflection point near 1. The effect will be exaggerated as n increases; as n becomes very large, the family of curves approaches a step function, in which $v = 0$ below the inflection point and $v = V_x$ above that point. Somewhat speculatively, one may consider this as a model for a system with a threshold or trigger action, of the type that is common in biology. As X is displaced very slightly, from just below to just above the inflection point, the system jumps from one state to another (no enzyme activity to maximum enzyme activity).

7. Inactivation of enzymes and denaturation

Since we have assumed that enzyme activity depends on the conformation of the enzyme protein, it is to be expected that physical factors which disturb the conformation in certain ways would lower activity. We shall consider thermal inactivation here, since it has been studied most assiduously; but inactivation by extremes of pH may be considered to be somewhat closely related.

The mechanism that seems reasonable for denaturation of proteins (a radical change leading to loss of specific conformation without any necessary rupture of primary valence bonds) is cleavage of hydrogen bonds, both within and between α helices. Breakage of disulfide bonds between chains or parts of a single chain may or may not enter the picture. To relate this mechanism to loss of enzyme activity, we observe that the unfolding of the highly-structured native protein may lead to separation of groups that form part of the binding site for substrate, as well as the separation from these of neighboring groups that may be involved in the catalytic action of the protein.

What kind of kinetic picture should one expect for the loss of conformation and the consequent loss of enzyme activity? The breakdown of protein conformation involves the breaking of a large number of hydrogen bonds. From what we know of systems like this, it is plausible to expect that significant denaturation will begin to occur only after a minimum number of adjacent bonds is broken, just as we know[27] that a stable helix will form only in a chain above a certain length.

To deal with this problem fully, one would need to apply the theory of runs[28]. However, one might approximate in a manner already familiar to students of radiation effects[29]. If bond breakage by thermal agitation is random, the probability of bond breakage should be given by a Poisson distribution, expressed as a function of the time t during which the agent (high temperature) is applied. The probability that a bond is unbroken will then be simply, e^{-kt}, where k is the number of effective hits per unit time. The probability that a bond is broken is then

$$(1 - e^{-kt})$$

If n bonds must be broken for the structure to begin breaking down, the probability for this is

$$(1 - e^{-kt})^n$$

The probability for a molecule to be undenatured, then, is

$$1 - (1 - e^{-kt})^n$$

This is an estimate of the fraction of surviving undenatured molecules after time t of exposure to heat, and therefore of the fraction of enzyme activity surviving. On a semilogarithmic scale, this multihit curve begins with a flat region, and then bends over to give a straight line with negative slope $-k$ and intercept on the survivor axis of n. The greater n, the more prolonged is the initial shoulder.

With one possible exception[30], I know of no cases of enzyme inactivation that behave like this. Most inactivation–time curves are linear on a semi-logarithmic plot, sometimes with a flattening at the tail-end of the curve. In short, such curves behave like single-hit curves. The implication, that there may be just one hydrogen bond whose breakage inactivates an enzyme molecule, is worth considering. If we take this interpretation seriously, it implies that the breakage of bonds occurring before this vital bond (which may be one of several such vital bonds) is broken does not count at all. This cannot be true without qualification; for it would imply that an enzyme molecule with the vital bonds intact would go calmly about its business while the rest of the protein was collapsing around it. Nothing that we know about enzymes and their delicate responses to influences that affect conformation encourages us to accept this view. The alternative is that at least one of the bonds vital to the maintenance of enzymatic activity is more labile than the majority of hydrogen bonds in the structure, so that it has a high probability of being broken before many of the others go.

Consider the simple irreversible reaction, occurring in the absence of substrate:

$$E \xrightarrow{3} E_d$$

where E_d is the inactive form. We get without difficulty:

References p. 164

$$v = VS\,e^{-k_3t}/(K + S) \tag{64}$$

for the rate measured by the usual assay after denaturation for time t. That is, the activity is the usual, modified by the exponential factor in the time due to inactivation. This is the expected result if inactivation is carried out in the absence of substrate. Assuming that substrate protects the enzyme absolutely:

$$v = VS\,e^{-kt}/(K + S) \tag{65}$$

where

$$k = k_3/(1 + S/K)$$

This is what we should expect if the form C is not subject to denaturation. If C is also denatured at the rate k_4C

$$k = (k_3 + k_4S/K)/(1 + S/K)$$

It is worth noting in this case that large values of S reduce the effective inactivation rate constant to k_4, not to 0 as in the previous case. Moreover, if by chance the complex C were more labile than E (which would be unusual), saturation with substrate would increase the rate of inactivation.

Some inactivation curves start linear, and then flatten out to some extent. There are two obvious mechanisms for this. One involves the assumption that denatured enzyme (and/or inert protein that may be present in the preparation) can combine with and protect active enzyme. Consider the scheme:

$$\begin{aligned} &E \xrightarrow{1} E_d \\ &E + P \underset{-2}{\overset{2}{\rightleftharpoons}} E' \\ &E + E_d \underset{-3}{\overset{3}{\rightleftharpoons}} E'' \end{aligned} \tag{66}$$

where P stands for non-enzyme protein. If the inactivation was carried out, as is usually the case, in the absence of substrate, we get for the time relation of the development of E_d:

$$k_1t = -2K_3E_d - M \ln(1 - E_d/E_t) \tag{67}$$

with

$$M = 1 + K_2P + 2K_3E_t$$

The analysis of this is similar to that of eqn. (9). If we plot

$$\ln(E_t - E_d)$$

the logarithm of residual active enzyme, against time, we do indeed get a diphasic curve, an early linear portion with slope of

$$-k_1/(1 + K_2P)$$

and an eventual slower linear segment with slope

$$-k_1/(1 + K_2P + 2K_3E_t)$$

Protein P, being present *ab initio*, reduces the rate at once; the effect of protection by denatured enzyme (the term $2K_3E_t$) becomes evident only after enough enzyme has been denatured. The presence of the term $2K_3E_t$ predicts the familiar effect of dilution on stability of enzymes; with sufficient dilution, E_t becomes so small that there is virtually no protection.

An alternative assumption to account for the falling off of inactivation rate with time is that inactivation is incomplete. Add to the usual enzyme scheme the reactions:

$$\begin{gathered} \mathrm{E} \xrightarrow{3} \mathrm{E}_d \\ \mathrm{E}_d + \mathrm{S} \underset{-4}{\overset{4}{\rightleftharpoons}} \mathrm{C}_d \xrightarrow{5} \mathrm{E}_d + \mathrm{P} \end{gathered} \tag{68}$$

Then we get:

$$v = (v_0 - v_d)e^{-k_3t} + v_d \tag{69}$$

where

$$v_0 = k_2E_tS/(K_1 + S)$$

the normal activity, and

$$v_d = k_5E_tS/(K_4 + S)$$

the activity when all enzyme has been inactivated. The semilogarithmic plot of v gives an initial linear portion with slope

$$(1 - v_d/v_0)k_3$$

The later portion of the curve is not linear, however, in contrast to the previous case. Instead, it is approximately exponential:

$$\ln v \sim \ln v_d + (v_0 - v_d)e^{-k_3t}/v_d \tag{70}$$

The plot of ln v will flatten off to a non-zero level, if carried far enough, and will not be really linear anywhere. The $\ln\{\ln (v/v_d)\}$ would be linear.

It is frequently argued that protein denaturation consists of two phases, one reversible and one irreversible. This would lead us to predict a somewhat odd kinetic curve. Let our model be one in which we inactivate at a certain temperature, then cool sufficiently to stop irreversible denaturation, and assay.

$$\mathrm{E} \underset{-3}{\overset{3}{\rightleftharpoons}} \mathrm{E}_d \xrightarrow{4} \mathrm{X} \tag{71}$$

at the inactivation temperature;

$$\mathrm{E} + \mathrm{S} \underset{-1}{\overset{1}{\rightleftharpoons}} \mathrm{C} \xrightarrow{2} \mathrm{E} + \mathrm{P} \;;\; \mathrm{E} \underset{-3'}{\overset{3'}{\rightleftharpoons}} \mathrm{E}_d$$

References p. 164

at the lower temperature where the prime (′) denotes the assay temperature. The solution is:

$$v = k_2 k_3 k_4 E_t[e^{-A_2 t}/A_2 - e^{-A_1 t}/A_1]Q(A_1 - A_2) \quad (72)$$

with

$$Q = 1 + (1 + 1/K_3')K_1/S$$

$$A_1 = \tfrac{1}{2}\{(k_3 + k_{-3} + k_4) + [(k_3 + k_{-3} + k_4)^2 - 4k_3 k_4]^{\frac{1}{2}}\}$$

and A_2 is the same expression with the + sign before the square root changed to a − sign.

The early part of the semilogarithmic plot is not linear, but parabolic:

$$\ln v \sim \ln(k_2 E_t/Q) - \tfrac{1}{2}k_3 k_4 t^2$$

The curve then proceeds downward for a while at an increasing slope, and then flattens somewhat to a slower linear tail with slope $- A_2$.

This would be similar to the other curves which show protection effects, if it were not for the initial parabolic segment with zero initial slope. The question is, whether this would be sufficiently prolonged to be detected in the presence of experimental error. The not very conclusive answer is that it depends on the magnitudes of k_3 and k_4—not surprisingly. If either of the constants is very small, the flat top of the curve will be relatively prolonged; if both are appreciable in magnitude, the curve will slope downwards so fast the flat top may be missed. It seems obvious that a search for kinetic evidence bearing on the question of a reversible phase of inactivation should be conducted under conditions where the rate constants would be diminished —preferably, one would think, at a temperature intermediate between the usual inactivation temperatures and the assay temperature for the enzyme.

8. Conclusion

The reader should realize that this chapter is a very condensed version of a very large subject. Some topics have been slighted because they are considered elsewhere in this volume, some because their exposition would be unduly lengthy. The latter is true of a rather general and analytically rather powerful theory of pH effects in enzyme activity. The reader is referred to ref. 7 for such material. On the subject of enzyme inhibition, in addition to ref. 7, an excellent compendium, including experimental as well as theoretical material, is now available[31].

The application of kinetic methods demands patience and ingenuity. As the foregoing pages should have demonstrated, appearances can be deceiving; and even when a diagnostic plot (*e.g.*, of the reciprocal type) is simple in appearance, its slope and intercept must be further investigated, in order to decide whether they behave (*e.g.*, as functions of E_t) in a simple and expected way or not.

When the reader has progressed beyond this point, and enjoyed the experience of developing his own kinetic treatment to deal with a problem that does not fit any of the published variants, he is likely to become an addict. But it should be pointed out that kinetics is neither a ritual, as it sometimes seems to be in the literature of enzymology (purify the enzyme, get K and V, file and forget!), nor an amusement that exists for its own sake alone. It has, in my opinion, two major kinds of significance: (*1*) Kinetic analysis can be a guide in studies of mechanism in the deeper sense, particularly when a series of substrates and inhibitors of well-defined structure can be applied, not only to the study of activity but also to the study of protection against denaturation and to the analysis of pH effects; and (*2*) Kinetic analysis is a tool for unravelling the events occurring in complex systems, from extracts to intact cells[7,32,33], and as such is an important part of the larger area of mathematical biophysics.

References p. 164

REFERENCES

1 J. M. REINER AND S. SPIEGELMAN, *J. Phys. Chem.*, 49 (1945) 81.
2 E. A. MOELWYN-HUGHES, *Ergeb. Enzymforsch.*, 6 (1937) 23.
3 J. LOEB, *Proteins and the Theory of Colloidal Behavior*, McGraw-Hill, New York, 1924.
4 S. W. BENSON, *Foundations of Chemical Kinetics*, McGraw-Hill, New York, 1960.
5 H. E. BRIGGS AND J. B. S. HALDANE, *Biochem. J.*, 19 (1925) 338.
6 B. CHANCE, *Advan. Enzymol.*, 12 (1951) 153.
7 J. M. REINER, *Behavior of Enzyme Systems*, Burgess, Minneapolis, 1959.
8 H. LINEWEAVER AND D. BURK, *J. Am. Chem. Soc.*, 56 (1934) 658.
9 A. J. BROWN, *Chem. Soc. (London), Trans.*, 81 (1902) 373.
10 F. J. W. ROUGHTON, *Discussions Faraday Soc.*, 17 (1954) 116.
11 E. C. SLATER AND W. D. BONNER, *Biochem. J.*, 52 (1952) 185.
12 J. B. S. HALDANE, *Enzymes*, Longmans, Green, London, 1930.
13 D. E. KOSHLAND JR., *Advan. Enzymol.*, 22 (1960) 45.
14 P. K. STUMPF, W. D. LOOMIS AND C. MICHELSON, *Arch. Biochem.*, 30 (1951) 126.
15 A. L. LEHNINGER, *Physiol. Rev.*, 30 (1950) 393.
16 H. BOREI, *Biochem. Z.*, 312 (1942) 160.
17 J. M. REINER, *Dissertation*, University of Minnesota, 1946.
18 M. LONDON, R. MCHUGH AND P. B. HUDSON, *Arch. Biochem. Biophys.*, 73 (1958) 72.
19 J. M. REINER, K. K. TSUBOI AND P. B. HUDSON, *Arch. Biochem. Biophys.*, 56 (1955) 165.
20 B. A. ASKONAS, *Dissertation*, University of Cambridge, 1952.
21 S. A. KUBY, L. NODA AND H. A. LARDY, *J. Biol. Chem.*, 210 (1954) 65.
22 V. MASSEY, *Biochem. J.*, 55 (1953) 172.
23 D. E. GREEN, D. HERBERT AND V. SUBRAHMANYAN, *J. Biol. Chem.*, 138 (1941) 327.
24 A. KORNBERG, *J. Biol. Chem.*, 182 (1950) 805.
25 N. B. MADSEN AND C. F. CORI, *J. Biol. Chem.*, 223 (1956) 1055.
26 J. F. AMBROSE, G. B. KISTIAKOWSKY AND A. G. KRIDL, *J. Am. Chem. Soc.*, 73 (1951) 1232.
27 B. H. ZIMM, in M. A. STAHMANN (Ed.), *Polyamino Acids, Polypeptides and Proteins*, University of Wisconsin Press, Madison, Wis., 1962, p. 229.
28 W. FELLER, *An Introduction to Probability Theory and its Applications*, Wiley, New York, 1950.
29 K. C. ATWOOD AND A. NORMAN, *Proc. Natl. Acad. Sci., U.S.*, 35 (1949) 696.
30 E. J. CASEY AND K. J. LAIDLER, *J. Am. Chem. Soc.*, 73 (1951) 1455.
31 J. L. WEBB, *Enzymes and Metabolic Inhibitors*, Academic Press, New York, 1963.
32 J. M. REINER, *Arch. Biochem. Biophys.*, 46 (1953) 53, 80.
33 C. W. SHEPPARD, *Basic Principles of the Tracer Method*, Wiley, New York, 1962.

Chapter VI

Metal Coordination and Enzyme Action

BERT L. VALLEE AND JOSEPH E. COLEMAN

Biophysics Research Laboratory, Division of Medical Biology, Department of Medicine, Harvard Medical School and Peter Bent Brigham Hospital, Boston, Mass. (U.S.A.)

1. Introduction

Metal ions were first observed to catalyze organic reactions in the early nineteenth century. Davy first recorded the platinum-catalyzed oxidation of acetic acid in 1820. The oxidation of cysteine catalyzed by iron and first studied by Baumann in 1883 was readily attributed to the formation of iron–cysteine complexes on the basis of the color changes observed. Proof that metal ions also participate in biological catalysis awaited the isolation of enzymes. The iron-containing oxidative enzymes, peroxidase, catalase and the cytochromes, were studied first and most extensively. They were recognized by MacMunn in 1885 as a result of their prominent absorption spectra which he associated with cellular oxidations. The history of this development has been detailed by Warburg[1]. The participation of metal ions in enzymatic reactions both as integral parts of purified crystalline enzymes and as activators of various enzyme systems has now been reaffirmed many times[1-4].

Parallel with the development of enzyme chemistry, the chemistry of metal ions themselves, especially that of the complexes they form with a large variety of organic and inorganic ions and molecules, has been studied intensively, beginning with the establishment of coordination chemistry by Werner in the early twentieth century. Although most metal ions form complex ions, investigations have centered particularly on the coordination complexes of the metals of the first transition period from vanadium to copper. Perhaps reflecting their versatile coordination chemistry, ions of the second half of this series, manganese, iron, cobalt, nickel, and copper, are

References p. 231

found associated with or can activate many enzymatic systems. The following metal ions are additionally important in enzymology: the IIB group, zinc, cadmium, and mercury; a single member of the second transition period, molybdenum; the alkali metals, sodium and potassium; and the alkaline earths, calcium and magnesium. Those enzymes which contain the first transition metals and zinc have received the most detailed study and will be the major subject of this discussion.

The transition metals form complexes with a wide variety of ligands through bonds which leave their d shell electronic orbitals only partially filled. Most of the interesting properties of these complexes can be attributed in one way or another to the d-shell electrons occupying these orbitals. However, ions with filled d shells, *e.g.* the IIB metals, share many of the complexing properties of the transition series and complement the understanding of transition-metal chemistry.

Where these metal ions interact with biological molecules to form complexes, certain properties analogous to those found with smaller ligands may be expected. The distinctive absorption maxima of many metalloproteins in the visible spectrum are a case in point. At the same time, the special properties of these ligands may impart physicochemical or biochemical characteristics not observed in complexes with smaller molecules.

In the following, a brief summary of the chemistry of simple coordination and chelate compounds will be given, followed by a discussion of the properties of metalloenzymes relating their chemistry to that of these metal ions. In many cases, of course, this cannot as yet be done with any degree of completeness, either because of lack of detailed study or because the models may only imperfectly approach the properties of metalloproteins.

2. Properties of metal–ligand complexes

A variety of changes in physicochemical properties accompanies the formation of metal–ligand complexes in solution. These properties have been employed both to detect the presence and to determine the stoichiometry of these complexes. Thus alterations in absorption spectra, pH, electrical conductivity, magnetic susceptibility, optical activity and aqueous solubility have served this purpose. The isolation of many of these complex ions as crystalline solids has allowed the determination of their elemental composition and the direct determination of their three-dimensional structure by X-ray, neutron, or electron-diffraction methods. In this manner, complex ions have been shown to form through the formation of coordinate bonds between the metal ion and, in most instances, from one to six neutral or negatively charged donor atoms. Ligands which contribute only one donor atom to a complex are termed monodentate. Dependent on the number of donor atoms contributed, ligands are termed bidentate, tridentate, etc. *Chelate* is the term reserved for *ring* compounds resulting from such coordination.

The physicochemical properties of these metal–ligand complexes arise from three sources, (*1*) properties primarily associated with the metal ion which are altered by the ligand, (*2*) properties of the ligand which are altered by the metal ion, and (*3*) certain properties that are characteristic of the complex ion and do not exist separately as such in its components.

Those properties of transition metal ions which are associated with their d-shell electrons belong to the first category: the absorption maxima of d-shell electronic transitions, the paramagnetism induced by unpaired d-shell electrons, and the several stable oxidation states of these ions which on formation of the complex undergo alteration in relative stability. These properties give rise to various spectrophotometric, electron spin resonance and polarographic methods for the study of complexes. Table I gives the outer electron configurations for the metal atoms of the first transition and IIB group of metals, and those of their monovalent, divalent and trivalent ions as well as the corresponding ionization potentials. These ions will be dealt with most frequently in this Chapter.

Alterations in the electronic structure and changes in the ionization of hydrogen ions associated with the ligand belong to the second category. The former often lead to chemical changes in the ligand structure which, in fact, the metal ion catalyzes. The competition between metal and hydrogen ions for the donor sites of the ligand generate the widely employed titration methods for the study of metal–ligand complex formation. Nuclear magnetic resonance methods have also been employed to detect alteration in proton equilibria, especially those associated with coordinated water molecules.

The third category includes the isomerism of asymmetric chelate rings and their resultant optical activity, certain intense charge-transfer spectra, and marked changes in solubility of some complexes compared to either those of the metal ion or the ligand alone. The intense charge-transfer bands, in conjunction with the low solubility of many complex ions in aqueous solution and their high solubility in organic solvents, have served importantly in analytical methods for the sensitive detection of metal ions.

(*a*) *Coordination number and stereochemistry*

The coordination theory of metal complexes was first originated in the late nineteenth century by the Swiss chemist Alfred Werner to explain certain compositional features of the so-called double salts of metal ions which were not readily explained by simple ionic theory[6]. Werner recognized the existence of two forms of several metal compounds with the same empirical

References p. 231

TABLE 1

OUTER ELECTRON CONFIGURATIONS, IONIZATION POTENTIALS, AND IONIC RADII FOR THE FIRST TRANSITION AND II B METALS

Element	Outer electron configuration				Ionization potentials (eV)			Ionic radii (Ångstroms)		
	Me	*Me*$^{+}$	*Me*$^{2+}$	*Me*$^{3+}$	*1st*	*2nd*	*3rd*		*P*	*G*
Sc	$(3d)^1(4s)^2$	—	—	$(3d)^2(3p)^6$	6.56	12.80	24.75	Sc^{3+}	0.81	0.68
Ti	$(3d)^2(4s)^2$	—	$(3d)^2$	$(3d)^1$	6.83	13.57	27.47	Ti^{4+}	0.68	0.60
V	$(3d)^3(4s)^2$	—	$(3d)^3$	—	6.74	14.65	29.31			
Cr	$(3d)^5(4s)^1$	—	$(3d)^4$	$(3d)^3$	6.76	16.49	30.95	Cr^{3+}		0.55
Mn	$(3d)^5(4s)^2$	—	$(3d)^5$	$(3d)^4$	7.43	15.64	33.69	Mn^{2+}	0.80	0.80
Fe	$(3d)^6(4s)^2$	—	$(3d)^6$	$(3d)^5$	7.90	16.18	30.64	Fe^{2+}	0.75	0.76
Co	$(3d)^7(4s)^2$	—	$(3d)^7$	$(3d)^6$	7.86	17.05	33.49	Co^{2+}	0.72	0.70
Ni	$(3d)^8(4s)^2$	—	$(3d)^8$	—	7.63	18.15	35.16	Ni^{2+}	0.69	0.68
Cu	$(3d)^{10}(4s)^1$	$(3d)^{10}$	$(3d)^9$	—	7.72	20.29	36.83	Cu^{+}	0.96	0.95
								Cu^{2+}		0.92
Zn	$(3d)^{10}(4s)^2$	—	$(3d)^{10}$	—	9.39	17.96	39.70	Zn^{2+}	0.74	0.69
Cd	$(4d)^{10}(5s)^2$	—	$(4d)^{10}$	—	8.99	16.91	38.0	Cd^{2+}	0.97	0.92
Hg	$(5d)^{10}(6s)^2$	—	$(5d)^{10}$	—	10.41	18.74	34.3	Hg^{2+}	1.10	0.93

P – Pauling radii (Ref. 5)
G – Goldschmidt radii (Ref. 6)

formulae by their difference in color. For example, two forms of [$Co(NH_3)_4Cl_2$] were found, one green and the other violet. Werner postulated that in addition to its electrovalence, a metal ion possessed a coordination number which determined the total number of anions or neutral molecules which may be associated with the cation. For the above compounds, he postulated the structures I and II, terming them the *cis* and *trans* isomers respectively.

cis
I

trans
II

He applied a series of substitution reactions to his compounds to prove his structures. He showed, *e.g.*, that formation of the carbonate occurred only with I, since the carbonate requires the *cis* configuration to replace the chlorine. He also postulated the correct geometrical configuration of the above compounds believing the six coordinated donor atoms to be arranged in a regular octahedron. Similarly, two isomers of the cobaltic complex of ethylenediamine [$Co(H_2NCH_2CH_2NH_2)_2Cl_2$] were observed and assigned analogous structures, each ethylenediamine molecule contributing two nitrogen donors. The isomerism of such compounds will be discussed further in section *2f* (p. 181). The compounds of platinum containing four donor groups were assigned the square-planar structures III and IV to account for the two forms.

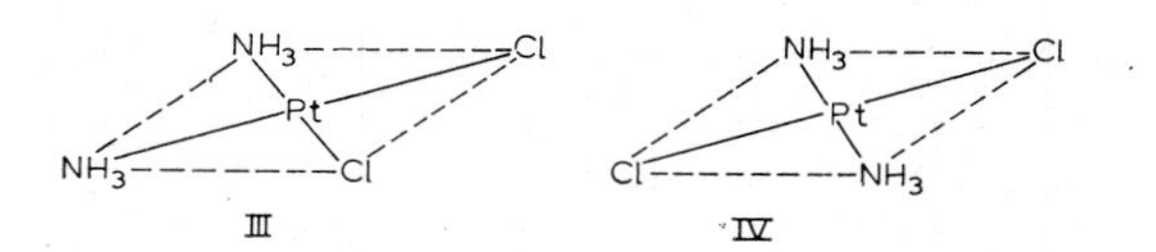

Since Werner's time, X-ray diffraction studies on the crystalline forms of thousands of these compounds have amply confirmed his postulates. Coordination numbers all the way from 2 to 9 have been observed in certain metal complexes. It is the custom to write the donor groups within the coordination sphere of the metal ion within square brackets and any anions associated outside the square brackets, *e.g.*, [$Pt(NH_3)_6$]Cl_4 for the amine of Pt^{4+} coordinating six ammonia molecules.

The even coordination numbers 2, 4, and 6 are by far the most common. Among the transition metals, octahedral, six coordination is most frequent. The lighter IIB metals, Zn^{2+} and Cd^{2+}, both prefer four coordination in which

References p. 231

the donors are arranged in a regular tetrahedron. Such division, however, is not absolute. Tetrahedral complexes of the transition metals are known, *e.g.* $[Co(NCS)_4]^{2-}$, $[CoCl_4]^{2-}$, and $[FeCl_4]^{2-}$, as well as octahedral complexes of Zn^{2+}, *e.g.* $[Zn(NH_3)_6]^{2+}$ and $[Zn(o\text{-phenanthroline})_3]^{2+}$. An uncomplicated electrostatic theory suffices to explain the occurrence of the frequently observed tetrahedral and octahedral configurations. These configurations place four and six negatively charged (or dipole) donor atoms around a positive ion in such fashion that the negative groups have minimal chance for interaction with each other. There are, however, notable deviations from these regular geometries which are not explained by simple theory. These will be mentioned briefly here and the theory will be touched upon in section *2d* (p. 177).

On the basis of simple ionic theory, large d^{10} ions like Ag^+, Au^+, Hg^{2+}, and Cu^+ would be expected to favor coordination with a large number of donor atoms. Structure determinations, however, show these ions to prefer linear coordination with two nearest donors. Mercuric chloride, $HgCl_2$, is such a species with two collinear nearest neighbors and four more neighbors, but at much longer distances. The crystal structure of Cu_2O and Ag_2O also show such linear coordination. It is not clear why Hg^{2+} prefers collinear coordination while its lighter d^{10} analogues, Zn^{2+} and Cd^{2+} do not, though several hypotheses have been advanced[6]. Hg^{2+} can occur, however, like Zn^{2+} and Cd^{2+}, in a tetrahedral geometry, *e.g.*, $[Hg(CN)_4]^{2-}$.

For a number of complex ions which demonstrate a coordination number of four, structure determinations show the geometry to be square-planar rather than tetrahedral, like the platinum compounds pictured above. Of the ions most frequently encountered in enzymology, Ni^{2+} and Cu^{2+} are the examples for which this geometry occurs commonly. Similar compounds for the analogues of Ni^{2+} in the second and third transition periods, Pd^{2+} and Pt^{2+}, also occur. Cu^{2+} is the most important biologically active metal ion to prefer this geometry (see section *2d*, p. 180).

Three, five, seven, eight, and nine coordination have been observed in special instances, but are not common. Discussions of these are found in Ref. 6.

It should be remembered that the above geometries are observed in metal–ligand complexes where the donor atoms of the ligand move reasonably freely relative to each other and thus the geometry would appear to be controlled by the preferred orientation of the metal–ligand bonds. If there is inherent spacial orientation, forced by rigidity in ligands such as the porphyrins and phthalocyanines, other factors may intervene. In fact, in large macromolecules, it is quite probable that many metal-binding sites have geometry conferred upon them by the molecular structure as well as by the preferred direction of the bonds with the metal ion.

From the ionization potentials in Table I, several points are apparent.

Scandium is the element most easily oxidized to the trivalent form and practically all of its chemistry deals with Sc^{3+} having the closed shell configuration $(3d)^2(3p)^6$. Compounds of Ni^{3+}, Cu^{3+}, Zn^{3+}, Cd^{3+}, and Hg^{3+} are non-existent, in keeping with the high value of the third ionization potentials. The high value of the second ionization potential of copper explains the stability of Cu^{+} relative to Cu^{2+} and accounts for the presence of this particular couple in a variety of situations. The ease of oxidation of Fe^{2+} to Fe^{3+} is indicated. The Co^{3+} ion is given since many ligands, amines for example, stabilize Co^{3+} relative to Co^{2+}, although the latter is usually the more stable species. This effect is less prominent with manganese, although its third ionization potential is similar to that of cobalt.

The "ionic radii" of the metal ions of the first transition and IIB metals are also included in Table I. These cannot, of course, be considered as constant or invariant and the values given are the result of X-ray measurements of bond distances in representative ionic solids. Sums or differences of ionic radii can be set up by this means and if independent measurements are then possible on a few single ions, the individual radii can be calculated. Pauling and Goldschmidt have both determined these by slightly different methods and the numbers derived from their respective calculations are indicated in Table I.

Normally, as electrons are added to the d shell of the transition series, one would expect the ionic radii to decrease steadily as the nuclear charge increases. The sequential addition of single electrons to the outer shell does not adequately shield the outer electrons from the increasing positive charge on the nucleus. Such a relation is seen in the decreasing radii of the rare earths for example. While it is difficult to get comparisons of the radii of similarly charged ions in the same geometry throughout the series, the ions of these metals do not show a steady decrease in radii. Mn^{2+} and Fe^{3+}, both of the d^5 configuration, appear to show a maximum compared to the ions on either side of them, while Cu^{2+} shows an anomalously high radius. Explanations for this variation as well as for the abnormal geometry of certain complexes mentioned earlier have come from deductions about the energies and distribution of the d-shell electrons of a metal ion when it is placed in a ligand-field[6] (see section *2d*, p. 177).

(*b*) *Stability constants and stability sequences*

The stability of coordination compounds has been that physicochemical characteristic which has been determined most frequently, aside from determinations of composition and structure. Stabilities are usually expressed as the reciprocals of the equilibrium constants, as measured in aqueous solution. For most of the metal ions of importance to enzymology, the ions

References p. 231

exist in water as the aquated species. Hence, the reaction between a ligand, L, and the metal ion is expressed by Eqn. (1),

$$Me(H_2O)_6 + nL \rightleftharpoons MeL_n(H_2O)_p \tag{1}$$

where n is the number of ligand molecules coordinating the metal ion and p the number of water molecules remaining in the coordination sphere of the metal ion. Six water molecules are usually arranged in a regular octahedron about the hydrated transition metal ions, although there are certain exceptions[7].

The stepwise stability constants describing Eqn. (1) for the formation of any complex are defined in terms of concentration as follows[8].

$$\begin{aligned} k_1 &= \frac{(MeL_1)}{(Me)(L)} \\ k_2 &= \frac{(MeL_2)}{(MeL_1)(L)} \\ &\vdots \\ k_n &= \frac{(MeL_n)}{(MeL_{n-1})(L)} \end{aligned} \tag{2}$$

where (L) is the ligand concentration and n is the maximum number of ligands which may be introduced. The overall, cumulative stability constant, K, is the product of the stepwise constants and equals $(MeL_n)/(Me)\,(L)^n$ and applies for any complex with n ligands attached. Concentrations in Eqn. (2) are determined by methods employing pH, polarography, spectrophotometry, and a number of procedures utilizing competition for the metal ion between two ligand-forming complexes of known and unknown stability respectively. The use of radioactive metals has been a convenient addition to the latter techniques. The reader is referred to the literature for detailed discussions of these methods[7-9].

The value of n which applies in a given instance is a function of the concentration of the metal ion, that of the ligand, the maximum number of ligand molecules which may be added, compatible with the preferred geometry of the complex, and the number of donor atoms on each ligand. On purely statistical grounds, there is expected to be a progressive decrease in the magnitude of the k_n's, as more ligands are added to the complex. This decrease in the firmness of binding reflects the lesser probability of the complex gaining and the greater probability of losing a ligand as the number of ligands in the complex increases. For monodentate ligands, the magnitude of k_n as a function of increasing number of ligands is expressed as a ratio of k_n/k_{n+1} (Eqn. 3), where N is the maximum number of ligands which can coordinate the metal ion and the probability of the nth complex acquiring

$$\frac{k_n}{k_{n+1}} = \frac{(N - n + 1)(n + 1)}{(N - n)(n)} \qquad (3)$$

a ligand is proportional to $(N-n)$ while the probability of the nth complex losing a ligand is proportional to n. For most complexes this ratio approaches 1 log unit. Experimentally, many complex ions show such stepwise decreases in the magnitudes of their measured k_n's. There are a number of common exceptions, however, including the zinc–ammonia and iron–*o*-phenanthroline complexes, and the complexes of copper with more than four monodentate or two bidentate ligands. In these instances, other factors, to be discussed in later sections, control the sequential k_n values. As determined by the usual techniques these are not true thermodynamic constants but reflect large concentrations of supporting electrolyte used to control ionic strength effects. The constants are then referred to a particular medium. For meaningful data to be obtained, the complexing ability for the metal ions of this supporting electrolyte should be very weak. Comparison between different constants must always take into account the specific medium employed, particularly when it does contain electrolytes or buffers with significant complexing affinity for the metal ions under study.

Oxygen, nitrogen, and sulfur are the ligand donor atoms of greatest biological interest. For a series of complexes of one ligand with several metal ions or of one metal ion with several ligands, specific series of stabilities have been observed to hold.

The IA, IIA, and IIIA metals of the periodic table form one series of stabilities when complexing with the same ligand and the stabilities fall in the order

$$Cs^+ < Rb^+ < K^+ < Na^+ < Li^+ < Ba^{2+} < Sr^{2+} < Ca^{2+} < Mg^{2+} < La^{3+} < Al^{3+}$$

This is the order of increasing electrostatic potential for these ions and this property largely accounts for their complexing ability. They usually form complexes with negatively charged donors and not with neutral molecules[10].

The stabilities of the complexes of large numbers of ligands with Mn^{2+}, Fe^{2+}, Co^{2+}, Ni^{2+}, Cu^{2+}, and Zn^{2+}, the divalent metal ions of the second half of the first transition series, have been catalogued[11]. The stabilities of their complexes with ligands containing oxygen and nitrogen as the donor atoms, fall in a typical sequence[10,12,13], which is illustrated in Fig. 1 for glycine and ethylenediamine respectively. The stabilities rise from Mn^{2+} to a maximum at Cu^{2+} and fall again to Zn^{2+} in the IIB group. If Cd^{2+} and Hg^{2+}, which also share some complex-forming characteristics with the metals of the first transition period, are included, the stabilities fall further to Cd^{2+} and then rise steeply to Hg^{2+}. It is apparent from these two series (Fig. 1) that

References p. 231

Co^{2+}, Ni^{2+}, and Cu^{2+} prefer nitrogen while Mn^{2+} prefers oxygen ligands, a general characteristic of their complexes.

If the large and highly polarizable sulfur atom is substituted for oxygen or nitrogen as one of the donor atoms, this sequence of stabilities is altered

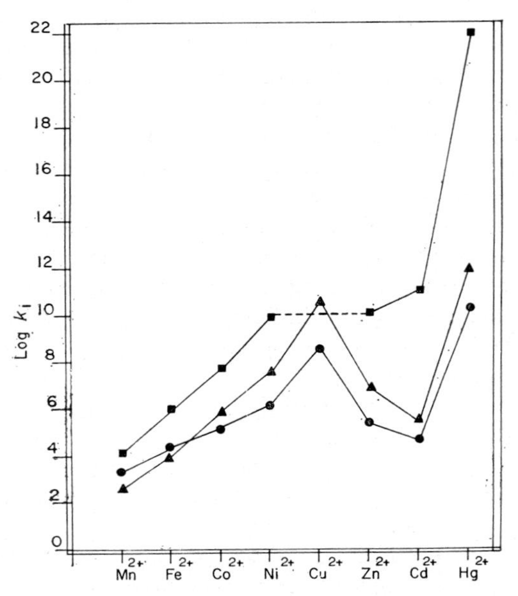

Fig. 1. Stability constant sequences for nitrogen–oxygen, nitrogen–nitrogen, and nitrogen–sulfur bidentate ligands. These have been indicated by plotting the log k_1 values (on the ordinate) for the 1 : 1 complexes of each ligand with the metal ions indicated on the abscissa. The nitrogen–oxygen ligand is glycine (●), while the nitrogen–nitrogen ligand is ethylenediamine (▲). The nitrogen–sulfur ligand represents values for mercaptoethylamine or cysteine (■). The values for Cu^{2+} are unavailable for the sulfur-containing ligands due to oxidation reactions catalyzed by this ion. All k_1 values are from Ref. 11.

as illustrated for the bidentate nitrogen–sulfur ligands[14] included in Fig. 1. The log k_1 values are raised for the entire series, but particularly for the IIB elements. The Zn^{2+} and Cd^{2+} complexes are now as stable or more stable than any of the first transition period complexes; the preference of Hg^{2+} for sulfur as the donor atom is apparent. Certain of the linear complexes of Hg^{2+} are extremely stable. The stability constant of the $HgCl_2$ complex, $K = 10^{13}$, should be remembered when employing Hg^{2+} in solutions containing high Cl^- concentration which will effectively reduce the equilibrium concentration of free Hg^{2+} ion to a very low level.

A single factor like the electrostatic potential cannot adequately account for the stabilities of the transition-metal complexes. Generally, three interdependent factors are thought to influence the formation of transition-metal complexes. (*1*) The *ionic radius* determines the number of donors which can be arranged about the central metal atom, to be in contact with it, but without interfering with one another. The "radius ratio rules" for coordination polyhedra are based on this parameter[15]. (*2*) The *electronegativity* of the metal atoms—"the power of an atom *in a molecule* to attract electrons to itself"—partially determines the bond strength. (*3*) The "d-state splitting" or change in energy of the d-shell electronic orbitals when a transition-metal ion is complexed contributes to complex stability by virtue of the decrease in the energy of the complex if the lower-energy more stable d orbitals are occupied by electrons leaving the higher-energy, less stable d orbitals vacant. The electronegativity of the ions in Fig. 1 follows very closely the stability series shown for their complexes with nitrogen–oxygen and nitrogen–nitrogen ligands. However, it is generally agreed that the third factor contributes importantly to these stabilities and, in addition, successfully explains stereochemical, spectral, and magnetic properties of these complexes as well (see section *2d*, p. 177).

(*c*) *pH, pM, pOH*

The donor atoms on the large variety of organic molecules making up the majority of multidentate ligands which bind metal ions, also have significant affinity for the simplest cation, hydrogen. Thus, in aqueous solution a second equilibrium usually accompanies that in Eqn. (1), where n now represents

$$\mathrm{LH}_n + \mathrm{Me} \rightleftharpoons \mathrm{MeL} + n\,\mathrm{H}^+ \tag{4}$$

the number of protonated donor atoms on the ligand L. The appropriate charges on each species will depend on the nature of the ligand and the valence of the metal ion. The hydrogen ion affinity will be reflected in the $\mathrm{p}K_a$ of the donor groups of the ligand and the metal ion affinity in the stability constant, as previously defined. This is illustrated experimentally in Fig. 2 using the formation of the Na^+, Li^+, Ba^{2+}, Mg^{2+}, and Ca^{2+} complexes of ethylenediamine tetraacetic acid (EDTA). Curve 1 is the titration of the acid in the absence of metal ions while curves 2–6 show the titrations performed in the presence of the series of metal ions as indicated. The competing metal ions now displace hydrogen ions from the ligand at much lower pH values. The effectiveness of each metal ion in this competition is related directly to the stability constants of its complex with EDTA, the midpoints of these curves being in the order (decreasing pH), $Na^+ < Li^+ < Ba^{2+} < Mg^{2+} < Ca^{2+}$, *i.e.*, that of the stability constants. Thus, formation of a given metal–ligand complex will depend on the pH as well as on the metal ion concentration, pM, the two being related by the respective dissociation constants for their complexes with the ligand. This relationship leads to the most widely used method for determining stability constants, in which titration of the ligand is performed in the presence and absence of the metal ion, followed by calculation of the k_n's needed to relate the two curves[7,9].

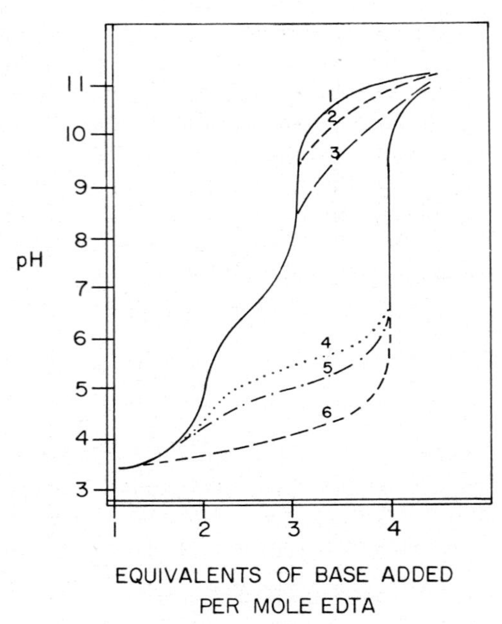

Fig. 2. Titration of ethylenediamine tetraacetic acid (EDTA) in the absence and presence of metal ions. Curve 1 (——), 10^{-3} M EDTA titrated with base in the absence of metal ions. Curves 2–6 are the same as 1 except in the presence of excess of Na^+ (-----), Li^+ (— — —), Ba^{2+} (····), Mg^{2+} (—·—·—), and Ca^{2+} (----) respectively. The curves are drawn after G. Schwarzenbach and H. Ackermann, *Helv. Chim. Acta*, 30 (1947) 1798.

The hydroxyl ion concentration has an equally marked influence on the metal ion equilibria though the *modus operandi* differs from that of H^+ ions. Hydroxyl ions exhibit affinity for the central metal ion rather than for the ligand; this is attested to by the stability and insolubility of many metal hydroxides. Thus, the OH^- ion, acting as a ligand, competes for the central metal ion, the oxygen with its lone pair of electrons being the donor atom. In contrast to H^+ ion equilibria, OH^- ion equilibria are not readily treated quantitatively. In an unbuffered aqueous solution the metal ions commonly precipitate as the insoluble hydroxides anywhere[4] from pH 2 for Hg^{2+} to pH 9 for Mn^{2+}. The hydrated metal ions have a tendency to lose protons from their coordinated water molecules.

$$Me(H_2O)_n^z \rightleftharpoons H^+ + Me(H_2O)_{n-1}(OH^-)^{z-1} \quad (5)$$

The equilibrium constant describing this reaction is dependent upon the metal ion species and is related to the pH at which precipitation may be expected; the smaller the dissociation constant for this release of protons, the less the tendency to precipitate. A variety of complexes, including soluble polynuclear hydroxide complexes, may form during this transformation and precise determination of all species present is difficult[4]. A number of detailed studies are on record on the various species of aquo and hydroxide complexes of zinc and the transition metals present in aqueous solution[4]. Most of these metals then, must be kept in solution near neutral pH by the presence of a ligand with which they form soluble complexes of sufficient stability to hold the metal ion in solution. This reduces the free-metal concentration to very low levels which must be considered when examining equilibria in such a medium.

(*d*) *Theory of transition-metal bonding*

A number of theories have been advanced to account for the coordinate bonds and their behavior in transition-metal complexes. These early attempts concerned donation of electron pairs by the ligand and this theory was extended by Pauling in the *valence bond theory*. In recent years this has been superseded by *ligand field theory* as developed by Van Vleck and coworkers. It is an outgrowth of the earlier purely electrostatic *crystal field theory*. It involves a quantum mechanical treatment of the interaction of ligand and metal ion orbitals and can be developed further into the more rigorous *molecular orbital theory*.

The electrons of the metals of the first transition period successively fill the five 3d orbitals as indicated in Table I. In the free or gaseous ions, which can be considered to be spherically symmetrical, these d-shell orbitals all have the same energy and the electrons have an equal probability of occupying any one of the orbitals.

It is the basis of the crystal and ligand field theories that these five 3d orbitals, all of the same energy in the free ion, acquire different energies in the complex. The nature of this split in the energies of the d orbitals is determined by the geometry of the complex and arises because the electron density of the metal prefers to avoid that of the ligand, thereby producing a more stable complex of lower energy. Compared to the random filling of the d orbitals as predicted by simple electrostatic theory, the d electrons can stabilize the system by filling the low-energy orbitals preferentially.

References p. 231

Thus, in addition to the electrostatic and electronegativity factors, the properties of the complex may be expected to depend on which of the d orbitals of the metal ion are occupied by electrons. This "d-state" splitting, induced by the crystal or ligand field, predicts many thermodynamic, stereochemical, magnetic and spectral characteristics of these complexes not explained by a purely electrostatic theory. In general, a complex will gain additional stability if the lower-energy d orbitals can be occupied and the higher-energy d orbitals left vacant. This additional gain in bonding

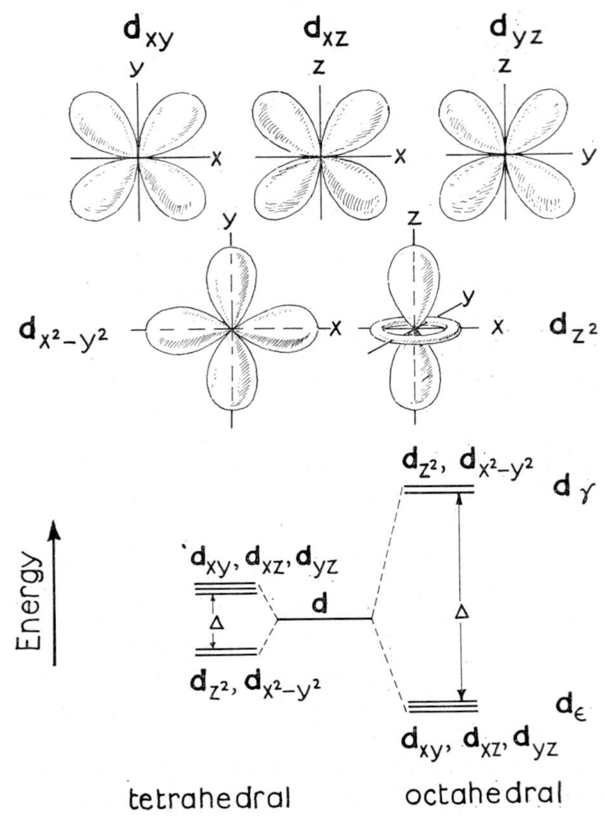

Fig. 3. Distribution of the electron density in the five d orbitals and their energy levels in tetrahedral and octahedral crystal fields relative to their energy in the free ion. All d orbitals have the same energy in the free ion indicated by d. In a tetrahedral field, three orbitals, d_{xy}, d_{xz}, and d_{yz}, have higher energy separated by energy Δ from two, $d_{x^2-y^2}$ and d_{z^2}, of lower energy. An octahedral field results in two orbitals of higher energy, $d_{x^2-y^2}$ and d_{z^2}, designated d_γ (often e_g) and three of lower energy, d_{xy}, d_{xz}, and d_{yz}, designated d_ε (often t_{2g}). Assuming the same bond distances, Δ in a tetrahedral complex equals 4/9 Δ in an octahedral complex.

energy is referred to as *cr̰ stal* or *ligand field stabilization* (CFSE). The transition metals all have less than ten 3d electrons and hence can leave some of the high-energy d orbitals at least partially unoccupied and gain stabilization from the crystal field. On the other hand, a complex of a d^{10} ion like Zn^{2+} with five fully-occupied orbitals or a d^5 ion like Mn^{2+} with five half-occupied orbitals will have no crystal field stabilization. Hence, all other factors being equal, Zn^{2+} and Mn^{2+} will both be expected to form less stable complexes with the same ligand than Co^{2+}, Ni^{2+}, or Cu^{2+}. The presence of particular donor atoms of the ligand, *i.e.*, sulfur, may alter this generalization, of course.

All of the theories of coordinate bonding are based on a knowledge of the shapes or calculated electron densities of the 3d orbitals and their interaction with the electron density of the ligand orbitals. The shapes of these 3d-shell orbitals are indicated in Fig. 3 and can be used to illustrate the origin of the d-state splitting. In an octahedral complex, the ligand electron density is along the x, y, and z axes (the bond directions). Hence, three of the metal ion orbitals, d_{xy}, d_{xz}, and d_{yz}, are concentrated away from the bond directions and acquire lower energy in the complex, while two, d_{z^2} and $d_{x^2-y^2}$, are concentrated along the bond directions and acquire higher energy. Thus, in an octahedral complex the d-shell orbitals split into three of lower energy, d_ε, and two of higher energy, d_γ, separated by energy Δ (Fig. 3). The magnitude of the splitting energy, Δ, is a measure of the strength of the ligand field. This can be determined by the energy of the absorption bands of these complexes which reflect the $d_\varepsilon \rightarrow d_\gamma$ electronic transitions from the filled to the unoccupied d orbitals. The crystal or ligand field strength will, of course, be a function of the chemical nature of the ligand. For the octahedral complexes of the transition metals, spectral evidence indicates an increasing order of ligand field strength for a variety of common ligands as follows:

$$I^- < Br^- < Cl^- < OH^- < COO^- < F^- < H_2O < SCN < NH_3 <$$
$$\text{ethylenediamine} < NO_2 < o\text{-phenanthroline} < CN^-$$

Prior to ligand field theory, these ligands were first arranged in this order, known as the spectrochemical series, on the basis of the energies of their absorption bands. These bands are now known to reflect the energy, Δ, and hence, the strength of the ligand field. *o*-Phenanthroline and cyanide, the ligands producing the most stable complexes by virtue of especially high ligand fields, are familiar in enzymology because of the ease with which they compete for metal ions bound to protein ligands. They have been employed widely as inhibitors of enzymes. To compete successfully, protein ligands must produce equally high ligand fields. Of course, the higher the ligand field, the more stabilization can be achieved in the complex by pairing all the electrons in the lower-energy d_ε orbitals. Since octahedral complexes

References p. 231

produce greater ligand fields (Δ's) than tetrahedral complexes (Fig. 3), the transition metals are found more commonly in octahedral environments while d^{10} ions like Zn^{2+} and Cd^{2+}, which are not stabilized by the ligand field, are found more commonly in tetrahedral environments.

Thus, the existence of very stable spin-paired diamagnetic complexes of Fe^{2+}, in which all 6 electrons are paired in the d_ε orbitals, and the existence of similar diamagnetic complexes of Co^{3+}, *e.g.*, the cobaltic cobalamin complexes, are explicated by theory. Since the d orbitals are unequally occupied, these ions cannot be considered spherically symmetrical and consideration of this asymmetry leads to explanations for the square-planar geometry of Cu^{2+}, Ni^{2+}, Pd^{2+}, and Pt^{2+} as well as the variation in the ionic radii of these ions. In addition, the spectra of these complexes, long known to be due to transitions between filled and unfilled d orbitals, receive a quantitative interpretation. A detailed development of the ligand field arguments is beyond the scope of this Chapter. Excellent non-mathematical treatments of these theories are given by Orgel[15] and Cotton and Wilkinson[6] to which the reader is referred for further discussion.

(*e*) *Spectral and magnetic properties*

(*i*) *Absorption spectra*

Transition-metal complexes characteristically have weak visible absorption maxima with molar extinction coefficients[15,16] between 0.01 and 100. These bands reflect the electronic transitions between occupied and unoccupied d orbitals and their energies are thus a measure of Δ or the ligand field strength. Such weak d–d electronic transitions are forbidden by the usual selection rules for electronic energy level shifts. These "forbidden transitions" are of two types, corresponding to the two selection rules which are broken. In the free atom, transitions are forbidden in which the number of unpaired electron spins changes; they are referred to as the *spin* or *multiplicity* forbidden transitions. Transitions which involve redistribution of electrons in a single quantum shell are also forbidden even if there is no change in the spin direction, such as any change in the d^n configuration. Actually both types of d–d transition are observed in the transition-metal complexes and account for most of their absorption spectra. These "forbidden" d–d transitions are postulated to occur because of some d–p orbital mixing in the complexes. d^{10} ions like Cu^{2+} or Zn^{2+} should not show these d–d transitions and their complexes are observed to lack visible absorption maxima.

Certain transition-metal complexes do show intense visible absorption maxima with extinction coefficients above 10^3, typical of allowed electronic transitions. These charge-transfer bands occur through the transfer of an electron from an orbital of the metal ion to a ligand orbital or *vice versa*.

(ii) Magnetic properties

The paramagnetism induced in transition-metal complexes by the unpaired d-shell electrons of the metal was mentioned in section *2d* (p. 180). The number of unpaired d electrons in any given complex depends in general on the strength of the ligand field and would be expected to shift from high to lower spin as the strength of the ligand field increases. The existence of these shifts in the number of spins, and, hence, magnetic moments have now been observed in a great many instances for the complexes of those ions where two configurations of the d-shell electrons are possible. In addition, the shift in the number of unpaired electrons and the magnetic moment accompanying oxidation or reduction of a metal ion in a complex have proven most useful in determining the oxidation state of the metal ion. Most measurements are now carried out by observing the microwave absorption of a substance placed in a constant magnetic field. The frequency of the microwave absorption reflects the energy required to reverse the spin directions of the unpaired electrons which prefer alignment opposite to that of the applied magnetic field. Such electron spin resonance has been discussed in detail in Volume 3. It is being applied with increasing success to those metalloenzymes which catalyze oxidation–reduction reactions.

(f) Optical rotatory properties

With metal–chelate complexes, two types of isomerism are possible, geometrical and optical isomerism, as illustrated below for the isomers of [Co(ethylenediamine)$_2$Cl$_2$]Cl. I has a geometrical isomer II, while II, the *cis* geometrical isomer, has an optical isomer, III.

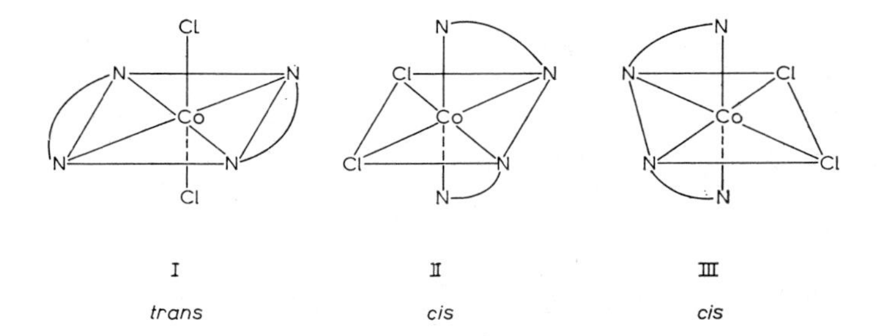

A substance which is optically active will rotate the plane of polarized light due to unequal velocity of the two circularly polarized components. If, in addition, the substance is chromophoric, unequal *absorption* of the left and right circularly polarized components will produce unequal amplitudes of these components in the emergent light or *circular dichroism*. The com-

References p. 231

bination of these effects gives rise to elliptically polarized light. This results in the phenomenon known as anomalous rotatory dispersion or the "Cotton effect". The rotation of the plane-polarized light produced by such a compound passes through a maximum and minimum as the wavelength of the incident polarized light passes through that of the chromophore. Such a rotatory dispersion curve is illustrated diagrammatically in Fig. 4 and compared to a plain or normal dispersion curve. It should be pointed out that a normal dispersion curve is simply the reflection of an optically active chromophore at lower wavelengths[17]. However, instrumental limitations

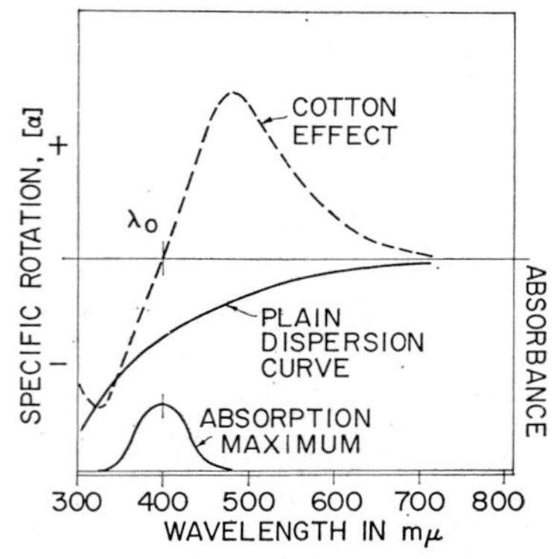

Fig. 4. Theoretical positive Cotton effect for an optically active absorption band resulting from a single electronic transition. The point of zero rotation is at the wavelength of the absorption maximum. A "plain" or "normal" dispersion curve resulting from a Cotton effect at lower wavelengths is shown for comparison.

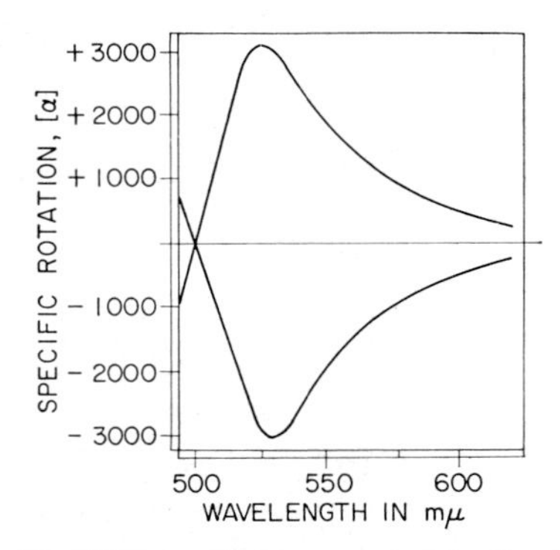

Fig. 5. Positive and negative Cotton effects generated by the two optical isomers of the octahedral cobaltic complexes of ethylenediamine. The curves are drawn after A. P. Smirnoff, *Helv. Chim. Acta*, 3 (1920) 177. The upper curve is D-$[Co(en)_3]^{3+}$ while the lower curve is L-$[Co(en)_3]^{3+}$.

have prevented the measurement of dispersion curves at wavelengths low enough to observe these Cotton effects. If the absorption band is due to a single electronic transition, the wavelength of zero rotation should be that of the absorption maximum[17].

Since chelate compounds are both optically active and chromophoric, anomalous dispersion curves should be observed and indeed formed part of the early study of these compounds. Fig. 5 shows the rotatory dispersion curves for the tris-ethylenediamine Co^{3+} isomers resolved by Smirnoff in 1920, showing Cotton effects of opposite sign for the two isomers. Such optically active absorption bands have now been observed in many metalloproteins and will be discussed in section 3*e* (p. 211).

(*g*) *Catalysis by metal ions*

The catalysis of enzyme substrates or their analogues by metal ions has held particular interest since such reactions may reveal mechanistic features characteristic of catalysis by metalloenzymes. A great number of such reactions have been investigated and it is not certain as yet that their features pertain to enzymes containing a given metal and catalyzing a similar reaction. Several of these "model" systems which have analogies among enzyme-catalyzed reactions are listed in Table II along with the catalytically effective metal ions. Three groups of reactions have received the most attention as possible analogues of enzymatic reactions: decarboxylations, hydrolysis of esters, and reactions involving pyridoxal and metal ions.

(*i*) *Pyridoxal reactions*

Almost all of the reactions catalyzed by the pyridoxal-dependent enzymes have been duplicated in a model system[24,25] using pyridoxal and the metal ions listed in Table II. The general reactions of pyridoxal with amino and keto acids forming Schiff base intermediates have been discussed earlier in this series. Though such reactions proceed at measurable rates in the absence of metal ions, metal ions greatly accelerate these model systems. Complexes between the carboxyl group of the amino acid and the phenolic hydroxyl of pyridoxal have been demonstrated[24,25] as intermediates, I and II. Such a complex would aid electron withdrawal from the bond to the α-carbon of the amino acid residue, labilize the α-hydrogen and promote the other electron shifts in the resulting conjugated system as indicated by the arrows in the scheme below for a transamination. The metal ion might also promote the initial formation of the Schiff base[25].

While the mechanism is most plausible, its occurrence in an actual enzyme remains to be demonstrated. Few of the enzymes employing pyridoxal as a coenzyme have been obtained in sufficiently pure form to permit meaningful

References p. 231

TABLE II

REACTIONS OF SMALL MOLECULES CATALYZED BY METAL IONS

Reaction	Activating metal ions	Conditions	Ref.
A. Hydrolytic reactions			
1. Hydrolysis of amino acid esters	$Cu^{2+} > Co^{2+} > Mn^{2+} > Ca^{2+} > Mg^{2+}$	pH 7.5, 25°	18
2. Reactions of phosphate esters			
Hydrolysis of α-glycerol phosphate	$La^{3+} > Ce^{2+} > Th^{2+}$	alkaline pH	19
Transphosphorylation of ATP with phosphate and carboxylate ions	Ca^{2+}, Cd^{2+}, Mn^{2+}	alkaline pH	20
3. Hydrolysis of amide and peptide bonds			
Glycine amide	$Cu^{2+} > Ni^{2+} > Co^{2+}$	pH 9–10, 65°	21
Phenylalanylglycine amide	Cu^{2+}	pH 5, 75°	
(both amide and peptide bonds)	Cu^{2+}, Ni^{2+}, Co^{2+}	alkaline pH	21
B. Decarboxylation reactions			
1. Decarboxylation of oxaloacetic acid	$Cu^{2+} > Ni^{2+} > Zn^{2+} > Co^{2+} > La^{2+} > Pb^{2+} > Fe^{2+} > Mn^{2+} > Cd^{2+} > Mg^{2+} > Ca^{2+} > Ba^{2+}$		22
2. Decarboxylation of dimethyloxaloacetic acid	$Fe^{3+} > Cu^{2+} > Al^{3+} > Ni^{2+} > Mn^{2+}$	a variety of pH values, see references	22
3. Decarboxylation of acetonedicarboxylic acid	$Cu^{2+} > Ni^{2+} > Co^{2+} > Zn^{2+} > Cd^{2+} > Mg^{2+}$		23
C. Reactions catalyzed by pyridoxal and metal ions			
1. Transaminations between keto and amino acids	$Zn^{2+} < Cu^{2+} > Ni^{2+} > Co^{2+} > Mn^{2+} > Al^{3+} > Fe^{3+}$	alkaline pH	24, 25
2. Racemization of amino acids	$Zn^{2+} < Cu^{2+} > Ni^{2+} > Co^{2+} > Mn^{2+} > Al^{3+} > Fe^{3+}$	alkaline pH	24, 25
3. Aldol reactions $RCHOHCHNH_2COOH \rightleftharpoons RCHO + NH_2CH_2COOH$	Cu^{2+}, Al^{3+}, Fe^{3+}	alkaline pH	24, 25
4. Elimination reactions $RCHXCHNH_2COOH + H_2O \rightleftharpoons HX + NH_3 + RCH_2COCOOH$	Cu^{2+}, Al^{3+}, Fe^{3+}	alkaline pH	24, 25
5. Decarboxylation reactions	Cu^{2+}, Al^{3+}, Fe^{3+}	alkaline pH	24, 25

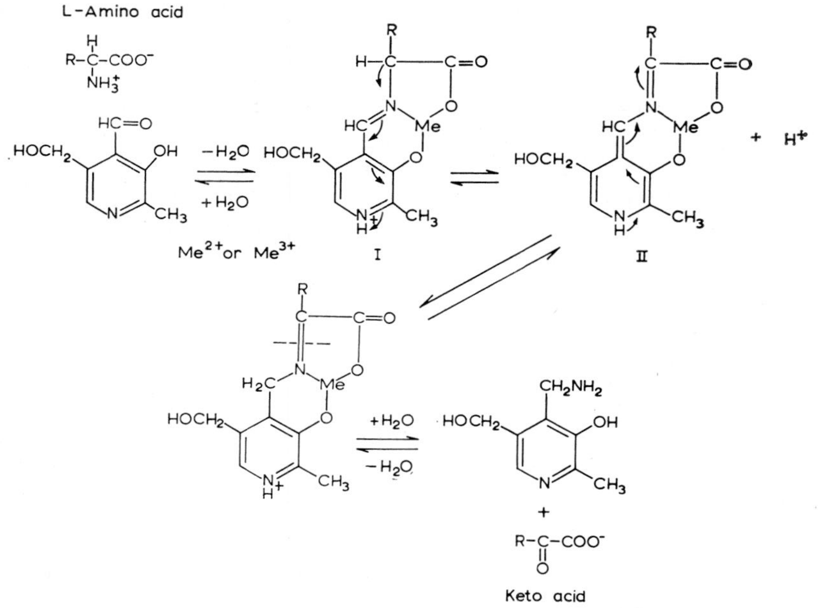

L-Amino acid

Keto acid

metal analyses. The transaminase from chicken liver, one of the few obtained in a high degree of purity, neither contains metal ions nor is activated by them[25a]. However, the histidine decarboxylase from *E.coli* and an amino-benzoate decarboxylase from *E. coli*[25] which are in a lesser state of purity do require pyridoxal and metal ions for full activation.

(ii) Decarboxylation reactions

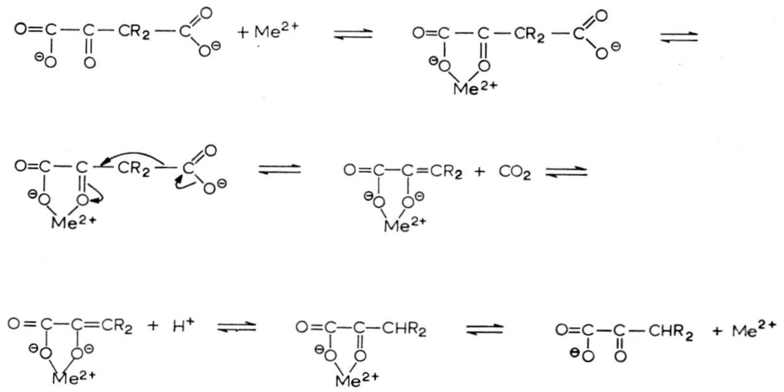

A model system has been developed for non-oxidative decarboxylation in which the decarboxylation of oxaloacetic acid is catalyzed by a variety of metal ions[22,22a,22b]. Neither thiamine pyrophosphate nor pyridoxal is required. At low concentrations of metal (10^{-3} to 10^{-4} *M*), the catalytic efficiency of a series of metal ions follows the order shown in Table II. For the transition and IIB metals this is the order of the stabilities of their complexes as predicted by the Irving–Williams series (Fig. 1, p. 174), suggesting that their catalytic efficiency is related to their ability to form complexes. The reaction is postulated to follow the scheme pictured above[22].

The pertinence of this mechanism to the action of the decarboxylating enzymes which do not utilize pyridoxal or thiamine is not yet clear.

(iii) Hydrolytic reactions

Several hydrolytic reactions catalyzed by metal ions have been studied, including the hydrolysis of phosphoric acid and amino acid esters, amide and peptide bonds. Among these, ester hydrolysis has received the greatest attention since model reactions under relatively mild conditions can imitate enzymatic catalysis. Model systems for peptide or amide bond hydrolysis on the other hand, require extremes of pH and temperature[21]. Studies of ester hydrolysis may, however, be pertinent to the study of the hydrolysis of peptides. A number of the pancreatic proteases, for instance, hydrolyze both types of substrates, and two of them, carboxypeptidases A and B, are metalloenzymes (see Table IV, p. 190). Certain alkaline phosphatases are the only true esterases known thus far to be metalloenzymes.

The hydrolysis of a variety of amino acid esters is catalyzed by metal ions at 25° and near neutral pH (Table II). Kroll[18] studied the hydrolysis of glycine ethyl ester, glycine methyl ester, and glycine benzyl ester between pH 7.5 and 8.5. The hydrolysis is catalyzed by Cu^{2+}, Co^{2+} and Mn^{2+} ions. The catalysis was also dependent on hydroxide ion concentration, the logarithm of the rate constants showing a linear increase with pH. It was proposed that catalysis occurs through the formation of a complex between the α-amino group of the ester and the carbonyl oxygen as pictured below.

$$Me^{2+} + H_2N\overset{R}{\overset{|}{C}}HCOOR' \rightleftharpoons \text{R–CH(NH}_2\text{)–C(=O)–OR' (NH}_2\text{, O} \rightarrow Me^{2+}) \rightleftharpoons \text{R–CH(NH}_2\text{)–}\overset{\oplus}{C}\text{(O}^{\ominus}\text{)–OR' (NH}_2\text{, O}^{\ominus} \rightarrow Me^{2+}) + OH^{\ominus} \rightleftharpoons$$

$$\text{R–CH(NH}_2\text{)–C(OR')(OH)–O}^{\ominus}\text{ (NH}_2\text{, O}^{\ominus} \rightarrow Me^{2+}) \rightleftharpoons \text{R–CH(NH}_2\text{)–C(=O)–O}^{\ominus}\text{ (NH}_2\text{, O}^{\ominus} \rightarrow Me^{2+}) + R'OH$$

A hydroxide ion attack on the chelate intermediate would then give the products of the reaction.

Kinetic studies of the cupric ion-catalyzed hydrolysis of glycine methyl ester, phenylalanine methyl ester, and phenylalanine ethyl ester in glycine buffer at pH 7.3 led Bender and Turnquest[26] to propose the accompanying mechanism for the hydrolysis of phenylalanine ethyl ester by Cu^{2+} ions.

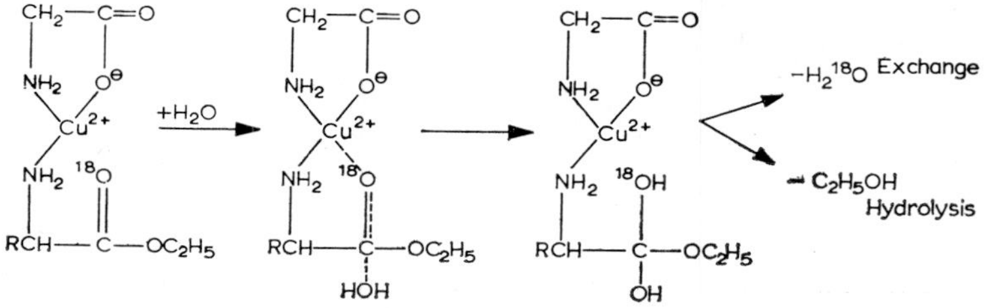

CH_2—C=O, NH_2, $O^{\ominus}$, Cu^{2+}, NH_2, ^{18}O, RCH—C—OC_2H_5
$+H_2O$ →
CH_2—C=O, NH_2, $O^{\ominus}$, Cu^{2+}, NH_2, ^{18}O, RCH—C—OC_2H_5, HOH
→
CH_2—C=O, NH_2, $O^{\ominus}$, Cu^{2+}, NH_2, ^{18}OH, RCH—C—OC_2H_5, OH
I
$-H_2{}^{18}O$ Exchange
$-C_2H_5OH$ Hydrolysis

Cupric ions accelerate the hydrolysis of DL-phenylalanine ethyl ester by a factor of 10^6 over alkaline hydrolysis alone. Using ester, labelled with ^{18}O in the carbonyl oxygen, exchange was observed to take place during the reaction indicating the formation of the addition intermediate I shown above. Interaction of the cupric ion with the α-amino and the alkoxyl oxygen atom of the ester group would be a possible alternative to the above scheme. Recent studies have indicated that such features of ester catalysis may be applicable to ester hydrolysis by the metallocarboxypeptidases[27].

3. Metal–enzyme interactions

(a) *Metalloenzymes and metal–enzyme complexes*

Based on the stability of the complexes, the interactions of metals with enzymatic proteins have divided themselves experimentally into two groups which have been designated as *metalloenzymes* and *metal–enzyme complexes*[2,4,28]. Metalloenzymes refer to those proteins containing functional metal atoms which are bound firmly enough to remain associated with the protein throughout isolation procedures and to be present in the final purified material in stoichiometric amounts relative to the protein. Such metals are not removed by the usual dialysis procedures. The firm association of a given metal with a given protein permits the deduction that this unique chemical association has specific biological significance.

Metal–enzyme complexes on the other hand, has been the designation for proteins with loosely bound, freely dialyzable, but functional metal ions. The metal ion must be added subsequent to isolation procedures to restore the activity associated with the protein and lost by dialysis.

References p. 231

TABLE

METAL CONTENT[a] OF FRACTIONS ATTENDING THE

From Vallee and Neu

Fraction	*Zinc (μg/g protein)*	*Zinc[b] / Protein*	*Activity[c] (C)*	*Activity / Zinc × 10*
Pancreatic juice	310	0.16	0.18	0.58
Euglobulin precipitate	590	0.31	1.43	2.43
Supernatant solution	450	0.24	0.05	0.11
$Ba(OH)_2$ extract	1 410	0.21	0.05	0.12
1st crystals	1 870	0.98	13.2	7.05
2nd crystals	1 860	0.98	*	*
3rd crystals	1 850	0.97	14.5	7.85
4th crystals	1 880	0.99	14.0	7.45
5th crystals	2 000	1.05	18.6	9.30

[a] Unless otherwise indicated, metal content is given in micrograms per gram of protein. All zinc determinations by the dithizone method in duplicate, and in quadruplicate for the cystalline enzyme preparations. Copper determined by the sodium dithiocarbamate method. Spectrographic analyses were done in duplicate, and separately on two different instruments.

The stability of metal-containing proteins, like that of simpler metal–ligand complexes, may be expected to span a considerable and continuous range of values depending on the number of donors and the geometry of the binding site.

While the choice of the above terminology might be considered arbitrary, the differentiation between metalloenzymes and metal–enzyme complexes is meaningful *operationally* and has proved useful and convenient from the point of view of the experimental procedures which may be applied to each group[28]. It focuses attention on the extremes of stability rather than on the middle range where overlapping behavior may be expected. Few quantitative studies have been carried out to determine the stability constants involved, but available values range from $2 \cdot 10^5$ *M* for Zn^{2+} enolase[29], a typical metal–enzyme complex, to $3.2 \cdot 10^{10}$ *M* for the metalloenzyme Zn^{2+} carboxypeptidase[30]. Both constants were determined by equilibrium dialysis techniques. The constants of the iron–heme complexes and some of the copper proteins on the other hand have been estimated to be much higher, the metal not even being dissociated by strong acid[31].

The experimental techniques that can be applied to a metalloenzyme containing a stoichiometric amount of firmly bound metal have made the correlation of their structure, composition and function particularly accessible to investigation[2]. Since the metal ions exhibit properties and reactivity which are distinctly different chemically from the surrounding protein groups, metalloenzymes have provided convenient models for the study of

TION OF CARBOXYPEPTIDASE FROM PANCREATIC JUICE

:en from Ref. 28

Other metals[d]										
Sr	*Ba*	*Ca*	*Mg*	*Al*	*Fe*	*Mn*	*Mo*	*Cu*	*Cr*	*Pb*
0.3	1.6	520	1 160	1.9	65.0	4.7	—	19.0	—	—
2.4	6.9	71.0	29.0	19.0	460	—	—	*	1.7	33.0
0.7	5.7	300	1 250	20.0	66.0	5.2	—	43.0	—	—
135	1 000	212	1 050	11.0	760	3.7	41.0	51.0	—	—
3.9	1 000	32.0	13.0	32.0	130	—	—	82.0	—	—
1.1	219	23.0	20.0	12.0	36.0	—	—	*	—	—
—	98.0	33.0	1.5	4.2	—	—	—	*	—	—
—	52.0	30.0	43.0	12.0	51.0	—	—	*	—	—
—	28.0	50.0	29.0	12.0	50.0	—	—	*	10.0	—

[b] The zinc–protein ratio has been calculated as the moles of zinc/molecular weight of carboxypeptidase.
[c] Expressed as first-order rate constant (in decimal logarithms) per mg of enzyme-N per cubic centimeter.
[d] The symbol — denotes not found; * not determined.

the mechanism of enzyme action[32].

Procedures and analytical methods applicable to the isolation of metallo-enzymes have been reviewed[28] and are briefly illustrated in Table III for the zinc metalloenzyme, carboxypeptidase A from bovine pancreas. In the purified protein, the ratios of metal to protein, enzymatic activity to protein, and metal to activity approach a fixed limit. With complete purification, the metal to protein ratio in gram atoms of metal per mole of protein reaches an integral number, attesting to the specificity of the association and implying stoichiometry. At the same time, metal ions not related to function are removed and decrease to negligible values in the final material, as illustrated in Table III. With a functional metal content of 2 000 micrograms per gram of protein determined on a few milligrams of enzyme, methods must be sensitive and samples free of contamination. Such methods for analysis and the avoidance of contamination have been documented in detail[33].

Although the size of the ligand molecules differs markedly, considerable similarity in physicochemical properties of metal–protein and small metal–ligand complexes with identical donor atoms would be expected. Thus, the firmness of binding between proteins and a given metal ion should be predictable on the basis of model compounds, once the identity of donors at the protein binding site is known. The fact that many biologically important molecules appear to exist in nature and are isolated complexed with a specific metal ion probably reflects a ligand site of the molecule with a particularly high affinity for that metal ion, favored by the relative abundance of metal

References p. 231

TABLE

Type of reaction / Specific enzyme	Metal	Other cofactors	Mol. wt.
			A. METAL
I. HYDROLYSES			
(a) Hydrolysis of peptide bonds			
1. Carboxypeptidase A	Zn^{2+}(Mn^{2+}, Fe^{2+}, Co^{2+}, Ni^{2+}, Cd^{2+}, Hg^{2+}, Pb^{2+})	none	34 300
2. Carboxypeptidase B	Zn^{2+} (Co^{2+}, Cd^{2+})	none	34 300
3. Carboxypeptidase B	Zn^{2+}	none	34 000
(b) Hydrolysis of phosphoric esters			
1. Alkaline phosphatase	Zn^{2+} (Co^{2+}, Hg^{2+})	none	80 000
2. Alkaline phosphatase	Zn^{2+}	highly purified	several components in th ultracentrifu
3. Alkaline phosphatase	Zn^{2+}	highly purified	several components in t ultracentrifu
II. HYDROGEN TRANSFERS			
(a) Oxidation of —$CHNH_2COOH$ to —CO—COOH			
1. L-Glutamate dehydrogenase	Zn^{2+}	NAD	1 000 000
(b) Oxidation of other nitrogenous groups			
1. NADH–cytochrome *c* reductase	Fe	Flavin nucleotide	84 000
2. Nitrate reductase	Mo	FAD	
3. Nitrite reductase	Cu, Fe	Flavin	partially purified
4. Photosynthetic pyridine nucleotide reductase	Fe	none	17 000
(c) Oxidation of —CHOH to —CO—			
1. Alcohol dehydrogenase	Zn^{2+}	NAD	84 000
2. Alcohol dehydrogenase	Zn^{2+}	NAD	150 000
3. Alcohol dehydrogenase	Zn^{2+}	NAD	87 000
4. Lactate dehydrogenase	Zn^{2+}	NAD	—
5. Malate dehydrogenase	Zn^{2+}	NAD	40 000
6. D-Glyceraldehyde 3-phosphate dehydrogenase	Zn^{2+}	NAD	137 000

...or ...ometry ...mole)	*Source*	*Substrate or reaction*	*Reference*
'YMES			
2+	Bovine pancreas	C-terminal bonds of proteins, peptides, N-acyl amino acids, and analogous esters (aromatic C-terminal side-chain)	30, 34–36
2+	Porcine pancreas	C-terminal bonds of proteins, peptides, and analogous esters (lysine or arginine C-terminal side-chain). Also has A activity	37
2+	Bovine pancreas	Same as for porcine pancreas	38
2+	*E. coli*	Hydrolyzes most orthophosphoric monoesters	39, 40
2+	Mammalian kidney	Hydrolyzes most orthophosphoric monoesters	41
2+	Human leucocytes	Hydrolyzes most orthophosphoric monoesters	41a
'n2+ NAD	Bovine liver	L-Glutamate + $NAD^+ \rightleftharpoons \alpha$-keto-glutarate + NADH + NH_3	42
'e ...vins	Porcine heart	NADH + cytochrome *c* $\rightleftharpoons$ NAD^+ + reduced cytochrome *c*	43
	Neurospora crassa, soybean leaves	Nitrate + NADPH $\rightleftharpoons$ nitrite + $NADP^+$ + H_2O	44
	Bacteria	2 NO_2 + NADPH $\rightleftharpoons$ 2 NO + $NADP^+$ + 2 H_2O	45
	Spinach leaves	Catalyzes the photochemical reduction of $NADP^+$ and certain heme-proteins in the presence of chloroplasts	139–139b
2+ .D	Equine liver	Alcohols + $NAD^+ \rightleftharpoons$ aldehydes + NADH	46
2+ .D	Yeast	Alcohols + $NAD^+ \rightleftharpoons$ aldehydes + NADH	47
2+ .D	Human liver	Alcohols + $NAD^+ \rightleftharpoons$ aldehydes + NADH	48, 49
	Rabbit muscle	L-Lactate + $NAD^+ \rightleftharpoons$ pyruvate + NADH	50
'n2+	Porcine heart	L-Malate + $NAD^+ \rightleftharpoons$ oxaloacetate + NADH	51
2+ .D	Rabbit muscle, bovine muscle, yeast	D-Glyceraldehyde 3-phosphate + NAD^+ + $PO_4 \rightleftharpoons$ D-glyceric acid 1,3-diphosphate + NADH	52, 53

(continued overleaf)

TABLE

Type of reaction / Specific enzyme	Metal	Other cofactors	Mol. wt.
7. Xanthine oxidase	Fe Mo	FAD	300 000
8. Xanthine oxidase	Fe	FAD	—
			cofactor sto metry calcu per flavin
9. Xanthine oxidase	Fe Mo	FAD	—
10. Aldehyde oxidase	Fe Mo	FAD Coenzyme Q_{10}	300 000
11. Lactate dehydrogenase D(−)Lactate-cytochrome *c* reductase	Zn^{2+}	FAD	50 000
(*d*) *Oxidation of CH—CH₂ to C=CH—*			
1. Succinate dehydrogenase	Fe	Flavin nucleotide	200 000
2. Succinate dehydrogenase	Fe	Flavin nucleotide	200 000
3. Dihydroorotic acid dehydrogenase	Fe	FAD FMN	62 000
III. OTHER OXIDATIONS			
1. Phenolases (tyrosinases)			
α (high-cresolase)	Cu	none	(inhomogene
β (cresolase–catecholase)	Cu	none	118–119 000
γ (high-catecholase)	Cu	none	118 000
δ (cresolase–catecholase)	Cu	none	119 000
Phenolases	Cu (crystalline polymerizes)	none	35–120 000
2. Phenolases	Cu	none	30–35 000 100 000
3. Phenolase (DOPA oxidase)	Cu	none	—
4. Ascorbic acid oxidase	Cu	none	146 000
5. Laccase	Cu	none	120 000
6. Uricase	Cu	none	120 000
7. Ceruloplasmin	Cu	none	151 000
8. Cytochrome oxidase	Cu	Fe–heme	200 000–1 0 polymolecu aggregate

inued)

or ometry mole)	Source	Substrate or reaction	Reference
D	Milk	Xanthine + O_2 ⇌ urate + H_2O_2	54, 55
D	Mammalian liver	Xanthine + O_2 ⇌ urate + H_2O_2	56
D	Bird liver	Xanthine + O_2 ⇌ urate + H_2O_2	57
D	Porcine liver	Aldehyde + O_2 ⇌ acid + H_2O_2	58
Q_{10} +)	Yeast	D(-)Lactate + FAD + cytochrome *c* ⇌ pyruvate + FAD + reduced cytochrome *c*	59
vin	Bovine heart	Succinate + certain dyes ⇌ fumarate + reduced dyes	60
vin	Yeast	Succinate + certain dyes ⇌ fumarate + reduced dyes	61
) N	*Zymobacterium oroticum*	Orotic acid + NADH ⇌ dihydroorotic acid + NAD^+	61a, 166
	Mushroom (*Agaricus bispora*)	Oxidation of monohydric phenols (cresol) to the *o*-dihydric compound and oxidation of the *o*-dihydric phenols (catechol) to the *o*-quinone stage	62
	Neurospora crassa		62a
	Mushroom	Same as for item (1)	63, 64
	Mammalian tissue	Both cresolase and catecholase activity	65, 66
	Squash, cucumber	L-Ascorbate + O_2 ⇌ dehydroascorbate + H_2O	67–69
	Latex (laquer tree)	*p*-Diphenols + O_2 ⇌ *p*-quinones + H_2O	70
	Mammalian liver	Urate + O_2 ⇌ unstable products (not allantoin)	31
	Human plasma	Oxidizes *p*-phenylenediamine, ascorbic acid, and some *o*- and *p*-dihydroxyphenols	71, 72
eme	Bovine heart	Reduced cytochrome *c* + O_2 ⇌ oxidized cytochrome *c* + H_2O	73, 73a

(continued overleaf)

TABLE

Type of reaction / Specific enzyme	Metal	Other cofactors	Mol. wt.
9. Monoamine oxidase	Cu	none	255 000
10. Spermine oxidase	Zn^{2+}	none	
11. Diamine oxidase	Cu	?Pyridoxal phosphate	96 000
12. D-Galactose oxidase	Cu	none	75 000
IV. ADDITION OF GROUPS TO DOUBLE BONDS (HYDRATION REACTIONS)			
1. Carbonic anhydrase	Zn^{2+} (Co^{2+}, Ni^{2+}, Fe^{2+})	none	30 000
2. Carbonic anhydrase	Zn^{2+}	none	28 000
V. ADDITION OF GROUPS TO A CARBONYL			
1. Aldolase	Zn^{2+} (Fe^{2+}, Co^{2+})	none	65–75 000
VI. FIXATION OF CO_2			
1. Ferredoxins	Fe	none	12 000

B. METAL–ENZ

Type of reaction / Specific enzyme	Metal	Other cofactors	Mol. wt.
I. HYDROLYSES			
(*a*) *Hydrolysis of peptide bonds*			
1. Metal-activated peptidases			
a. Glycylglycine dipeptidase	Co^{2+}, Mn^{2+}	none	
b. Glycylleucine dipeptidase	Mn^{2+}, Zn^{2+}	none	
c. Carnosinase	Zn^{2+} (Mn^{2+}, Co^{2+}, Cd^{2+})	none	homogene in the ultr centrifuge
d. Anserinase	Zn^{2+}	none	
e. Imidodipeptidase (prolidase)	Mn^{2+}	none	
f. Iminodipeptidase (prolinase)	Mn^{2+}	none	
g. Acetylornithinase	Co^{2+}	none	
h. Leucine aminopeptidase	Mn^{2+}, Mg^{2+}	none	300 000 (p kidney)

ntinued)

tor iometry /mole)	*Source*	*Substrate or reaction*	*Reference*
1	Bovine plasma	$RCH_2NH_2 + O_2 + H_2O \rightleftharpoons RCHO + NH_3 + H_2O_2$	74
	Bovine plasma	$RCH_2NH_2 + O_2 + H_2O \rightleftharpoons RCHO + NH_3 + H_2O_2$	75
1	Pea seedlings	Catalyzes the oxidation of a great variety of monoamines and diamines by molecular oxygen	75a
	Polyporus circinatus (Dactylium dendroides)	D-Galactose + $O_2 \rightleftharpoons$ D-galactohexodialdose + H_2O_2 (also oxidizes polysaccharides with galactose end groups)	75b
$^{2+}$	Bovine erythrocytes	$CO_2 + H_2O \rightleftharpoons H_2CO_3$	76–78
$^{2+}$	Human erythrocytes	$CO_2 + H_2O \rightleftharpoons H_2CO_3$	79
$^{2+}$	Yeast	Dihydroxyacetone phosphate + D-glyceraldehyde 3-phosphate $\rightleftharpoons$ D-fructose 1,6-diphosphate	80
e	*C. pasteurianum, C. acidi-uridi*	Essential for the formation of acetylphosphate and hydrogen from pyruvate	80a, 80b

PLEXES

	Source	*Substrate or reaction*	*Reference*
	Mammalian tissue	Hydrolyzes glycylglycine and sarcosylglycine	81, 82
	Mammalian tissue	Hydrolyzes glycyl-L-leucine	81
	Porcine kidney	Hydrolyzes dipeptides of L-histidine and their amides	81, 83, 84
	Fish muscle	Hydrolyzes anserine giving 1-methylhistidine and β-alanine	85
	Porcine intestine	Hydrolyzes glycyl-L-proline and glycyl-L-hydroxyproline, and glycylsarcosine	82
	Animal tissues	Hydrolyzes L-prolylglycine and L-hydroxyprolylglycine	81
	E. coli	Hydrolyzes α-*N*-acetyl-L-ornithine and *N*-acetyl-L-methionine	86
	Mammalian intestine, bacteria, plants	Hydrolyzes peptides or amides with a free α-amino group on the N-terminal leucine	87

(continued overleaf)

TABLE

Type of reaction *Specific enzyme*	*Metal*	*Other cofactors*	*Mol. wt.*
(*b*) *Hydrolysis of amines*			
1. Arginase	Mn^{2+}, Co^{2+}, Ni^{2+}	none	138 000
2. Glycocyaminase	Mn^{2+}	none	
(*c*) *Other hydrolyses*			
1. β-Sulphinylpyruvate desulphinase	Mn^{2+}	none	
2. Oxaloacetase	Mn^{2+}	none	all partially purified
3. Enzymes hydrolyzing organophosphorous compounds	Mn^{2+}, Co^{2+}, Mg^{2+}, Fe^{2+}, Ba^{2+}, Cd^{2+}, Zn^{2+}, Cu^{2+}, Hg^{2+}	none	
II. Non-oxidative Decarboxylation			
1. Pyruvate decarboxylase	Mg^{2+}, Mn^{2+}, Co^{2+}, Cd^{2+}	Thiamine PP	75–85 000
2. Oxaloacetate decarboxylase	Mn^{2+}, Cd^{2+}, Co^{2+}	none	crystalline, inhomogenec
3. Acetolactate decarboxylase	Mn^{2+}	none	—
4. Aminobenzoate decarboxylase	Fe^{3+}	Pyridoxal P	—
III. Fixation of CO_2			
1. Phosphoenolpyruvate carboxylase	Mg^{2+}, Mn^{2+}, Zn^{2+}, Co^{2+}, Ca^{2+}	none	
2. Ribulose diphosphate carboxylase	Mn^{2+}, Mg^{2+}, Co^{2+}, Ni^{2+}, Fe^{2+}	none	300 000
IV. Transfer of Phosphate Groups			
1. Gluconokinase	Mg^{2+}, Mn^{2+}, Zn^{2+}, Co^{2+}, Ca^{2+}	ATP	
2. 2-Keto-3-deoxy-D-glucuronate kinase	Mn^{2+}, Mg^{2+}, Co^{2+}	ATP	
3. Phosphoribulokinase	Mg^{2+}, Mn^{2+}, Ca^{2+}, Co^{2+}, Cd^{2+}	ATP	
4. Pantetheine kinase	Mg^{2+}, Mn^{2+}	ATP	
5. Pyridoxal kinase	Mn^{2+}, Mg^{2+}, Co^{2+}, Zn^{2+}, Ni^{2+}	ATP	
6. Mevalonate kinase	Mn^{2+}, Mg^{2+}, Zn^{2+}, Co^{2+}, Fe^{2+}, Ca^{2+}	ATP	all partially purified pre tions
7. Phosphomevalonate kinase	Mg^{2+}, Co^{2+}, Zn^{2+}, Fe^{2+}, Mn^{2+}	ATP	
8. Arginine kinase	Mn^{2+}	ATP	43 000 (crystallizec
V. Transfer of Substituted Orthophosphate Groups			
1. Adenylcarbonate pyrophosphatase	Zn^{2+}	ATP	partially purified

inued)

or ometry mole)	*Source*	*Substrate or reaction*	*Reference*
	Mammalian liver	Citrate ⇌ *cis*-aconitate + H_2O ⇌ D-isocitrate	113
2+	Yeast, rabbit muscle, potato	D-2-Phosphoglycerate ⇌ phosphoenol-pyruvate + H_2O	29, 114
	Neurospora crassa, E. coli	D-*erythro*-Imidazoleglycerol phosphate ⇌ imidazoleaceto phosphate + H_2O	115
	Pseudomonas	6-Phosphogluconate ⇌ 2-keto-3-deoxy-6-phosphogluconate + H_2O	116
	E. coli	β-Dihydroxy-β-methylvaleric acid ⇌ α-keto-β-methylvaleric acid + H_2O	117
	Bacteria	Dihydroxyacetone phosphate + D-glyceraldehyde 3-phosphate ⇌ D-fructose 1,6-diphosphate	80

ing to the reaction types they catalyze. If a single metal ion serves in nature, as in the metalloenzymes, it is listed *first* in Column II. If other metal ions have been shown to substitute *in vitro*, they are listed in brackets. For those systems where it has not been possible to identify a particular metal among several as operating in nature, no distinction is made. The following columns give additional cofactors involved, the molecular weight and cofactor stoichiometry if they are available, the source of the enzyme, and a brief description of the reaction catalyzed. The references include a review article if one exists.

A scan of Column II reveals the metals involved in these enzymatic reactions to be limited to the alkaline earths, Ca^{2+} and Mg^{2+}, the metals of the second half of the first transition period, the IIB metals, Zn^{2+}, Cd^{2+}, and Hg^{2+}, and a single metal from the second transition period, molybdenum.

The distribution of metalloenzymes and metal–enzyme complexes among the various reaction types is not particularly different from that for non-metal enzymes. The largest number catalyze either a hydrolysis or a hydrogen transfer. This, however, is not a distinction of metalloenzymes, but reflects a general pattern[118]. Examination of the enzymes listed in Table IV for the distribution of metals among the various reactions reveals no preferred distribution except for molybdenum and copper. Molybdenum has been encountered so far exclusively in the metalloflavoproteins[119], while copper enzymes catalyze a series of oxidation–reduction reactions without the aid of additional cofactors. Present evidence indicates a reversible reduction of

References p. 231

Cu^{2+} to Cu^{+} during the reactions. The favorable relationship between the first and second ionization potentials of copper has previously been mentioned. Copper is notably absent as an essential participant in hydrolytic systems. This lack of function has been attributed to the high stability of the complexes formed between copper and its ligands, too great to permit rapid breakdown. The unusual geometry induced by copper may be another possible factor.

Valence states for molybdenum from Mo^{+} to Mo^{6+} can be stabilized by various combinations of ligands. The reader is referred to Williams[120] for a discussion of the various properties of the Mo^{5+}–Mo^{6+} couple that might make it likely to operate in biological oxidation–reduction systems.

For all the oxidative enzymes involving metals other than copper, an additional cofactor, either pyridine nucleotide or a flavin, is required. The metalloflavoproteins include the only examples where two different non-heme linked metals, Fe and Mo, occur simultaneously as integral parts of one enzyme molecule, *e.g.*, the xanthine and aldehyde oxidases. Copper and heme–Fe both occur in cytochrome oxidase. Since there is usually some doubt as to the valence state and as to whether the metal itself undergoes oxidation–reduction during the reaction, the valences have not been included for the oxido-reductases in Table IV, except for Zn^{2+}.

Among the metalloenzymes, restoration of esterase activity to metal-free carboxypeptidase A by Hg^{2+} and Pb^{2+} and to metal-free alkaline phosphatase (*E. coli*) by Hg^{2+} are the only examples in which these heavy metals are active. However, activation by Cd^{2+} has been observed in many of the enzymes in which Zn^{2+} is also an efficient activator. The occurrence of Zn^{2+} among every category of the metal–enzyme catalyzed reactions emphasizes the varied roles of this metal ion.

The alkaline earths, Ca^{2+} and Mg^{2+}, activate a great number of the enzyme systems involving ATP as indicated by the partial list in Table IV under the phosphate transfer reactions. In many of these instances, first transition metals can also activate. Whether the action of the alkaline earths and the first transition-metal ions are the same in all cases remains to be elucidated. In at least one instance, the zinc metalloenzyme alkaline phosphatase of *E. coli*, the activating effect of Mg^{2+} and the function of the catalytically essential zinc ion would appear to be quite different[39,40].

(*c*) *Metal ion exchanges, apoenzymes, and stability constants*

Table V gives some examples both of metal–enzyme complexes and of metalloenzymes in which a variety of metal ions have been shown to induce activity. The native carboxypeptidases and carbonic anhydrase are all isolated as zinc enzymes. In these instances zinc is first removed and the activating metal species is substituted for it. In each instance the metals are

TABLE V

METAL ION ACTIVATION AND INHIBITION OF METAL–ENZYME COMPLEXES AND METALLOENZYMES

Enzymes	*Activating metal ions*	*Inhibiting metal ions*	*Reference*
Metal–enzyme complexes			
Enolase	$Mg^{2+} > Zn^{2+} > Mn^{2+} > Fe^{2+} > Cd^{2+} > Co^{2+}$	Be^{2+}, Ca^{2+}, Sr^{2+}, Ba^{2+}, Cd^{2+}, Hg^{2+}	29
Carnosinase	$Cd^{2+} > Mn^{2+} > Zn^{2+} > Co^{2+}$	$Be^{2+} > Ni^{2+} > Fe^{2+} > Hg^{2+}$	81, 83, 84
Arginase (liver)	$Mn^{2+} > Co^{2+} > Ni^{2+}$		88
Arginase (jack bean)	$Co^{2+} > Mn^{2+} > Ni^{2+}$		88
Oxaloacetic decarboxylase	$Mn^{2+} > Co^{2+} \geqslant Cd^{2+} > Zn^{2+} > Fe^{2+} > Ni^{2+}$		96, 97
Metalloenzymes			
Carboxypeptidase A			
Cbz–Gly–L-Phe as substrate	$Co^{2+} > Ni^{2+} > Zn^{2+} > Mn^{2+} > Fe^{2+}$	$Hg^{2+} > Cd^{2+} > Pb^{2+} > Cu^{2+}$	30, 36
Bz–Gly–L-Phe as substrate	$Zn^{2+} > Co^{2+} > Ni^{2+} > Mn^{2+}$		30
Bz–Gly–L-Phenyllactate as substrate (ester)	$Cd^{2+} > Hg^{2+} > Zn^{2+} > Co^{2+} > Ni^{2+} > Mn^{2+}$	Cu^{2+}	30
Carboxypeptidase B			
Bz–Gly–L-Arg as substrate	$Co^{2+} > Zn^{2+}$	Cd^{2+}	37
Bz–Gly–L-Argininic acid as substrate (ester)	$Cd^{2+} > Zn^{2+} > Co^{2+}$		37
Carbonic anhydrase	$Zn^{2+} > Co^{2+}$	Cu^{2+}	77

References p. 231

arranged in the order of their effectiveness as activators. In some cases other metals may act as inhibitors and are shown for comparison. It has been tempting to relate the activities of these metal–enzymes to some physico-chemical property such as the stability of the complexes formed. If the various examples given in Table V are considered, a definite correlation between *biological effectiveness* and *chemical properties* of these metals is not immediately apparent unless one wishes to emphasize the obvious fact that the "active" ions are part of the first transition and IIB series. The effectiveness of these ions as activators does not follow any of the three stability series presented in Fig. 1 (p. 174). Where comparative data are available, activity with a given metal ion depends on either the particular substrate being attacked (carboxypeptidase) or on the particular source of the enzyme (arginase) or both (carboxypeptidase).

While activation of one enzyme by a series of metal ions has been in the past limited to metal–enzyme complexes, two methods are becoming increasingly useful in studying metal ion interactions with the active sites of metalloenzymes. The first is metal ion exchange. Under the proper conditions of ionic strength, external metal ion concentration, temperature, and in the presence or absence of substrates, it is possible to exchange the metal at the active site either for another metal ion species or for a radioactive isotope of the native ion. The three metalloenzymes listed in Table V all readily undergo such exchange reactions. The ability of substituted metal ions to impart activity can then be measured.

It has been shown that the copper of ascorbic acid oxidase will only exchange with externally added $^{64}Cu^{2+}$ when the enzyme is actively oxidizing substrates[72,121]. In contrast, under a variety of conditions, substrates for carboxypeptidase A *prevent* metal ion exchange reactions[122,123] (see p. 224).

The preparation of stable, metal-free apoenzymes by removal of the native metal ion with competing chelating agents has yielded another valuable procedure for the study of metalloenzymes. Under proper conditions of pH, temperature, concentration, and ionic strength, various chelating agents, but particularly *o*-phenanthroline, have been used successfully for this purpose. While a number of metalloenzymes undergo irreversible inactivation and alteration in three-dimensional structure when the metal ion is removed[124], others have been shown to form stable, metal-free inactive apoenzymes to which activity can be fully restored by re-addition of metal ions. Examples of metalloenzymes in which this procedure has been carried out are listed below.

The preparation of a stable apoenzyme implies that a completely reversible equilibrium governs the metal–protein interaction analogous to the interaction of metal ions with small molecules; hence, methods applicable to such reversible equilibria may be applied.

METALLOENZYMES WHICH FORM STABLE APOENZYMES

Carboxypeptidase A[36,125]
Carbonic anhydrase[77,79]
Alkaline phosphatase[40]
Tyrosinase[63]
Laccase[126]
Ascorbic acid oxidase[127]
Ceruloplasmin[128]

When a functional metal ion can be reversibly removed from the protein with concurrent loss and restoration of enzymatic activity, it becomes possible to employ a metal or series of metal ions as "site-specific" reagents to determine the nature of the active enzymatic site. The use of radioactive metal ions has been a particularly powerful tool in this regard. At the same time, the more usual organic reagents can be used to explore the metal-binding groups of the protein uncovered by removal of the metal (*vide infra*). In the case of carboxypeptidase A, ions of the first transition period including Mn^{2+}, Fe^{2+}, Co^{2+}, Ni^{2+}, and the IIB ions, Zn^{2+}, Cd^{2+}, Hg^{2+}, all produce enzymatically active metallocarboxypeptidases on binding to the inactive apocarboxypeptidase[30]. Many of these metallocarboxypeptidases exhibit activities which differ markedly both in magnitude and specificity from that of the native enzyme. Table V indicates the changing orders of activation and inhibition induced by several metal ions when the enzyme acts on different substrates. These studies permit the physicochemical events which govern metal–protein binding to be correlated with the ensuing enzymatic consequences.

Fig. 6 illustrates a metal ion exchange experiment on carboxypeptidase A using Zn^{2+} and Cd^{2+}. Each metal imparts characteristic and different functional characteristics to the enzyme when bound at the active site. Precise correspondence between metal ion exchange and enzymatic characteristics thereby induced can be shown directly.

Cadmium replaces zinc in the enzyme with simultaneous abolition of peptidase activity and increase in esterase activity. Throughout the experiment, the total metal content remains 1 gram atom of metal per mole of protein demonstrating that this interaction takes place at a single binding site and accounts for all the functional changes observed.

Similar exchange experiments have been carried out with carboxypeptidase B from porcine pancreas using cobalt and cadmium to replace zinc, but measuring activity only[37]. The activities of cobalt and cadmium carboxypeptidase B relative to those of the native enzyme are indicated in Table V.

Cobalt has also been exchanged for zinc at the active site of bovine carbonic anhydrase. The cobalt enzyme has several visible absorption maxima

References p. 231

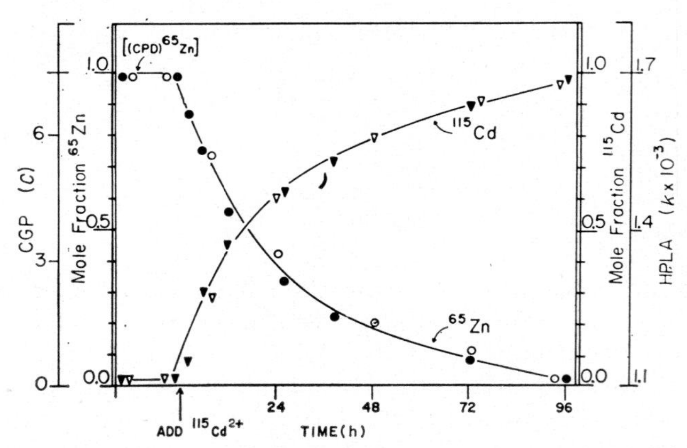

Fig. 6. Effect of cadmium replacement on peptidase and esterase activities of zinc carboxypeptidase. The graph beginning at the top shows the ^{65}Zn content of the enzyme and its peptidase activity (left-hand ordinates). The graph beginning at the bottom shows the ^{115}Cd content of the enzyme and its esterase activity (right-hand ordinates). The experiment was performed in a medium containing 1 *M* NaCl–0.05 *M* Tris, pH 8.0, 4°. Peptidase assays were performed with 0.02 *M* carbobenzoxyglycyl-L-phenylalanine, 0.1 *M* NaCl–0.02 *M* sodium veronal, pH 7.5, 0°, and are expressed as the proteolytic coefficient, *C*. Esterase assays were performed with 0.01 *M* hippuryl-*dl*-*β*-phenyllactate–0.01 *M* NaCl–0.001 *M* Tris, pH 7.5, 25°, and are expressed as the zero order velocity constants, $k \times 10^{-3}$. ●, ^{65}Zn bound to $1 \cdot 10^{-4}$ *M* [(CPD)^{65}Zn], exposed to $1 \cdot 10^{-4}$ *M* $^{115}Cd^{2+}$ at 0 time; ○, proteolytic coefficient, *C*, of $1 \cdot 10^{-4}$ *M* [(CPD)^{65}Zn], exposed to $1 \cdot 10^{-4}$ *M* $^{115}Cd^{2+}$ at 0 time; ▼, $^{115}Cd^{2+}$ bound to $1 \cdot 10^{-4}$ *M* [(CPD)^{65}Zn] exposed to $1 \cdot 10^{-4}$ *M* $^{115}Cd^{2+}$ at 0 time; ▽, esterase activity, $k \times 10^{-3}$, of $1 \cdot 10^{-4}$ *M* [(CPD)^{65}Zn], exposed to $^{115}Cd^{2+}$ at 0 time. Both metal contents were measured simultaneously on the same sample with a two-channel *γ*-ray spectrometer, one channel focused on the 1.12 MeV peak of ^{65}Zn and the other on the 1.30 MeV peak of ^{115}Cd. The solid curves (——) represent peptidase and esterase activities *calculated* on the basis of the mole fractions of [(CPD)Zn] and [(CPD)Cd] present at any given time. Esterase activity is plotted from $1.1 \cdot 10^3$, typical of [(CPD)Zn] to $1.7 \cdot 10^3$, typical of [(CPD)Cd]. Taken from J. E. Coleman, *Doctoral Dissertation*, Massachusetts Institute of Technology, 1963.

between 500 and 600 mμ and demonstrates 45% of the activity of the native enzyme[77,129]. Ni^{2+} imparts a very low activity while Cu^{2+} produces an inactive enzyme with an absorption maximum at about 700 mμ.

The stability constants for a series of metallocarboxypeptidases measured by equilibrium dialysis are the only instance of a complete series of stability constants for the complexes of the transition and IIB metal ions with a specific and known site of a metalloenzyme known to date. The logarithms of the stability constants are presented in Table VI and compared to the log k_1 values for the complexes of the same metals with bidentate nitrogen–sulfur, nitrogen–oxygen, and nitrogen–nitrogen ligands.

The stabilities of the metallocarboxypeptidases follow the order $Hg^{2+} > Cd^{2+} > Cu^{2+} > Zn^{2+} > Ni^{2+} > Mn^{2+}$, that expected for a sulfur-containing

TABLE VI

STABILITIES OF METALLOCARBOXYPEPTIDASES AND OF METAL CHELATES OF KNOWN STRUCTURE

Taken from Coleman and Vallee[30]

Metal	*Log k* *Metallocarboxypeptidases*[a]	*Log k_1*		
		2-Mercapto-ethylamine (*N–S*)	*Glycine* (*N–O*)	*Ethylenediamine* (*N–N*)
Mn^{2+}	5.6	4.1[b]	3.4	2.7
Co^{2+}	7.0	7.7	5.2	5.9
Ni^{2+}	8.2	9.9	6.2	7.7
Cu^{2+}	10.6	—[c]	8.6	10.7
Zn^{2+}	10.5	10.2	5.2	5.7
Cd^{2+}	10.8	11.0	4.8	5.5
Hg^{2+}	21.0	22.0	10.3	12.0

[a] Each contained 1 gram atom of metal per mole of protein.
[b] These values for 2-mercaptoethylamine are not on record; those given are for cysteine[11].
[c] The reasons for the unavailability of constants for the cupric complexes have been detailed[130].

ligand (Fig. 1, p. 174). The general magnitudes of the stability constants correlate closely with those expected for bidentate ligands, particularly nitrogen–sulfur ligands (Table VI). This stability series implies the presence of a sulfur and nitrogen atom as donors at the active metal-binding site. The required proof of the nature of the protein donor atoms must be obtained by independent experimental means. The analytical evidence regarding specific donor atoms in metalloproteins is detailed in section 3*f* (p. 219). The metallocarboxypeptidases formed with the ions of the IIB period metals, Zn^{2+}, Cd^{2+}, and Hg^{2+}, are very stable and contain stoichiometric amounts of metal which are not freely dialyzable. As expected, from the magnitude of the stability constants, equilibrium is reached when the concentrations of free metal ions are extremely low. On the other hand, the affinity of Mn^{2+}, Co^{2+} and Ni^{2+} for the site is much lower, and hence, the respective metalloenzymes readily lose a fraction of the functional metal on dialysis. The full metal content and activity are maintained only in the presence of an excess of metal ion in the ambient medium[131]. If the Mn^{2+}, Co^{2+}, or Ni^{2+} enzymes were to exist in nature, their detection would be complicated by this circumstance since the metal would dissociate readily during isolation. Further, minor changes in pH during isolation would assist dissociation and result in an inactive apoenzyme which would not be detected.

Another zinc metalloenzyme, carbonic anhydrase, has been isolated in highly purified form from both human and bovine erythrocytes[77,77a]. Either enzyme can be further fractionated by column chromatography into two or three separate and electrophoretically distinct species. The molecular weight of each species is slightly different and the values span the range[77,77a] from 26 000 to 34 000. Each of these species has a different specific activity, but like the earlier, less pure, preparations of this enzyme, all species contain one gramatom of zinc per mole of protein.

Many of the experimental approaches, designs and procedures originally worked out for carboxypeptidase have subsequently served successfully in the delineation of similar features of carbonic anhydrase. Thus, completely inactive metal-free apocarbonic anhydrases have been prepared from both the human and bovine enzymes by removing the zinc with *o*-phenanthroline[77,79]. The bovine apocarbonic anhydrase can be completely reactivated by Zn^{2+}, but the enzyme when activated by Co^{2+} yields only one half the activity of the zinc enzyme. Ni^{2+} and Fe^{2+} have been reported to give low activity, but results have been variable and the possibility of zinc contamination has not been completely ruled out[77]. The Cu derivative is inactive.

The Co^{2+} and the Cu^{2+} carbonic anhydrases exhibit absorption maxima in the visible wavelength region, a characteristic of complexes of these ions (see Table VII, p. 212). Changes in these spectra subsequent to the binding of inhibitors, such as the sulfonamides, provide a significant new parameter for the study of these interactions. Equilibrium dialysis experiments measuring sulfonamide binding to Zn^{2+}, Co^{2+} and apocarbonic anhydrase indicate that the metal is involved in the binding of these inhibitors[77b].

Edsall and coworkers[79] have shown that the sulfhydryl group of the sole cysteine residue of the human enzyme is involved in Zn^{2+} binding (see section 3*f*, p. 221). In contrast to this work on the human enzyme, Malmstrom and coworkers[77c] have reported the complete absence of cysteic acid derivatives in the amino acid analysis of the bovine enzyme. Differences in amino acid composition of human erythrocyte carbonic anhydrases differing in electrophoretic mobility have also been reported[77c]. These in turn differ from similar ones obtained from the bovine. These differences in composition require further investigation since they are thought to be pertinent to metal binding[77c].

While the above properties indicate considerable similarity between carbonic anhydrase and carboxypeptidase as protein ligands, other properties deviate markedly from one another. Thus, in contrast to carboxypeptidase, all attempts to exchange the Zn of carbonic anhydrase for $^{65}Zn^{2+}$ have been unsuccessful under conventional conditions[77,78] at pH 7–8. Hence, at physiological pH, the zinc bound to the enzyme is not in rapid equilibrium with metal ions in the surrounding medium. In carboxypeptidase such exchange takes place readily[30]. Differences in the solubility of enzymes and the nature of the metal ion equilibria suggest caution in comparing pertinent physical–chemical parameters such as stability constants. The apparent stability constant for Zn^{2+} carboxypeptidase has been determined to be $3.2 \cdot 10^{10}$ M in 1 M NaCl and for Zn^{2+} carbonic anhydrase is approximately $1 \cdot 10^{12}$ M in the absence of salt, indicating similar stabilities for the two enzymes. The exchange data, however, indicate considerable difference in the kinetics of the association–dissociation reaction which controls binding of the metal. More experimental data will be needed before the similarities and differences between the various metalloenzymes catalyzing widely differing reactions can be elucidated.

(*d*) *Hydrogen ion equilibria*

In addition to the usual hydrogen ion equilibria of the amino acid residues of proteins, in accordance with the principles outlined in section 2*c* (p. 175), a metalloenzyme may be expected to be affected by the hydrogen ion equilibria which affect primarily the metal atom and its binding site. It may prove difficult to separate these two equilibria unless careful analytical studies are pursued along with the investigation of the effect of pH on enzymatic function. Such studies on carboxypeptidase A may again serve to illustrate the principle.

The peptidase pH–rate profile of carboxypeptidase obtained by varying the pH of the reaction mixture in standard fashion is bell-shaped with a maximum at pH 7.5, and inflections at pH 6.7 and 8.5 (Curve B, Fig. 7). However, this pH–activity profile does not reflect the stability of the zinc–protein complex. Over the range of pH from 6 to 9, the complex is completely stable and zinc ions begin to be displaced only below pH 6.0 (Curve A, Fig. 7). This is shown by the formation curves (see section 2*c*, p. 176) measured by either $^{65}Zn^{2+}$ binding or activity. Hence, the normal pH maximum of peptidase activity must involve ionizations of groups on the protein which are not directly involved in binding the metal ion.

By analogy to the formation of metal–coordination complexes, the formation of a metal–protein complex at any given pH will displace protons from those donor atoms which are protonated at that pH. The instantaneous interaction of metal ions with a stable, metal-free apoenzyme provides the opportunity to test this hypothesis. Such a *complexometric difference titration* of carboxypeptidase is shown in Fig. 8. Zinc ions were added to the apoenzyme at each indicated pH and the number of H^+ ions released per mole of protein were titrated with a pH Stat. Determination of the number of displaced protons as a function of pH gave the apparent pK_a values of the donor groups involved. Over the range pH 6.0 to 9.0, where the zinc enzyme is formed 100%, Zn^{2+} binds to two protonated groups, having pK_a's of 7.7 and 9.1 (Fig. 8). By this means, the hydrogen ion equilibria for the two metal-binding groups can be isolated, whereas they would be lost among the large number of ionizations in a continuous titration curve.

References p. 231

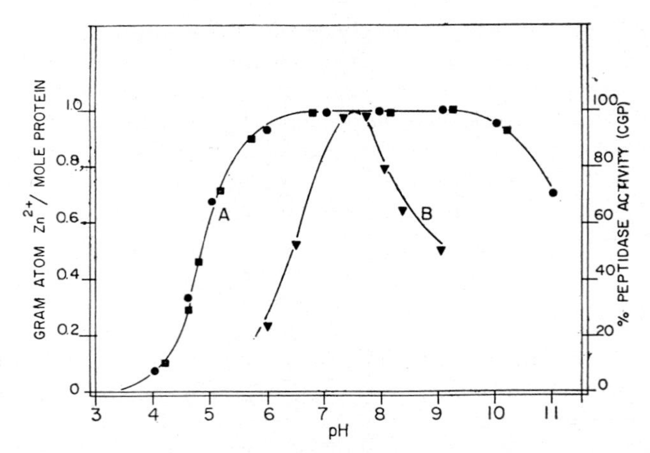

Fig. 7. (A) Enzyme-bound $^{65}Zn^{2+}$ (●) and peptidase activity (■) of carboxypeptidase as a function of pH; (B) pH–rate profile for peptidase reaction. $^{65}Zn^{2+}$ binding was determined by equilibrium dialysis[131] at each pH. The accompanying peptidase activity (■) was determined[131] by assaying an aliquot of each sample at pH 7.5. The pH–rate profile (▼), on the other hand, was determined by varying the pH of the reaction mixture[27].

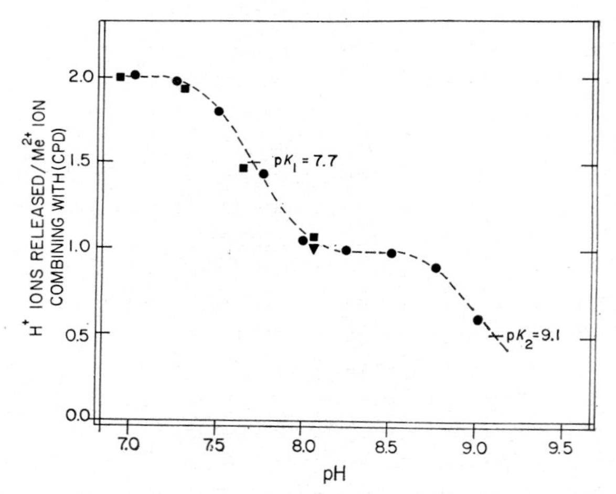

Fig. 8. The displacement of protons from apocarboxypeptidases, (CPD), by Zn^{2+} ions (●), Cd^{2+} ions (■), and Co^{2+} ions (▼). The reaction was carried out at the pH values indicated by the experimental points in 1 *M* NaCl–0.00025 *M* citrate at 25°. Protons released from the protein due to its interaction with the metal ions were measured by means of a pH Stat. The ratio of H^+ released to Me^{2+} combined = 1 corresponds to 0.32 ± 0.01 μmole H^+ measured. In the case of the Zn^{2+} interaction, a reduction in NaCl concentration from 1 to 0.5 *M* resulted in a shift of pK_1 from 7.7 to 7.8. Cd^{2+} ions give a titration very similar to Zn^{2+} ions while Co^{2+} can be used only at pH 8.0 since the enzyme is 100% formed only at pH 8.0. The Zn^{2+} data are taken from Coleman and Vallee[30].

The isolation of the ionizations of the zinc-binding groups of carboxypeptidase allows the construction of the formation curve, analogous to that shown for the EDTA complexes in Fig. 2 (p. 176). This construction is illustrated in Fig. 9. The two curves are related by the three simultaneous equilibria described by the two acid dissociation constants and the stability constant

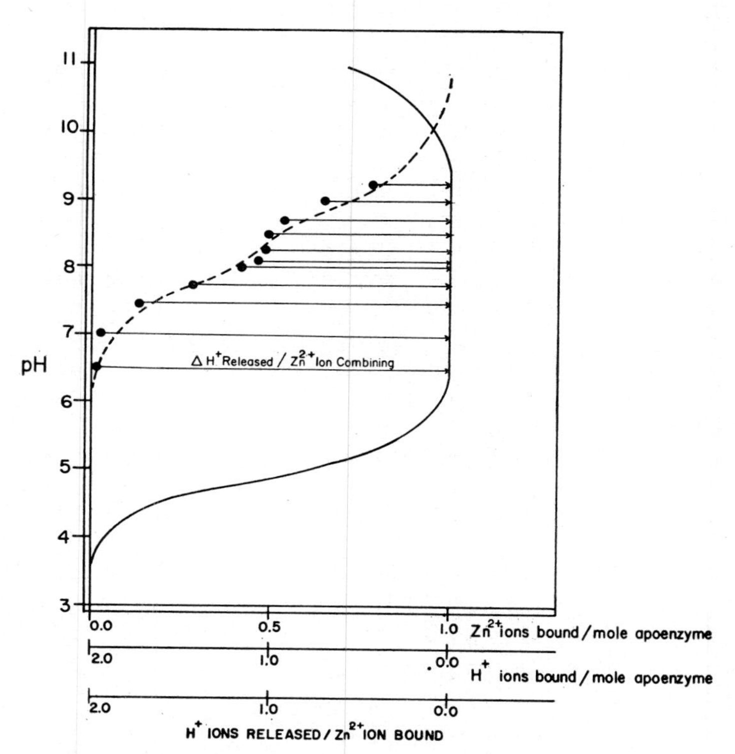

Fig. 9. Relationship between the complexometric titration curve (Fig. 8) and the pH–formation curve (Fig. 7) for zinc carboxypeptidase. The experimental points (●) are the complexometric titration curve for zinc carboxypeptidase from Fig. 8. (-----) represents the theoretical curve for two independent ionizations of pK 7.7 and pK 9.1. (———) is the formation curve for zinc carboxypeptidase taken from Fig. 7 for $^{65}Zn^{2+}$ binding. Between pH 6.5 and pH 9.5 the metalloenzyme normally contains its full complement of metal, 1.0 gram atom per mole, and the metal-binding groups bind no hydrogen. On the other hand, the apoenzyme binds two hydrogen ions per mole at pH 6.5, the average number decreasing along the curve given by the complexometric titration. The addition of Zn^{2+} ions to the apoenzyme serves to transform the protein from the point on the apoenzyme titration curve to the corresponding point on the formation curve. The bound hydrogen ions are displaced as indicated by the arrows. Below pH 6.5, the hydrogen ion concentration is high enough to begin to displace the more firmly bound Zn^{2+} ion. The two curves pictured in this graph are quantitatively related by the stability constant for the metal–protein chelate and the pK_a's of the donor groups.

for the zinc carboxypeptidase complex. Their relationship is illustrated schematically by the arrow in Fig. 9. Addition of Zn^{2+} ions to the apoenzyme results in the shift from the hydrogen ion dissociation curve of the apoenzyme to the formation curve for the zinc enzyme by the release of two hydrogen ions and the binding of one zinc ion. Below pH 6.0, of course, only partial formation of the zinc enzyme would occur and a portion of the donor atoms would remain protonated.

Formation of a carboxypeptidase of less stability than the zinc enzyme would be expected to shift the formation curve to higher pH values. Cobalt carboxypeptidase, for example, follows such a curve, the enzyme containing one gram atom of ^{60}Co per mole only over a very narrow pH range[131] around 8.0. It would thus be difficult to separate the pH-dependence of cobalt binding from the pH–rate profile for peptidase action. Yet, the data with zinc show the two profiles to involve different ionizations. Hence, for the less stable metal–enzyme complexes, it may be very difficult to separate the pH–rate profiles observed from the pH-dependence of metal binding when different activating metal ions are employed, *e.g.*, arginase[132,133].

Thus, through the determination of the acid dissociation constants of the donor groups such complexometric titrations yield indirect information regarding their chemical nature. In conjunction with the other analytical data, the donor groups in carboxypeptidase A have been assigned to the α-amino groups of the N-terminal asparagine and the sulfhydryl group of the single cysteine residue of the molecule[27,134] (*vide infra*).

(*e*) *Spectral, optical rotatory, and magnetic properties*

The absorption spectra of metalloproteins containing metals of the first transition period with unfilled d-shell orbitals exhibit the expected visible absorption maxima corresponding to electronic transitions involving these d-shell electrons. The position of the absorption maxima and their molar extinction coefficients are listed in Table VII for a variety of these proteins.

In keeping with coordination to a d^{10} ion, zinc metalloproteins do not have absorption maxima in the visible part of the spectrum. When zinc is bound to an —SH group, a charge-transfer maximum at 215 mμ is observed[147]. The spectral interference of aromatic residues in most proteins plus end-absorption precludes the detection of this chromophore in most zinc proteins. When it has been possible to substitute a first transition period metal for the zinc atom of a protein, the absorption spectrum predicted for the substituted ion appears. The Co^{2+} and Cu^{2+} derivatives of carbonic anhydrase and carboxypeptidase constitute the most prominent examples. Their spectral characteristics are included in Table VII. The absorption bands and extinction coefficients of the hydrated metal ion species $[Me(H_2O)_6]^{2+}$, are given for comparison at the top of each heading.

The extinction coefficients of the absorption bands of metalloproteins are greater than those of the corresponding hydrated ions, but usually considerably less than those expected for allowed electronic transitions. For comparison, the charge transfer Co^{3+}–cobalamin bands due to these allowed transitions are shown in juxtaposition to the much weaker ones of cobalt carboxypeptidase and cobalt carbonic anhydrase.

From the general position of these bands, it is very difficult to draw firm conclusions concerning the nature of the donor atoms forming the complex. The assignment of the bands in the near-ultraviolet spectrum of some copper proteins to sulfur bonding has been made[72]. It has been stated that the 530-mμ band of cobalt carboxypeptidase compared to the 510-mμ band of the hydrated ion indicates binding to a sulfur donor[149]. While sulfur has been shown to be one of the donor atoms in carboxypeptidase by analytical methods, a variety of Co^{2+}–peptide complexes which do not contain sulfur also absorb maximally between 510 mμ and 600 mμ, with coefficients of absorptivity[150] ranging from 100 to 500. Hence, neither the location of the maximum nor its coefficient of absorptivity can be considered to be unique properties of specific donor atoms.

If the d^9 cupric ion were placed in an octahedral environment, there would be expected to be a single absorption band corresponding to the transition from a d_ε orbital to the single unfilled d_γ orbital analogous to the single absorption band observed in the d^1 Ti^{3+} ion. However, copper is not usually found in an octahedral environment and while most copper complexes do have a single absorption maximum in the visible part of the spectrum it is usually very broad and is believed to be made up of transitions from several of the occupied d-orbitals to the partially filled $d_{x^2-y^2}$ orbital. In addition to the near-ultraviolet band, mentioned previously, most copper proteins exhibit this broad absorption band between 600 and 800 mμ accounting for their blue color.

If the Cu^{2+} ion undergoes reduction to Cu^+ and the d^{10} state, this band should disappear. Both ascorbic acid oxidase and ceruloplasmin undergo decolorization when exposed to the substrate, ascorbic acid[68,71]. The blue color of laccase is bleached by addition of its hydroquinone substrate, and the color is restored by oxygenation[151]. This has led to the hypothesis that part of the enzymatic mechanism in these copper oxidases involves a reversible electron transfer to the copper ion. Electron spin resonance studies support this conclusion (*vide infra*).

Some copper proteins, *e.g.*, tyrosinase and uricase are colorless or absorb only in the near-ultraviolet. It is not clear yet whether or not this reflects the oxidation state of the copper or other as yet unknown factors. Recent data show the major portion of the copper in mushroom tyrosinase to be in the cuprous form[62], thus accounting for the lack of the visible absorption band.

References p. 231

TABLE VII

ABSORPTION BANDS OF METALLOPROTEINS

Metal-protein	λ_{max} ($m\mu$)	*Molar extinction coefficient*	*Reference*
$Mn(H_2O)_6^{2+}$	multiple bands 300–550	0.01–0.04	135
Mn^{3+}–conalbumin	429	~4800	136
Mn^{3+}–transferrin	429	~4800	137
$Fe(H_2O)_6^{2+}$	970	poorly characterized	16
$Fe(H_2O)_6^{3+}$	700–800		16
	~238 (charge transfer)		
Hemerythrin	330	—	138
	380	—	
	500	—	
Iron–photosynthetic pyridine nucleotide reductase	327	—	139
	420	—	
	460	—	
Fe^{3+}–conalbumin	470	~3280	140
Fe^{3+}–transferrin	470	~3280	141, 142
$Co(H_2O)_6^{2+}$	510	10	131
Carboxypeptidase	530	150	131
Carbonic anhydrase	530	300	129
	555	400	
	630	300	
	640	290	
Co^{3+}–cobalamin	500–600	$\sim 10^4$	143

TABLE VII *(continued)*

Metal-protein	λ_{max} *(mμ)*	*Molar extinction coefficient*	*Reference*
$Cu(H_2O)_6^{2+}$	800	~12	16
Hemocyanin	575 340–350	600 6000	138
Erythrocuprein	655	140	138
Ceruloplasmin	605 370	1200 ~500	128
Ascorbic acid oxidase	606 412	770 ~500	138
Laccase	615 410	1400 ~500	144
Carbonic anhydrase	775	~100	129
Carboxypeptidase	790	<100	145
Cu^{2+}–albumin	375	~2000	146
Cu^{2+}–conalbumin	440	~1600	140
Zn^{2+}–proteins	No visible absorption maxima		
Zn^{2+}–thionein	215 (charge transfer)	$2 \cdot 10^4$	147
Cd^{2+}–thionein	250 (charge transfer)	$1.45 \cdot 10^4$	147
$[(LADH)Cd_2]$	250	$1.5 \cdot 10^4$	148

— Precise values not available.

References p. 231

Like isomers of simple metal-coordination compounds, asymmetric metal–ligand sites of proteins frequently exhibit pronounced optical rotatory power. These sites may generate optically active absorption bands of sufficient rotatory strength to be discernible above the background rotatory dispersion of the protein and are manifested by highly characteristic Cotton effects. Such effects may be single or multiple and simultaneously reflect the chemical composition of the metal–protein ligand site, its configuration, and the spacial disposition of this chromophoric site with respect to neighboring groups[152]. Delineation of these Cotton effects appears to provide a powerful new approach to the study of metalloproteins and the stereochemistry of metal–protein complexes[152].

The metalloproteins which, thus far, have been found to display anomalous rotatory dispersion or frank Cotton effects, are listed in Table VIII, along with a brief description of their rotatory dispersion curves. In all instances, the Cotton effects are dependent upon both the presence of the metal atom and an intact secondary and tertiary structure of the protein. For example, the multiple Cotton effect curve of the iron enzyme, photosynthetic pyridine nucleotide reductase (Fig. 10), is obliterated either by removal of the metal

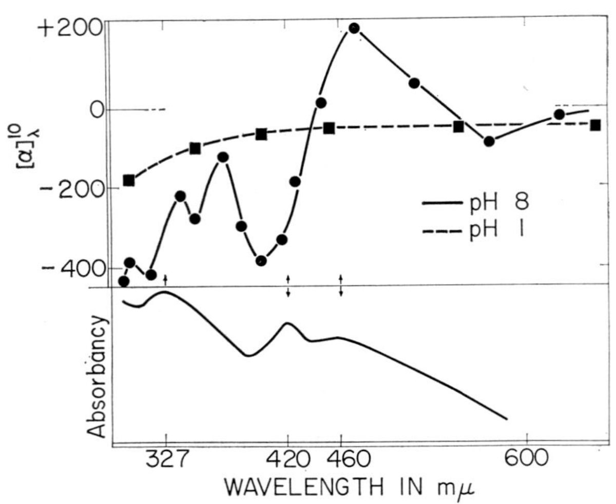

Fig. 10. The effect of acid on the optical rotatory dispersion of photosynthetic pyridine nucleotide reductase. Specific rotation at 10°, —$[\alpha]^{10}_{\lambda}$, and absorbancy are plotted against wavelength. At pH 8.0, the native enzyme, the absorption band at 420 mμ generates a positive Cotton effect with a magnitude of more than 500 degrees, while a smaller positive Cotton effect is associated with the absorption band at 227 mμ. At pH 1, the denatured enzyme, these absorption bands disappear, and rotatory dispersion becomes plain. Conditions: enzyme 0.3–0.7 mg/ml, in 0.005 *M* Tris (hydroxymethyl)-aminomethane, at pH 8.0 (●——●) and pH 1.0 (■---■). Taken from Ulmer and Vallee[152].

atom with chelating agents or by denaturation[152] of the protein at low pH. Moreover, the Cotton effects sensitively reflect the interaction of metal–protein ligand sites with other agents. For example, the anomalous dispersion of the heme proteins is markedly altered when cyanide binds to the 6th coordination position of the iron atom[152]. Similarly, binding of oxygen to the iron–ligand site of hemerythrin induces profound changes in the Cotton effect of that protein[152]. It has been observed that metal atoms such as iron and manganese, which may form octahedral complexes with proteins and, therefore, serve as asymmetric centers, are more likely to generate anomalous rotatory dispersion than are ions such as copper, which prefer square planar complexes, and cannot serve readily as asymmetric centers[152].

Due to instrumental limitations, spectropolarimetric studies of metalloproteins have been mostly restricted to those with chromophoric metal sites which absorb radiation between 300 and 700 mμ. A notable exception, metallothionein, exhibits the ascending limb of a positive Cotton effect due to a cadmium–sulfur absorption band[155] at 250 mμ; study of this protein was facilitated by the virtual absence of aromatic amino acids, permitting measurements of rotatory dispersion at wavelengths much shorter than is ordinarily feasible.

Thus far, it has not been possible to delineate the intrinsic Cotton effects of zinc metalloenzymes which absorb at wavelengths below 250 mμ, but anomalous dispersion of these proteins does result from the asymmetric binding of chromophoric coenzymes and inhibitors at the zinc sites[154]. Cotton effects of the complexes of liver alcohol dehydrogenase with DPNH and chelating agents have proven important in eliciting new information concerning the mechanism of enzymatic action and inhibition of this protein[159,160] and the details of its interaction with coenzymes and substrates[154,161].

Magnetic properties

The magnetic properties of several of the metalloenzymes have been investigated by means of electron spin resonance. Most of this work has centered on the copper proteins.

A number of the blue copper proteins yield ESR signals which indicate the presence of the Cu^{2+} ion. These are listed in Table IX along with the observed g values. The g value for the copper complexes of dithiocarbamate which coordinates the copper through four sulfur atoms and for phthalocyanine which coordinates through four nitrogen atoms are shown for comparison. Up to the present, only tentative interpretations have been offered for variations in the hyperfine structure of ESR signals of such proteins. Both in cytochrome oxidase and ceruloplasmin, the structure of the ESR signal has been interpreted to indicate the presence of a Cu^{+}–Cu^{2+} couple in very close proximity[128,162]. However, copper–copper interactions

References p. 231

TABLE VIII

METALLOPROTEINS FOR WHICH ANOMALOUS ROTATORY DISPERSION OR COTTON EFFECTS HAVE BEEN OBSERVED IN THE PROTEINS OR THEIR COMPLEXES WITH COENZYMES OR INHIBITORS

Protein	*Wavelength of optically active absorption bands (mμ)*	*Description of rotatory dispersion curve*	*Reference*
Catalase	407 530 622	Negative Cotton effect associated with the Soret band at 407 mμ, anomalous dispersion at 530 mμ (β-band of porphyrin ring), anomalous dispersion at 622 mμ	152, 153
Ceruloplasmin	600	Small perturbations in the rotatory dispersion at copper absorption band, no Cotton effects	152
Conalbumin–Fe^{3+}	470	Negative Cotton effect at the absorption peak of the iron–conalbumin complex, trough 505 mμ, peak 420 mμ, breadth 85 mμ, amplitude 16°	137
Conalbumin–Mn^{3+}	429	Cotton effect at the absorption maximum of the manganese–conalbumin complex	137
Oxy-hemerythrin	380 500	Cotton effect of 20° amplitude associated with the 380-mμ band, positive Cotton effect associated with the 500-mμ band, amplitude 70°	152
Met-hemerythrin	380	The Cotton effect at 500 mμ disappears while that at 380 mμ increases in amplitude to more than 150°	152
Liver alcohol dehydrogenase–NADH complex[a]	327	Negative Cotton effect associated with the absorption maximum of the LADH·DPNH complex, trough 355 mμ, peak 305 mμ, breadth 50 mμ, amplitude 70°, analogues of DPNH also produce Cotton effects on binding to LADH	154
Metallothionein	250	Ascending limb of positive Cotton effect associated with the cadmium–mercaptide chromophore	155

TABLE VIII *(continued)*

Protein	*Wavelength of optically active absorption bands (mμ)*	*Description of rotatory dispersion curve*	*Reference*
Ferrihemoglobin Ferrimyoglobin	410	Positive Cotton effect associated with the Soret band at 410 mμ, smaller positive Cotton effect at 530 mμ	156
Iron–photosynthetic pyridine nucleotide reductase	327 420	Multiple Cotton effects, principal one is positive of more than 500° amplitude and associated with the band at 420 mμ, a smaller Cotton effect is associated with the 327-mμ band	152
Hemocyanin	340 580	Single pronounced negative Cotton effect at 340 mμ, additional perturbation in the rotatory dispersion curve at 580 mμ	157
Transferrin–Fe^{3+}	470	Negative Cotton effect almost identical to that of iron–conalbumin, amplitude 13°	137
Transferrin–Mn^{3+}	429	Cotton effect associated with the manganese–transferrin absorption band, very similar to that observed for manganese–conalbumin	137
Peroxidase	403 530 641	Positive Cotton effect associated with the Soret band at 403 mμ, amplitude more than 200°, perturbation in the rotatory dispersion curve at 530 mμ (β-band of porphyrin ring), anomalous dispersion at the non-porphyrin band at 641 mμ	152, 153
Yeast alcohol dehydrogenase–*o*-phenanthroline complex	288	Negative Cotton effect associated with the absorption of the zinc–*o*-phenanthroline chromophore, trough 290 mμ, peak 289 mμ, amplitude 140°	158

[a] The LADH · NADH complex generates a Cotton effect which is here cited as an example of others yet to be detected due to the interaction of other coenzymes, inhibitors or substrates with their respective enzymes at the absorption bands of these complexes. Such Cotton effects, in fact, have been demonstrated recently for the complexes of pyridoxal and pyridoxamine with aspartic aminotransferase (glutamic–aspartic transaminase)[25b], which is not a metalloenzyme, however[25a].

TABLE IX

g VALUES FOR THE ESR SPECTRA OF SOME METALLOPROTEINS AND MODEL COMPLEXES

Protein or ligand	*g*	*Coordination*	*Reference*
Expected for a free electron	2.0023		
Oxidized laccase	2.048	unknown	162
Reduced laccase	none		
Oxidized ceruloplasmin	2.056	unknown	128, 162
Reduced ceruloplasmin	none		
Copper carboxypeptidase	2.060	sulfur–nitrogen	162
Erythrocuprein	2.063	? sulfur	162
Cu^{2+}-phthalocyanine	2.045	4 nitrogens	162
Cu^{2+}-dithiocarbamate	2.047	4 sulfurs	162
Oxidized xanthine oxidase	none		163
Reduced xanthine oxidase	2.004 and 1.971	unknown	

inferred on the basis of the hyperfine structure of the ESR signal have been questioned[164].

The most useful information to come from these studies so far has concerned alterations in the oxidation states of these ions in the course of enzymatic reactions. Cytochrome oxidase which contains one copper ion per heme-prosthetic group[73] exhibits an ESR spectrum associated with Cu^{2+} which disappears on oxidation of the substrate, cytochrome *c*. This has been interpreted to indicate the reduction of Cu^{2+} to Cu^{+} during the oxidation of substrate. The disappearance and reappearance of the signal parallels the oxidation state of the heme moiety as measured spectrophotometrically[73].

Similar studies have been carried out with laccase and ceruloplasmin. Both the ESR spectrum and color disappear on exposure to "substrate"[128,162].

A variety of flavin enzymes contain metal ions firmly incorporated into the molecule (*vide supra*). While spectrophotometric and ESR methods have established the reversible oxidation and reduction of the flavin component[165], the additional participation of the metal ions in the oxidation sequence is not documented extensively.

Most of these enzymes contain either iron or molybdenum or both, metals which readily alternate between two oxidation states.

The hypothesis is therefore attractive that these metals serve this function in these enzymes. Recent ESR studies on xanthine and aldehyde oxidases have tended to corroborate the hypothesis. Xanthine oxidase contains flavinadeninedinucleotide, iron and molybdenum. The enzyme itself gives no ESR signal indicating that the resting enzyme neither contains free flavin radicals nor paramagnetic ions (Fe^{3+}, Mo^{5+}, or Mo^{3+})[163]. When the substrate, xanthine, is added aerobically, two ESR absorption maxima appear. After exhaustion of the substrate both signals disappear. One of the peaks, with a g value of 2.004 appears on *partial* reduction and is abolished by an excess of dithionite and has been attributed to a flavin free radical. The second signal with a g value of 1.971 has been assigned to a paramagnetic form of molybdenum, either Mo^{3+} or Mo^{5+}. Both flavin and molybdenum are postulated to undergo reduction during the oxidation of substrate[163]. The role of the non-heme iron requires further investigation. More recent ESR studies indicate a series of reductions involving the sequence molybdenum–flavin–iron and the reverse sequence on reoxidation[166]. The iron, molybdenum and FAD contents of aldehyde oxidase from rabbit liver are very similar to those of xanthine oxidase, and similar ESR signals have been observed for this enzyme[166].

(*f*) *Evidence for specific donor atoms*

Knowledge of the precise nature and configuration of the donor atoms of biological ligands has been restricted largely to the nitrogen coordination sites of the porphyrin ring in the heme proteins and the corrin ring of the derivatives of vitamin B_{12}. In some of the heme proteins, the additional donor contributed to the coordination sphere of the iron is known to be a nitrogen of a histidine side-chain[167,168]. The distinctive chemical features of these prosthetic groups both increase the ease of determining the metal-binding sites and restrict the number of coordination sites contributed by the protein. Determination of the specific donor atoms constituting the metal-binding site of metalloproteins lacking a prosthetic group has presented formidable obstacles quite analogous to the identification of side-chains of specific amino acid residues involved in the activity of non-metal enzymes.

Data on the nature of the donor atoms at the metal-binding sites of the enzymatic metalloproteins are not extensive. Carboxypeptidase A from bovine pancreas has been studied most extensively in this regard though some data are now also available on human carbonic anhydrase and some details will be presented to illustrate what may be regarded as the modest beginnings of the elaboration of general principles.

Ag^{+}, *p*-mercuribenzoate, or ferricyanide titrate only one —SH group in apocarboxypeptidase A and none in the zinc metalloenzyme[134]. If aliquots of Zn^{2+} between 0.1 and 1.0 gram atom/mole are added to the apoenzyme, the —SH titer decreases in inverse proportion to the amount of Zn^{2+} added (Table X). The sum of the zinc content and —SH titer is always close to unity (Table X).

The magnitude of the stability constants for a series of metallocarboxypeptidases discussed in the previous section indicated the additional participation of a nitrogen donor[30]. The experiments suggesting that the α-amino group of the N-terminal asparagine residue of γ-carboxypeptidase may be the second donor group for zinc binding were quite analogous to those employed for the —SH group. On exposure to fluorodinitrobenzene or phenylisothiocyanate, the apoenzyme readily formed DNP–aspartic acid (DNP–Asp) or PTH–asparagine (PTH–AspNH$_2$), respectively, while the yields from the metalloenzyme were significantly less. Zinc was displaced from the enzyme in proportion to the reaction of these reagents with the N-terminal asparagine[169]. The sum of the number of gram atoms of zinc bound per mole of enzyme and the moles of product was unity (Table X).

The identity of the sulfur donor as that of a cysteine side-chain has been confirmed by isolation of the peptide containing the single cysteine residue of carboxypeptidase[170]. Protection of the active center of the enzyme during reduction and alkylation by a powerful competitive inhibitor, β-phenyl-

TABLE X

COMPLEMENTARITY OF —SH AND —NH$_2$ GROUPS WITH ZINC CONTENT OF [(CPD)Zn][a]

From Vallee *et al.*[27]

Sample	*Zn^{2+}*[b] *(gram atom/mole)*	*—SH*[c] *(moles/mole)*	*Σ(Zn^{2+} + —SH)*
[(CPD)Zn][d]	1.00	0	1.00
(CPD) + 0.5 g atom Zn^{2+}	0.57	0.42	0.99
(CPD) + 0.25 g atom Zn^{2+}	0.27	0.63	0.90
(CPD)	0	0.91	0.91
		DNP–Asp (moles/mole)	*Σ(Zn^{2+} + DNP–Asp)*
[(CPD)Zn][e]	1.0	0	1.00
[(CPD)Zn][f]	0.77	0.25	1.02
(CPD) + 0.5 g atom Zn^{2+}	0.47	0.52	0.99
[(CPD)Zn][g]	0.23	0.70	0.93
		PTH–AspNH$_2$ (moles/mole)	*Σ(Zn^{2+} + PTH–AspNH$_2$)*
[(CPD)Zn] + PTC[h] 2 min	0.72	0.28	1.00
[(CPD)Zn] + PTC 15 min	0.44	0.47	0.91
[(CPD)Zn] + PTC 30 min	0.38	0.69	1.07

[a] Apocarboxypeptidase is designated (CPD), zinc carboxypeptidase is [(CPD)Zn] in accord with previous usage (B. L. Vallee, *Advan. Protein Chem.*, 10 (1955) 317).
[b] Determined by chemical analysis[131].
[c] —SH groups titrated[134] with Ag$^+$.
[d] Native and fully reconstituted zinc carboxypeptidase.
[e] Native zinc carboxypeptidase, not treated with 1-fluoro-2,4-dinitrobenzene (FDNB).
[f] Native zinc carboxypeptidase, FDNB, 2 h, 25°, pH 7.0.
[g] Native zinc carboxypeptidase, FDNB, pH 9.0.
[h] Native zinc carboxypeptidase, phenylisothiocyanate (PTC) 22°, Whatman No. 1 paper strip.

propionate, followed by removal of the inhibitor and realkylation with ^{14}C-labelled iodoacetamide, resulted in the identification of a [^{14}C]carboxymethylcysteine-containing peptide (Table XI)[170]. β-Phenylpropionate requires the presence of the zinc ion for binding at the active site[171], and, thus, its ability to prevent the alkylation of the single cysteine —SH of the enzyme clearly implicates this group as that involved in zinc binding. The bidentate nature of the metal-binding site of carboxypeptidase was further supported by complexometric titrations (Fig. 8, p. 208).

TABLE XI

SULFUR-CONTAINING PEPTIDE ISOLATED FROM THE ACTIVE CENTER OF CARBOXYPEPTIDASE A

From Kumar *et al.*[170a]

Gly · Lys · Ala · (Ala, Ser) · Ser · (Pro, Ser, *Cys*) · Ser · Glu · Thr · Tyr

The cysteine residue was isolated either as the yellow compound produced by alkylation with *N*-(4-dimethylamino-3,5-dinitrophenyl)-maleimide or as the carboxymethylcysteine produced on alkylation with [^{14}C]iodoacetamide.

A similar procedure was subsequently applied to carbonic anhydrase from human erythrocytes by Edsall and coworkers[79]. In the native enzyme, no free —SH groups are detectable by titration with *p*-mercuribenzoate or Ag^+ ions. After removal of the Zn^{2+} ions, one —SH group is titrable with Ag^+ ions[79]. On treatment with urea, the —SH group of the apoenzyme reacts with both Ag^+ and *p*-mercuribenzoate. While *p*-mercuribenzoate apparently does not react with the undenatured apoenzyme, prior treatment of the metal-free enzyme with *N*-ethylmaleimide prevents subsequent reaction both with Zn^{2+} and *p*-mercuribenzoate. Amino acid analysis of the protein revealed one cysteine residue per mole of protein[79].

By metal ion exchange methods, it has been possible to exchange the zinc ion at the active sites of horse-liver alcohol dehydrogenase with cadmium ions. On exchange, the charge-transfer band typical of cadmium mercaptides appears at 250 mμ, implicating a sulfur as involved in binding the metal in this enzyme[148].

(*g*) *Functional and structural role of the metal ion*

The function of the metal ion in catalysis by metal–enzymes has been postulated variously to be based on a number of mechanisms: (*1*) The metal may participate in binding the substrate, cofactors, or both. (*2*) It could activate the enzyme–substrate complex once formed. (*3*) It may participate both in (*1*) and (*2*). (*4*) The metal ion has been thought to maintain secondary, tertiary or quaternary structure or to interact with side-chains such that the ensuing coordination complex can function catalytically. (5) Certain metal ions undergo oxidation–reduction during the enzymatic reaction and thus are considered to transfer electrons in oxidative processes.

In most metalloenzymes, the available information does not allow such a microscopic interpretation of the function of metal ions. However, with many of these systems, the precise definition is being approached rapidly. For a number of the metalloenzymes it has now been proved that the metal ions are an absolute requirement for catalytic activity. An *inactive*, metal-free apoenzyme can be prepared by removal of the metal ion with chelating agents or low pH. Activity can then be fully restored by the readdition of the metal ion. Enzymes for which such a procedure have been carried out were listed in section 3*c* (p. 202). However, in some metalloenzymes like yeast alcohol dehydrogenase, removal of the metal ion results in irreversible changes in protein structure, and a stable apoenzyme to which activity can be restored by readdition of a metal ion has not been prepared[124].

On the other hand, X-ray diffraction studies of inactive, crystalline apo-carboxypeptidase A show its unit cell dimensions to be within 2% of those for the native metalloenzyme[125]. Similarly, electrophoretic, ultracentrifugal and optical rotatory behavior of the apoenzyme closely resembles that of the native protein. Such data suggest that the zinc atom is not critical to the three-dimensional structure of this enzyme.

It has not been easy to demonstrate such an absolute dependence of catalytic activity on the presence of the metal for many of the "metal-activated" systems. The lack of analytical data often complicates the problem of interpretation. The supposedly metal-free enzyme often exhibits low but definite enzymatic activity as exemplified by arginase[132,133]. Other metal-activated enzymes, however, are extremely unstable in the absence of metal ions and reactivation has been difficult to achieve[4]. Several metal–enzyme complexes such as carnosinase and enolase undoubtedly can be prepared with less than 10% of the activity that can be restored by adding the activating metal ions[29,83,84].

It would appear that in a number of cases the metal ion is essential to catalysis, but does not play a major role in maintaining the three-dimensional structure of the protein, while in others it may serve a major and crucial structural role.

When loss and restoration of activity have been found to be directly correlated to loss and restoration of the metal ion, the specificity of the active metal-binding site for the particular metal ion present in the native enzyme has been shown *not* to be absolute. Thus, Zn^{2+}, Mn^{2+}, Fe^{2+}, Co^{2+}, and Ni^{2+} all restore peptidase activity to apocarboxypeptidase A[30,34], while Zn^{2+} and Co^{2+} restore activity to apocarbonic anhydrase[77]. Both native enzymes only contain zinc and it is not known whether these other metal ions operate in the biological actions of these enzymes. The copper-containing oxidases apparently constitute the exceptions to this general observation; their apoenzymes have so far only been reactivated by copper. Such a result is compatible with the operation of copper as a Cu^{+}–Cu^{2+} couple (*vide supra*). While many enzymes do not exhibit a high degree of specificity for a particular metal ion, the metal ion species present does markedly influence the enzymatic rate. Further, in the hydrolytic enzymes, carboxypeptidase A and B, the metal ion also profoundly affects substrate specificity. These enzymes hydrolyze a variety of peptides with free C-terminal carboxyl groups as well as the analogous esters. The ions Zn^{2+}, Co^{2+}, Ni^{2+}, Mn^{2+}, Cd^{2+}, Hg^{2+} and Pb^{2+} all produce active carboxypeptidases A. The activities of various metallocarboxypeptidases against three peptides and the ester, hippuryl-β-phenyllactate, are shown in Table XII. The carboxypeptidases A formed with the first transition metals and zinc are both peptidases and esterases[30]. The relative magnitude of the hydrolytic rates depends both on the metal ion species present at the active site and on the substrate structure. For example, with carbobenzoxyglycyl-L-phenylalanine as substrate, both the Co^{2+} and Ni^{2+} carboxypeptidase A are more active peptidases than the native zinc enzyme. The enhanced activity of the

TABLE XII

PEPTIDASE AND ESTERASE ACTIVITIES OF METALLOCARBOXYPEPTIDASES

From Coleman and Vallee[30]

[(CPD) Me][a]	*Peptidase activity*[b] *(C)*			*Esterase activity*[c] *($k \times 10^{-3}$)*
	A Carbobenzoxy-glycyl-L-phenylalanine	B Carbobenzoxy-glycyl-L-tryptophan	C Benzoyl-glycyl-L-phenylalanine	D Hippuryl-*dl*-β-phenyl-lactate
[(CPD)Zn]	7.5	2.8	5.5	1.15
[(CPD)Co]	12.0	2.7	5.2	1.10
[(CPD)Ni]	8.0	2.0	2.0	1.00
[(CPD)Mn]	2.8	0.6	0.6	0.40
[(CPD)Cu]	0	0	0	0
[(CPD)Hg]	0	0	0	1.34
[(CPD)Cd]	0	0	0	1.75
[(CPD)Pb]	0	0	0	0.60

[a] Me, 1 gram atom per mole of enzyme

[b] Assays were carried out at pH 7.5, 0°, with 0.02 *M* substrate in 0.02 *M* sodium veronal, containing 0.1 *M* NaCl.

[c] Assays were carried out at pH 7.5, 25°, with 0.01 *M* hippuryl-*dl*-β-phenyllactate in 0.005 *M* Tris, containing 0.1 *M* NaCl. The coefficient of variation for these measurements is 4%.

References p. 231

cobalt enzyme toward carbobenzoxyglycyl-L-phenylalanine is maintained over a wide range of substrate concentrations[32] and thus is not due to a radical shift in the velocity *versus* substrate curve. A different order of rates of hydrolysis is observed, however, for benzoyl-glycyl-L-phenylalanine.

In marked contrast, Cd^{2+}, Hg^{2+}, and Pb^{2+} carboxypeptidases are only esterases. They are inactive toward the peptide substrates, although the Cd^{2+} and Hg^{2+} enzymes are even more active esterases than the native zinc enzyme. Copper carboxypeptidase A, although containing 1 gram atom of copper at the active site, lacks both peptidase and esterase activity[30]. The inactivity of the copper enzyme can be reversed completely by replacement with Zn^{2+}, and thus is not due to a copper-catalyzed, irreversible oxidation of the enzyme[172].

Using the analogous carboxypeptidase B substrates, hippuryl-L-arginine and hippurylargininic acid, Cd^{2+} carboxypeptidase B is also active toward ester substrates while completely inactive against the peptide[37]. Cobalt carboxypeptidase B shows 200% of the activity of the native enzyme against hippuryl-L-arginine and also hydrolyzes the ester[37].

The failure of cadmium carboxypeptidase A to catalyze the hydrolysis of peptides and of the copper enzyme to catalyze the hydrolysis of either peptides or esters is not due to the failure of formation of an enzyme–substrate complex. Peptide substrates form complexes with the cadmium enzyme and prevent the exchange of cadmium[115] for zinc ions (Fig. 11). Similar results are obtained with the copper enzyme when either peptide or ester substrates are employed[123]. Moreover, D-isomers of these substrates[122] do not prevent metal ion exchange.

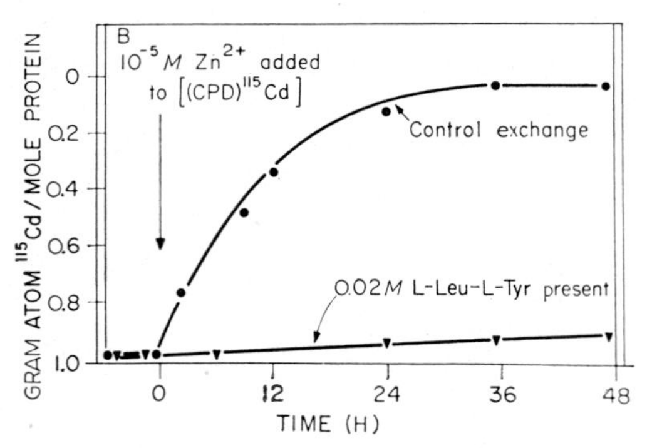

Fig. 11. The effect of L-Leu–L-Tyr on the exchange of $^{115}Cd^{2+}$ at the active site for Zn^{2+} ions. $1 \cdot 10^{-5}$ *M* [(CPD)^{115}Cd] was exposed to $1 \cdot 10^{-5}$ *M* stable Zn^{2+} ions at 0 time, and the enzyme-bound $^{115}Cd^{2+}$ (●) followed as a function of time. $1 \cdot 10^{-5}$ *M* [(CPD)^{115}Cd] was exposed to $2 \cdot 10^{-2}$ *M* L-Leu–L-Tyr for 2 h, $1 \cdot 10^{-5}$ *M* stable Zn^{2+} ions were added, and the enzyme-bound $^{115}Cd^{2+}$ (▼) followed as a function of time. Taken from Coleman and Vallee[122].

Thus, in certain cases the metal ion is an absolute requirement for catalytic activity and exerts an influence on the substrate specificity of the enzyme as well; apparently, this is accomplished through an effect on the catalytic step, not on substrate binding.

Isotopic binding and exchanges studies have provided further insight into the function of the metal ion in carboxypeptidase. Dipeptide substrates for this enzyme when added to the apoenzyme prior to the addition of zinc ions prevent the restoration of activity (Fig. 12). Examination of this phenom-

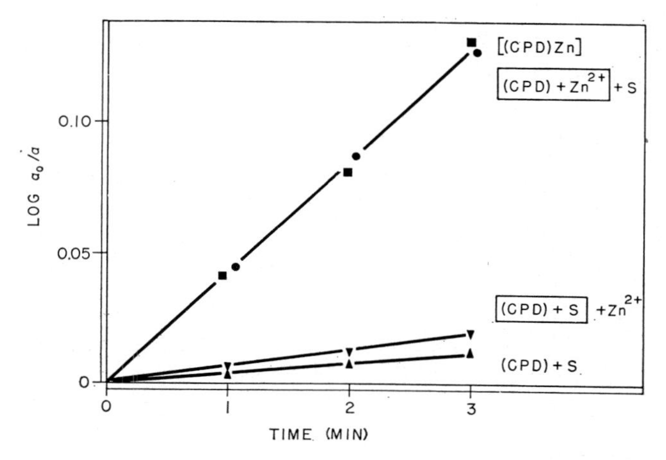

Fig. 12. Prevention of restoration of activity to apocarboxypeptidase, (CPD), by variation in the sequence of addition of Zn^{2+} ions and of the substrate, carbobenzoxyglycyl-L-phenylalanine, S. First-order progression curves; native zinc carboxypeptidase (■); (CPD) + S (▲) is the control; (CPD) was first incubated with 1 gram atom of Zn^{2+} ions for 1 min and substrate, S, was then added to start the reaction (●); (CPD) was first incubated with substrate, S, for 1 min and 1 gram atom of Zn^{2+} ions was then added to start the reaction (▼). Enzyme, $1 \cdot 10^{-6}$ *M*, peptidase assay conditions as described[30]. Preincubation of (CPD) with the substrate carbobenzoxyglycyl-L-phenylalanine, S, prevents restoration of activity with Zn^{2+} ions. Taken from Felber *et al.*[173].

enon by a gel-filtration method readily demonstrates that the peptide–substrate prevents the binding of $^{65}Zn^{2+}$ to the apoenzyme (Fig. 13). In the absence of substrate, $^{65}Zn^{2+}$ binds firmly to the protein and does not dissociate on passage over the Sephadex column (Fig. 13). Thus, dipeptide substrates for this enzyme form stable apoenzyme–substrate complexes which occlude the metal-binding site. The gel-filtration method can be used to measure the equilibrium constants, K_s, for these apocarboxypeptidase–substrate complexes. Measurements for several dipeptide substrates show the K_s values to agree closely in magnitude with K_m determined by the usual kinetic means[122]. Hence, dipeptide–substrate binding does not require

References p. 231

the metal ion and the major portion of the binding affinity appears to be accounted for by interaction with groups on the protein.

In marked contrast, the ester substrates of carboxypeptidase have no effect on ^{65}Zn binding and restoration of activity to apocarboxypeptidase (Fig. 13). Since the only difference in the peptide and ester substrates is the peptide-NH—, this group must be required for binding the substrate to the apoenzyme[123]. By this means it has been determined that three groups of a peptide substrate, indicated in brackets, are minimally required to form a

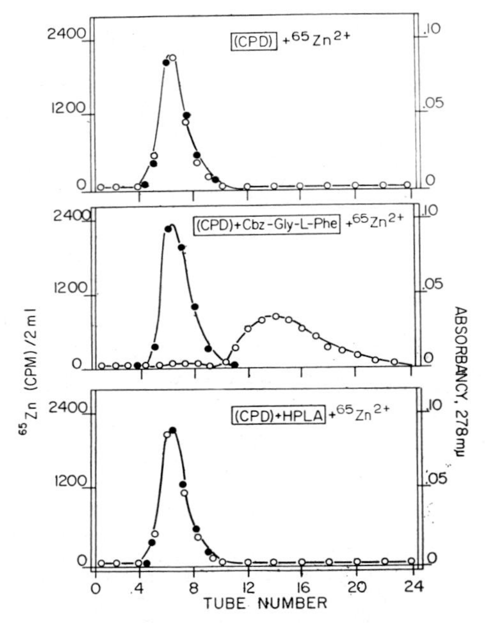

Fig. 13. The effect on $^{65}Zn^{2+}$ binding to apocarboxypeptidase produced by peptide substrate, carbobenzoxyglycyl-L-phenylalanine and ester substrate, hippuryl-β-phenyllactate. 1-ml samples of $5 \cdot 10^{-6}$ M apocarboxypeptidase plus $5 \cdot 10^{-6}$ M $^{65}Zn^{2+}$ (upper curve); $5 \cdot 10^{-6}$ M apocarboxypeptidase plus $5 \cdot 10^{-2}$ M Cbz–Gly–L-Phe plus $5 \cdot 10^{-6}$ M $^{65}Zn^{2+}$ (center curve); and $5 \cdot 10^{-6}$ M apocarboxypeptidase plus $4 \cdot 10^{-2}$ M hippuryl-*dl*-β-phenyllactate plus $5 \cdot 10^{-6}$ M $^{65}Zn^{2+}$ (lower curve) were passed over a 1×30 cm, G-25 Sephadex column at a flow rate of 1 ml/min. Absorbancy at 278 mμ (●) and $^{65}Zn^{2+}$, counts/min/2-ml fraction (○), were determined on successive 2-ml fractions. Ionic $^{65}Zn^{2+}$ passed over the column is retarded and emerges in fractions 12–24 with a maximum at fraction 14 while enzyme-bound $^{65}Zn^{2+}$ emerges with the protein. Data taken from Coleman and Vallee[122,123].

complex with apocarboxypeptidase: the —NH— function of the C-terminal residue, the —NH— function of the adjacent amino acid residue, and the R-group on the α-carbon of the C-terminal residue which may be either an aromatic or branched aliphatic side-chain.

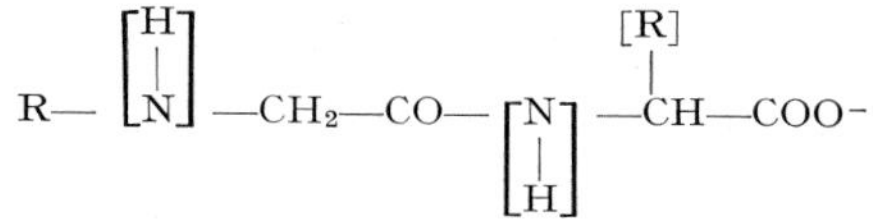

$$R\text{—}\begin{bmatrix}H\\|\\N\end{bmatrix}\text{—}CH_2\text{—}CO\text{—}\begin{bmatrix}N\\|\\H\end{bmatrix}\text{—}\overset{\overset{[R]}{|}}{CH}\text{—}COO^-$$

When either one of the two —NH— functions is lacking, the apoenzyme–substrate complex no longer forms, though a metalloenzyme–substrate complex still does form and hydrolysis still takes place. Removal of the R group destroys both the activity and formation of either complex.

Thus, for this particular metalloenzyme, the functions of the metal ion are being delineated. It participates both in the formation of certain enzyme–substrate complexes and also in the subsequent hydrolysis of these complexes. With dipeptide substrates, however, the metal does not seem required for binding, but it is for catalysis. Substrate binding in the metalloenzyme appears to be a concerted event involving both the metal ion and groups of the protein as well.

Evidence that the hydrolytic step is a concerted catalysis has come from recent studies on chemical modification of this protein[27,174,175]. If carboxypeptidase A is acetylated, iodinated, or photooxidized, peptidase activity is abolished while esterase activity against hippuryl-β-phenyllactate is increased between 300 and 600%. These changes are detailed in Table XIII and are illustrated for acetylation with acetylimidazole in Fig. 14. The metal content is unchanged and the enhanced esterase activity is still

TABLE XIII

SIMULTANEOUS ALTERATIONS IN ENZYMATIC ACTIVITY AND SPECIFICITY OF CARBOXYPEPTIDASE INDUCED BY METAL IONS, ANHYDRIDES, IODINATION AND IRRADIATION

From Vallee *et al.*[27]

Enzyme[a]	*Activity*	
	Esterase (%)	*Peptidase (%)*
[(CPD)Zn]	100	100
[(CPD)Hg]	116	0
[(CPD)Cd]	152	0
Iodinated [(CPD)Zn]	500	0
Acetyl [(CPD)Zn]	610	0
Succinyl [(CPD)Zn]	150	154
Acetyl-succinyl [(CPD)Zn]	780	0
Acetyl [(CPD)Zn] + NH_2OH	138	85
iso-Butyryl [(CPD)Zn]	134	83
n-Valeryl [(CPD)Zn]	162	80
n-Butyryl [(CPD)Zn]	191	64
Propionyl [(CPD)Zn]	342	49
Photooxidized [(CPD)Zn]	198	36

[a] Metallocarboxypeptidases were prepared as previously described[30]. Acetylations and iodinations of carboxypeptidase were carried out as previously described[27].

References p. 231

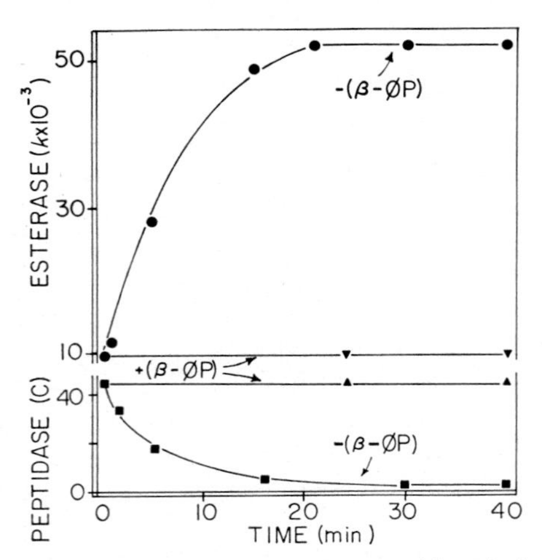

Fig. 14. Progression of changes in esterase (●) and peptidase (■) activities during acetylation of carboxypeptidase (4 mg/ml) with acetylimidazole (60-fold *M* excess) and in the presence (▼▲) and absence of β-phenylpropionate, as indicated. The reactions were performed in 0.02 *M* sodium veronal–2 *M* NaCl, pH 7.5, 23°. Activities were determined on hippuryl-*dl*-β-phenyllactate and carbobenzoxyglycyl-L-phenylalanine as previously described[30] immediately following dilution of an aliquot of the reaction mixture into the same buffer. Taken from Vallee[175].

dependent on the presence of metal ions. The changes induced by acetylation and iodination are completely prevented by the competitive inhibitor β-phenylpropionate (Fig. 14.). Apparently, these reagents modify a protein group (or groups) in the active center of this enzyme which participates together with the metal ion in catalysis. The unmodified form of this group (or groups) is absolutely essential for peptide catalysis, but actually inhibits ester catalysis. The enzymatic changes in Fig. 14 can be completely reversed by deacetylation with hydroxylamine. These data on chemical modification along with data on pH–rate profiles which differ markedly for esterase and peptidase activity[27] have led to the development of a tentative scheme for the mechanism of action of carboxypeptidase A (Fig. 15)[27]. Group B is postulated to be a nucleophile which initiates a nucleophilic attack on the carbonyl carbon of the substrate. The hydrolysis is assisted by the electron-withdrawing effect of the metal on the carbonyl oxygen and the peptide nitrogen. The coordination of the nitrogen also reduces the presence of those stabilizing canonical forms of the peptide bond in which the nitrogen is more negative, thus assisting destabilization. An additional acidic group of the protein, A, is postulated to donate a proton to the transition state. It is group B which may be modified by the chemical reactions mentioned above. It is also postulated that ester hydrolysis does not require nucleophilic

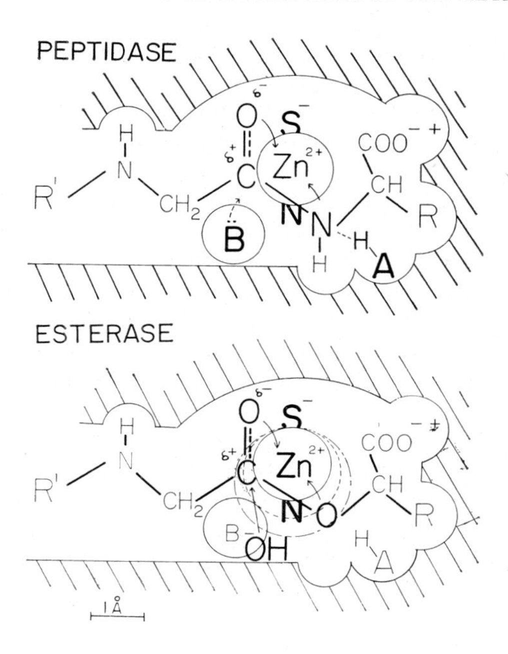

Fig. 15. Proposed mechanism of peptide and ester hydrolysis by carboxypeptidase A.

Mechanism of peptidase hydrolysis. The ionic radius[5] of Zn^{2+}, drawn to scale and indicated by the circle, is 0.74 Å. Alternative possibilities, such as have been suggested by Rabin[177] for prolidase, could include a water molecule between B and the carbonyl carbon atom, *i.e.*,

$$\begin{array}{c} B{:}\rightarrow \underset{|}{H}—\underset{|}{O}{:}\rightarrow \underset{|}{C}=O \\ \quad\quad H \quad\; N \end{array}$$

and A could represent the protein group toward which the NH-bond of the peptide linkage is directed, *i.e.*, —N—H···A—

Mechanism of ester hydrolysis. In addition to the ionic radius of zinc, 0.74 Å, the ionic radii[5] of Cd^{2+}, 0.97 Å, and Hg^{2+}, 1.10 Å, drawn to scale, are indicated. These radii are drawn-off-center to indicate their maximum latitude of coordination. Goldschmidt radii[6] of Cd^{2+} and Hg^{2+} (0.93 Å and 0.94 Å) also exceed that of Zn^{2+} (0.69 Å) by more than 0.2 Å, consistent with the postulate. Group B is drawn lightly and the hydroxide ion is added to indicate the lack of participation of B in the mechanism of hydrolysis by the modified enzymes, as described in the text. The other lightly drawn parts are identical with the peptidase figure. Taken from Vallee *et al.*[27].

attack and can be catalyzed by OH^- ions alone. Indeed, ester hydrolysis by this enzyme shows a linear dependence on pH while peptide hydrolysis shows a sharp maximum[27,174] at pH 7.5. Similar OH^- ion-dependent metal ion-catalyzed hydrolysis of amino acid esters has been observed in model systems[18]. Under comparable conditions, peptides are resistant[72]. The changes in specificity brought about by cadmium and mercury were thought

References p. 231

to result from their large ionic radii allowing them to interact with group B and prevent the nucleophilic catalysis.

Labelling the enzyme with [^{14}C]acetic anhydride in the presence and absence of β-phenylpropionate, followed by removal of the acetyl groups with hydroxylamine, has shown *two* groups to be protected from acetylation by β-phenylpropionate[176]. Based on the marked decrease in extinction coefficient and bathochromic shift produced on O-acetylation of tyrosine[176], difference spectra between the acetylated enzyme protected and unprotected by the competitive inhibitor show these groups to be *two* tyrosine residues of the protein. The acetylation and deacetylation, the appearance and disappearance of the difference spectra and the enzymatic changes of Fig. 14 all correlate[176]. The function of these residues in substrate binding, the ensuing hydrolytic step or both remains to be elucidated.

Rabin has postulated a similar concerted acid–base catalysis for the peptidase action of the manganese metal–enzyme complex, prolidase[177]. A basic group of the protein, B, is thought to initiate the attack of a water molecule on the carbonyl carbon, assisted by the metal ion chelated between the free amino groups of the substrate and the carbonyl oxygen. An acid group of the protein, A, is postulated to donate a proton in the transition state.

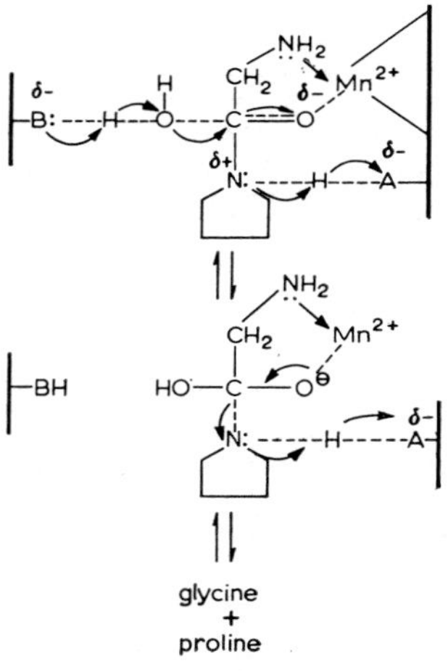

Catalysis by metalloenzymes is seen to involve both the metal ion and amino acid residues of the protein. Such concerted catalysis may explain why metalloenzymes are so much more efficient catalysts than are metal ions alone when operating on model compounds. Detailed studies of the function of the metal ion should soon be available on a number of metalloenzymes which are under scrutiny in several laboratories.

REFERENCES

[1] O. WARBURG, *Heavy Metal Prosthetic Groups and Enzyme Action*, Oxford University Press, London, 1949.
[2] B. L. VALLEE in P. D. BOYER, H. LARDY AND K. MYRBÄCK (Eds.), *The Enzymes*, Vol. 3, Academic Press, New York, 1959, p. 225.
[3] F. R. N. GURD AND P. E. WILCOX, *Advan. Protein Chem.*, 11 (1956) 312.
[4] B. G. MALMSTROM AND A. ROSENBERG, *Advan. Enzymol.*, 21 (1959) 131.
[5] L. PAULING, *Nature of the Chemical Bond*, Cornell University Press, Ithaca, N.Y., 1960.
[6] F. A. COTTON AND G. WILKINSON, *Advanced Inorganic Chemistry*, Interscience, New York, 1962.
[7] F. J. C. ROSSOTTI in J. LEWIS AND R. G. WILKINS (Eds.), *Modern Coordination Chemistry*, Interscience, New York, 1960, p. 1.
[8] J. BJERRUM, *Metal Amine Formation in Aqueous Solution*, P. Haase and Son, Copenhagen, 1941.
[9] A. E. MARTELL AND M. CALVIN, *Chemistry of the Metal Chelate Compounds*, Prentice-Hall, Englewood Cliffs, N.J., 1952.
[10] R. J. P. WILLIAMS in P. D. BOYER, H. LARDY AND K. MYRBÄCK (Eds.), *The Enzymes*, Academic Press, New York, 1959, p. 391.
[11] J. BJERRUM, G. SCHWARZENBACH AND L. G. SILLÉN, *Stability Constants of Metal-Ion Complexes, Chem. Soc. (London), Spec. Publ.*, No. 6 (1957).
[12] H. M. N. H. IRVING AND R. J. P. WILLIAMS, *J. Chem. Soc.*, 70 (1953) 3192.
[13] M. CALVIN AND N. C. MELCHIOR, *J. Am. Chem. Soc.*, 70 (1948) 3270.
[14] H. M. N. H. IRVING, *International Conference on Coordination Chemistry, Chem. Soc. (London), Spec. Publ.*, No. 13 (1959) 13.
[15] L. E. ORGEL, *An Introduction to Transition-Metal Chemistry*, Wiley, New York, 1960.
[16] T. M. DUNN in J. LEWIS AND R. G. WILKINS (Eds.), *Modern Coordination Chemistry*, Interscience, New York, 1960, p. 229.
[17] C. DJERASSI, *Optical Rotatory Dispersion*, McGraw-Hill, New York, 1960.
[18] H. KROLL, *J. Am. Chem. Soc.*, 74 (1952) 2036.
[19] W. W. BUTCHER AND F. H. WESTHEIMER, *J. Am. Chem. Soc.*, 77 (1955) 2420.
[20] J. M. LOWENSTEIN, *Biochem. J.*, 70 (1958) 222.
[21] L. MERIWETHER AND F. H. WESTHEIMER, *J. Am. Chem. Soc.*, 78 (1956) 5119.
[22] R. STEINBERGER AND F. H. WESTHEIMER, *J. Am. Chem. Soc.*, 73 (1951) 429.
[22a] J. F. SPECK, *J. Biol. Chem.*, 178 (1948) 315.
[22b] A. KORNBERG, S. OCHOA AND A. H. MEHLER, *J. Biol. Chem.*, 174 (1948) 159.
[23] J. E. PRUE, *J. Chem. Soc.*, (1952) 2331; J. J. HOPPE AND J. E. PRUE, *J. Chem. Soc.*, (1957) 1775.
[24] D. E. METZLER, M. IKAWA AND E. E. SNELL, *J. Am. Chem. Soc.*, 76 (1954) 648.
[25] E. E. SNELL, *Federation Proc.*, 20, Suppl. 10 (1961) 81.
[25a] P. FASELLA, G. G. HAMMES AND B. L. VALLEE, *Biochim. Biophys. Acta*, 65 (1962) 142.
[25b] P. FASELLA AND G. G. HAMMES, *Biochemistry*, 3 (1964) 530.
[26] M. L. BENDER AND B. W. TURNQUEST, *J. Am. Chem. Soc.*, 79 (1957) 1656.
[27] B. L. VALLEE, J. F. RIORDAN AND J. E. COLEMAN, *Proc. Natl. Acad. Sci. (U.S.)*, 49 (1963) 109.
[28] B. L. VALLEE, *Advan. Protein Chem.*, 10 (1955) 317.
[29] B. G. MALMSTROM in P. D. BOYER, H. LARDY AND K. MYRBÄCK (Eds.), *The Enzymes*, Vol. 5, Academic Press, New York, 1959, p. 471.
[30] J. E. COLEMAN AND B. L. VALLEE, *J. Biol. Chem.*, 236 (1961) 2244.
[31] H. R. MAHLER in C. A. LAMB, O. G. BENTLEY AND J. M. BEATTIE (Eds.), *Trace Elements*, Academic Press, New York, 1958, p. 311.
[32] B. L. VALLEE, *Federation Proc.*, 20, Suppl. 10 (1961) 71.
[33] R. E. THIERS in D. GLICK (Ed.), *Methods of Biochemical Analysis*, Vol. 5, Interscience, New York, 1957.
[34] B. L. VALLEE AND H. NEURATH, *J. Am. Chem. Soc.*, 76 (1954) 5006.

35 H. Neurath in P. D. Boyer, H. Lardy and K. Myrbäck (Eds.), *The Enzymes*, Vol. 4, Academic Press, New York, 1960, p. 11.
36 B. L. Vallee, J. A. Rupley, T. L. Coombs and H. Neurath, *J. Biol. Chem.*, 235 (1960) 64.
37 J. E. Folk, E. C. Wolff and E. W. Schirmer, *J. Biol. Chem.*, 237 (1962) 3100.
38 E. Wintersberger, D. J. Cox and H. Neurath, *Biochemistry*, 1 (1962) 1069, 1078.
39 D. J. Plocke, C. Levinthal and B. L. Vallee, *Biochemistry*, 1 (1962) 373.
40 D. J. Plocke and B. L. Vallee, *Biochemistry*, 1 (1962) 1039.
41 J. C. Mathies, *J. Biol. Chem.*, 233 (1958) 1121.
41a S. Trubowitz, D. Feldman, S. W. Morgenstern and V. M. Hunt, *Biochem. J.*, 80 (1961) 369.
42 S. J. Adelstein and B. L. Vallee, *J. Biol. Chem.*, 233 (1958) 589.
43 H. R. Mahler and D. G. Elowe, *J. Biol. Chem.*, 210 (1954) 165.
44 D. J. D. Nicholas and A. Nason, *J. Biol. Chem.*, 207 (1954) 352; 211 (1954) 183.
45 C. W. Chung and V. A. Najjar, *J. Biol. Chem.*, 218 (1956) 617, 627.
46 B. L. Vallee and F. L. Hoch, *J. Biol. Chem.*, 225 (1957) 185.
47 B. L. Vallee and F. L. Hoch, *Proc. Natl. Acad. Sci. (U.S.)*, 41 (1955) 327.
48 J. P. von Wartburg and B. L. Vallee, *Abstracts 145th Meeting Am. Chem. Soc.*, New York, Sept. 1963, p. 100-C.
49 J. L. Bethune, J. P. von Wartburg and B. L. Vallee, *Abstracts 145th Meeting Am. Chem. Soc.*, New York, Sept. 1963, p. 100-C.
50 B. L. Vallee and W. E. C. Wacker, *J. Am. Chem. Soc.*, 78 (1956) 1771.
51 J. H. Harrison, *Federation Proc.*, 22 (1963) 493.
52 B. L. Vallee, F. L. Hoch, S. J. Adelstein and W. E. C. Wacker, *J. Am. Chem. Soc.*, 78 (1956) 5876.
53 T. Keleti, S. Gyorgyi, M. Telegdi and H. Zaluska, *Acta Physiol. Acad. Sci. Hung.*, 22 (1962) 11.
54 P. G. Avis, F. Bergel and R. C. Bray, *J. Chem. Soc.*, (1955) 1100; (1956) 1219.
55 I. Fridovich and P. Handler, *J. Biol. Chem.*, 231 (1958) 899, 1581.
56 E. C. De Renzo, *Advan. Enzymol.*, 17 (1956) 293.
57 C. Remy, D. A. Richert, R. H. Doisy, I. C. Wells and W. W. Westerfeld, *J. Biol. Chem.*, 217 (1955) 293.
58 K. V. Rajagopalan, I. Fridovich and P. Handler, *J. Biol. Chem.*, 237 (1962) 922.
59 C. Gregolin and T. P. Singer, *Biochim. Biophys. Acta*, 67 (1963) 201.
60 T. P. Singer, E. B. Kearney and V. Massey, *Advan. Enzymol.*, 18 (1957) 65.
61 T. P. Singer, V. Massey and E. B. Kearney, *Arch. Biochem. Biophys.*, 69 (1957) 405.
61a H. C. Friedmann and B. Vennesland, *J. Biol. Chem.*, 235 (1960) 1526.
62 S. Bouchilloux, P. McMahill and H. S. Mason, *J. Biol. Chem.*, 238 (1963) 1699.
62a M. Fling, N. H. Horowitz and S. F. Heinemann, *J. Biol. Chem.*, 238 (1963) 2045.
63 F. Kubowitz, *Biochem. Z.*, 292 (1937) 221; 296 (1938) 443; 299 (1938) 32.
64 D. Kertész and R. Zito, *Nature*, 179 (1957) 1017.
65 A. B. Lerner, T. B. Fitzpatrick, E. Calkins and W. H. Summerson, *J. Biol. Chem.*, 178 (1949) 185; 187 (1950) 793; 191 (1951) 799.
66 D. Kertész, *J. Natl. Cancer Inst.*, 14 (1954) 1081, 1093.
67 P. L. Lovett-Janison and J. M. Nelson, *J. Am. Chem. Soc.*, 62 (1940) 1409.
68 F. J. Dunn and C. R. Dawson, *J. Biol. Chem.*, 189 (1951) 485.
69 E. H. Stotz, *J. Biol. Chem.*, 133 (1940) C.
70 D. Keilin and T. Mann, *Nature*, 145 (1940) 304.
71 C. G. Holmberg and C. B. Laurell, *Acta Chem. Scand.*, 2 (1948) 550.
72 W. D. McElroy and B. Glass (Eds.), *A Symposium on Copper Metabolism*, Johns Hopkins, Baltimore, 1950.
73 H. Beinert, D. E. Griffiths, D. C. Wharton and R. H. Sands, *J. Biol. Chem.*, 237 (1962) 2337.
73a M. Morrison, S. Horie and H. S. Mason, *J. Biol. Chem.*, 238 (1963) 2220.
74 H. Yamada and K. T. Yasunobu, *J. Biol. Chem.*, 237 (1962) 1511, 3077.

[75] V. Z. Gorkin, *Problems of Medical Chemistry (Moscow)*, 7 (1961) 632.
[75a] J. M. Hill and P. J. G. Mann, *Biochem. J.*, 91 (1964) 171.
[75b] D. Amaral, L. Bernstein, D. Morse and B. L. Horecker, *J. Biol. Chem.*, 238 (1963) 2281.
[76] D. Keilin and T. Mann, *Biochem. J.*, 34 (1941) 1163.
[77] S. Lindskog and B. G. Malmstrom, *J. Biol. Chem.*, 237 (1962) 1129.
[77a] E. E. Rickli, S. A. S. Ghazanfar, B. H. Gibbons and J. T. Edsall, *J. Biol. Chem.*, 239 (1964) 1065.
[77b] S. Lindskog, *J. Biol. Chem.*, 238 (1963) 945.
[77c] P. O. Nyman and S. Lindskog, *Biochim. Biophys. Acta*, 85 (1964) 141.
[78] R. P. Davis in P. D. Boyer, H. Lardy and K. Myrbäck (Eds.), *The Enzymes*, Vol. 5, Academic Press, New York, 1961, p. 545.
[79] E. E. Rickli and J. T. Edsall, *J. Biol. Chem.*, 237 (1961) PC 258.
[80] W. J. Rutter in P. D. Boyer, H. Lardy and K. Myrbäck (Eds.), *The Enzymes*, Vol. 5, Academic Press, 1961, p. 341.
[80a] K. Tagawa and D. I. Arnon, *Nature*, 195 (1962) 537.
[80b] B. B. Buchanan, W. Lovenberg and J. C. Rabinowitz, *Proc. Natl. Acad. Sci. (U.S.)*, 49 (1963) 345.
[81] E. L. Smith, *Advan. Enzymol.*, 12 (1951) 191.
[82] E. L. Smith, *J. Biol. Chem.*, 173 (1948) 9, 533, 571.
[83] A. Rosenberg, *Arch. Biochem. Biophys.*, 88 (1960) 83.
[84] A. Rosenberg, *Biochim. Biophys. Acta*, 45 (1960) 297.
[85] N. R. Jones, *Biochem. J.*, 60 (1955) 81.
[86] H. J. Vogel and D. M. Bonner, *J. Biol. Chem.*, 218 (1956) 97.
[87] E. L. Smith and R. L. Hill in P. D. Boyer, H. Lardy and K. Myrbäck (Eds.), *The Enzymes*, Vol. 4, Academic Press, New York, 1960, p. 37.
[88] D. M. Greenberg in P. D. Boyer, H. Lardy and K. Myrbäck (Eds.), *The Enzymes*, Vol. 4, Academic Press, New York, 1960, p. 257.
[89] J. Roche, G. Lacombe and H. Girard, *Biochim. Biophys. Acta*, 6 (1950) 210.
[90] E. B. Kearney and T. P. Singer, *Biochim. Biophys. Acta*, 11 (1953) 270, 276.
[91] O. Hayaishi, H. Shimazono, M. Katagiri and Y. Saito, *J. Am. Chem. Soc.*, 78 (1956) 5126.
[92] L. A. Mounter and A. J. Chanutin, *J. Biol. Chem.*, 204 (1953) 837.
[93] L. A. Mounter in P. D. Boyer, H. Hardy and K. Myrbäck (Eds.), *The Enzymes*, Vol. 4, Academic Press, New York, 1960, p. 541.
[94] D. E. Green, D. Herbert and V. Subrahmanyan, *J. Biol. Chem.*, 138 (1941) 327.
[95] T. P. Singer and J. Pensky, *J. Biol. Chem.*, 196 (1952) 375.
[96] M. F. Utter in P. D. Boyer, H. Lardy and K. Myrbäck (Eds.), *The Enzymes*, Vol. 5, Academic Press, New York, 1961, p. 319.
[97] D. Herbert, *Symp. Soc. Exptl. Biol.*, 5 (1951) 52.
[98] E. Juni, *J. Biol. Chem.*, 195 (1952) 715.
[99] D. Watt and L. O. Krampitz, *Federation Proc.*, 6 (1947) 301.
[100] W. G. McCullough, J. T. Piligian and J. D. Idus, *J. Am. Chem. Soc.*, 79 (1957) 628.
[101] D. A. Walker, *Biochem. J.*, 67 (1958) 557.
[102] A. Weissbach, B. L. Horecker and J. Hurwitz, *J. Biol. Chem.*, 218 (1956) 795.
[103] R. Nordlie and H. Lardy in P. D. Boyer, H. Lardy and K. Myrbäck (Eds.), *The Enzymes*, Vol. 6, Academic Press, New York, 1962, p. 3.
[104] I. G. Leder, *J. Biol. Chem.*, 225 (1957) 125.
[105] M. A. Cynkin and G. Ashwell, *J. Biol. Chem.*, 235 (1960) 1576.
[106] J. Hurwitz, A. Weissbach, B. L. Horecker and P. Z. Smyrniotis, *J. Biol. Chem.*, 218 (1956) 769.
[107] K. Levintow and G. D. Novelli, *J. Biol. Chem.*, 207 (1954) 761.
[108] J. Hurwitz, *J. Biol. Chem.*, 205 (1953) 935.
[109] T. T. Tchen, *J. Biol. Chem.*, 233 (1958) 1100.
[110] K. Block, S. Chaykin, A. H. Phillips and A. deWaard, *J. Biol. Chem.*, 234 (1960) 2595.

111 P. ELODI AND E. T. SZÖRÉNYI, *Acta Physiol. Acad. Sci. Hung.*, 9 (1956) 367.
112 B. K. BACHHAWAT AND M. J. COON, *J. Am. Chem. Soc.*, 79 (1957) 1505.
113 S. R. DICKMANN in P. D. BOYER, H. LARDY AND K. MYRBÄCK (Eds.), *The Enzymes*, Vol. 5, Academic Press, New York, 1961, p. 495.
114 F. WOLD AND C. E. BALLOU, *J. Biol. Chem.*, 227 (1957) 313.
115 B. N. AMES, *J. Biol. Chem.*, 228 (1957) 131.
116 J. MAGEE AND M. DOUDOROFF, *J. Biol. Chem.*, 210 (1954) 617.
117 J. W. MYERS AND E. A. ADELBERG, *Proc. Natl. Acad. Sci. (U.S.)*, 40 (1954) 493.
118 M. DIXON AND E. C. WEBB, *Enzymes*, Academic Press, New York, 1958.
119 T. P. SINGER AND V. MASSEY, *Record Chem. Progr. (Kresge-Hooker Sci. Libr.)*, 18 (1957) 201.
120 R. J. P. WILLIAMS in S. KIRSCHNER (Ed.), *Advances in Chemistry of the Coordination Compounds*, Macmillan, New York, 1961, p. 65.
121 H. DRESSLER AND C. R. DAWSON, *Biochem. Biophys. Acta*, 45 (1960) 508.
122 J. E. COLEMAN AND B. L. VALLEE, *J. Biol. Chem.*, 237 (1962) 3430.
123 J. E. COLEMAN AND B. L. VALLEE, *Biochemistry*, 1 (1962) 1083.
124 J. H. R. KÄGI AND B. L. VALLEE, *J. Biol. Chem.*, 235 (1960) 3188.
125 J. A. RUPLEY AND H. NEURATH, *J. Biol. Chem.*, 235 (1960) 609.
126 A. TISSIÈRES, *Nature*, 162 (1948) 340.
127 G. T. MEIKLEJOHN AND C. P. STEWART, *Biochem. J.*, 35 (1941) 755.
128 W. E. BLUMBERG, J. EISINGER, P. AISEN, A. G. MORELL AND I. H. SCHEINBERG, *J. Biol. Chem.*, 238 (1963) 1675.
129 S. LINDSKOG, *J. Biol. Chem.*, 238 (1963) 945.
130 W. STRICKS AND I. M. KOLTHOFF, *J. Am. Chem. Soc.*, 73 (1951) 1723.
131 J. E. COLEMAN AND B. L. VALLEE, *J. Biol. Chem.*, 235 (1960) 390.
132 L. HELLERMAN AND C. C. STOCK, *J. Biol. Chem.*, 125 (1938) 771.
133 C. C. STOCK, M. E. PERKINS AND L. HELLERMAN, *J. Biol. Chem.*, 125 (1938) 753.
134 B. L. VALLEE, T. L. COOMBS AND F. L. HOCH, *J. Biol. Chem.*, 235 (1960) PC 45.
135 C. K. JØRGENSON, *Acta Chem. Scand.*, 8 (1954) 1505.
136 J. K. INMAN, *Doctorate Thesis* in Biochemistry, Division of Medical Sciences, Harvard University, 1956.
137 D. D. ULMER AND B. L. VALLEE, *Biochem. Biophys. Res. Commun.*, 8 (1962) 331.
138 C. R. DAWSON, *Ann. N.Y. Acad. Sci.*, 88 (1960) 353.
139 A. SAN PIETRO in W. D. MCELROY AND B. GLASS (Eds.), *Light and Life*, Johns Hopkins, Baltimore, 1961, p. 631.
139a E. APELLA AND A. SAN PIETRO, *Biochem. Biophys. Res. Commun.*, 6 (1961) 349.
139b K. T. FRY AND A. SAN PIETRO, *Biochem. Biophys. Res. Commun.*, 9 (1962) 218.
140 R. C. WARNER AND I. WEBER, *J. Am. Chem. Soc.*, 75 (1953) 5094.
141 B. A. KOECHLIN, *J. Am. Chem. Soc.*, 74 (1952) 2649.
142 A. L. SCHADE, R. W. REINHART AND H. LEVY, *Arch. Biochem.*, 20 (1949) 170.
143 S. K. KON in R. T. WILLIAMS (Ed.), *The Biochemistry of Vitamin B_{12}*, *Biochem. Soc. Symp. (Cambridge, Engl.)*, No. 13 (1955) 17.
144 D. KEILIN AND T. MANN, *Nature*, 143 (1939) 23.
145 T. L. COOMBS AND B. L. VALLEE, unpublished data.
146 E. V. JENSEN, *Sulfur in Proteins*, Academic Press, New York, 1959, p. 75.
147 J. H. R. KÄGI AND B. L. VALLEE, *J. Biol. Chem.*, 236 (1961) 2435.
148 R. DRUYAN AND B. L. VALLEE, unpublished data.
149 R. J. P. WILLIAMS, *Nature*, 188 (1960) 322.
150 G. W. MILLER, B. T. GILLIS AND N. C. LI, *J. Biol. Chem.*, 235 (1960) 2840.
151 T. NAKAMURA, *Biochim. Biophys. Acta*, 30 (1958) 44.
152 D. D. ULMER AND B. L. VALLEE, *Biochemistry*, 2 (1963) 1335.
153 A. J. OSBAHR AND G. L. EICHHORN, *J. Biol. Chem.*, 237 (1962) 1820.
154 D. D. ULMER, T. K. LI AND B. L. VALLEE, *Proc. Natl. Acad. Sci. (U.S.)*, 47 (1961) 1155.
155 D. D. ULMER, J. H. R. KÄGI AND B. L. VALLEE, *Biochem. Biophys. Res. Commun.*, 8 (1962) 327.
156 S. BEYCHOK AND E. R. BLOUT, *J. Mol. Biol.*, 3 (1961) 769.

[157] D. D. Ulmer and B. L. Vallee, unpublished data.
[158] D. D. Ulmer and B. L. Vallee, *J. Biol. Chem.*, 236 (1961) 730.
[159] T. K. Li, D. D. Ulmer and B. L. Vallee, *Biochemistry*, 2 (1963) 482.
[160] T. K. Li, D. D. Ulmer and B. L. Vallee, *Biochemistry*, 1 (1962) 114.
[161] T. K. Li and B. L. Vallee, *J. Biol. Chem.*, 239 (1964) 792.
[162] B. G. Malmstrom and T. Vänngard, *J. Mol. Biol.*, 2 (1960) 118.
[163] R. C. Bray, B. G. Malmstrom and T. Vänngard, *Biochem. J.*, 73 (1959) 193.
[164] H. S. Mason, *Biochem. Biophys. Res. Commun.*, 10 (1963) 11.
[165] H. Beinert in P. D. Boyer, H. Lardy and K. Myrbäck (Eds.), *The Enzymes*, Academic Press, New York, 1960, p. 339.
[166] P. Handler, K. V. Rajagopalan and V. Aleman, *Federation Proc.*, 23 (1964) 30.
[167] M. F. Perutz, M. G. Rossmann, A. F. Cullis, H. Muirhead, G. Will and A. C. T. North, *Nature*, 185 (1960) 416.
[168] J. C. Kendrew, R. E. Dickerson, B. E. Standberg, R. G. Hart, D. R. Davies, D. C. Phillips and V. C. Shore, *Nature*, 185 (1960) 422.
[169] T. L. Coombs and Y. Omote, *Federation Proc.*, 21 (1962) 234.
[170] K. A. Walsh, K. S. V. S. Kumar, J. P. Bargetzi and H. Neurath, *Proc. Natl. Acad. Sci. (U.S.)*, 48 (1962) 1443.
[170a] K. S. V. S. Kumar, K. A. Walsh, J.-P. Bargetzi and H. Neurath in G. N. Ramachandran (Ed.), *Aspects of Protein Structure*, Academic Press, New York, 1963, p. 333.
[171] J. E. Coleman, *Federation Proc.*, 22 (1963) 594.
[172] T. L. Coombs, J. P. Felber and B. L. Vallee, *Biochemistry*, 1 (1962) 899.
[173] J. P. Felber, T. L. Coombs and B. L. Vallee, *Biochemistry*, 1 (1962) 231.
[174] J. F. Riordan and B. L. Vallee, *Biochemistry*, 2 (1963) 1460.
[175] B. L. Vallee, *Federation Proc.*, 23 (1964) 8.
[176] R. T. Simpson, J. F. Riordan and B. L. Vallee, *Biochemistry*, 2 (1963) 616.
[177] B. R. Rabin, *Biochem. Soc. Symp. (Cambridge, Engl.)*, 15 (1958) 21.

Chapter VII

Newer Aspects of Enzymatic Stereospecificity

H. HIRSCHMANN

Department of Medicine, Western Reserve University,
Cleveland, Ohio (U.S.A.)

1. Introduction

The stereospecificity of enzyme action can manifest itself in two distinct ways: (*1*) Enzymes can distinguish between stereoisomers. The most impressive demonstration of this faculty is their ability to differentiate between the two antipodal forms of an optically active compound as shown by their catalyzing exclusively the reaction of one of these enantiomeric forms. (*2*) Enzymes can distinguish, within a given molecule, bonds that differ merely in their steric relationships to the remainder of the molecule. The former of these manifestations of enzyme stereospecificity was discovered by Pasteur and, therefore, has been explored from the very beginnings of stereochemistry. This aspect of the stereospecificity of enzyme action[1] has been reviewed repeatedly and will be touched upon here only when it is related to phenomena of the second kind. Although it is clear in retrospect that the latter, too, have been known to the biochemist for a long time, the problem did not come into clear focus until 1948, when Ogston[2] challenged views which regarded a symmetrical intermediate incompatible with the asymmetric distribution of isotope in a final metabolite.

In 1941 two groups of investigators[3] found, contrary to expectation[4], that the isotopically labeled carbon dioxide which is incorporated into oxaloacetic acid (I) led to the labeling of only that carboxyl group of α-oxoglutaric acid (IV) which is adjacent to the keto group. It was concluded and generally accepted that citric acid (II) could not be an intermediate in such a process because citric acid is a symmetrical molecule in which the two carboxyl groups that are retained in α-oxoglutaric acid had occupied corresponding positions. The fallacy of this argument which had been applied also to other metabolic schemes was pointed out by Ogston[2] who showed that attachment of a symmetrical molecule like citric acid to an enzyme at three points could lead to the differentiation of like groups as is shown in Fig. 1.

$$\begin{array}{ccccccccc}
 & & & & \mathrm{COOH} & & \mathrm{COOH} & & \mathrm{COOH} \\
 & & \mathrm{COOH} & & \mathrm{H{-}C{-}H} & & \mathrm{CH_2} & & \mathrm{CH_2} \\
{}^*\mathrm{CO_2} & \longrightarrow & \mathrm{C{=}O} & \longrightarrow & \mathrm{HO{-}C{-}COOH} & \longrightarrow & \mathrm{H{-}C{-}COOH} & \longrightarrow & \mathrm{CH_2} \\
 & & \mathrm{CH_2} & & \mathrm{H{-}C{-}H} & & \mathrm{HO{-}C{-}H} & & \mathrm{C{=}O} \\
 & & {}^*\mathrm{COOH} & & {}^*\mathrm{COOH} & & {}^*\mathrm{COOH} & & {}^*\mathrm{COOH} \\
 & & \mathrm{I} & & \mathrm{II} & & \mathrm{III} & & \mathrm{IV}
\end{array}$$

Let the symmetrical substrate be represented by Caabd and the enzyme be so constituted that two of its three sites (A′ and A″) can combine only with the (a) groups and the third site (B) only with the (b) group. If reaction can occur only at the site (A′) and only if all three groups are engaged simultaneously, then differentiation between the (a) groups will take place because any attempt to move the unreactive (a) group from the site (A″) which it occupies in Fig. 1 to the active site (A′) while still retaining (b) at (B) will necessarily prevent the other (a) group originally at (A′) from engaging at the site (A″). Hence, only one active complex is possible which invariably places the same (a) group at the active site (A′). Discrimination between the two (a) groups would also result if the active complex required engagement of the groups (a, b, d) with the three enzymatic sites (A, B, D,

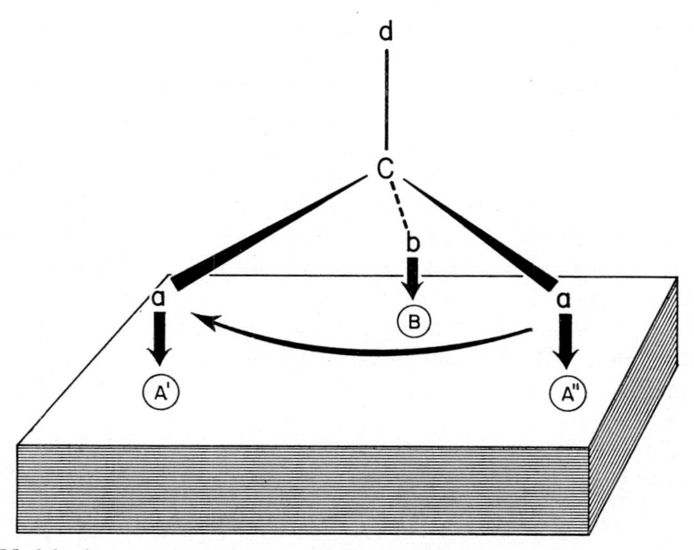

Fig. 1. Model of an enzyme that would cause differentiation of two (a) groups in Caabd by interaction at three sites (A′, A″, B). Only the site (A′) is assumed to be catalytically active.

respectively) because it would be impossible to bring the free (a) group to the active site (A) while retaining (b) at (B) and (d) at (D).

Although the implications of this enzymatic model seem quite clear, Ogston's prediction of discrimination between seemingly identical groups in symmetrical molecules has proved sufficiently baffling that a number of comments have been made which are clearly contrary to fact and which should, therefore, be examined more closely. For example, it has been stated that citric acid could be an intermediate of the asymmetrically labeled α-oxoglutaric acid if one is justified in assuming that citric acid undergoes further reaction on the same enzyme surface on which it is formed without ever leaving this enzyme surface. This interpretation which explains discrimination by postulating that the symmetric intermediate never existed in free form misses the cardinal point of the Ogston hypothesis which implies that there is only one way in which the active complex can form and that dissociation of substrate and enzyme, therefore, cannot alter the steric result which is unambiguously determined by the structure of the enzyme. Moreover, the "continuous association" hypothesis does not provide a valid explanation for the asymmetric labeling of α-oxoglutaric acid as was first shown by Potter and Heidelberger[5] who isolated radioactive citric acid from a liver homogenate containing labeled bicarbonate and converted the isolated compound to asymmetrically labeled α-oxoglutaric acid by incubation with a second liver homogenate. One must conclude from such experiments[5,6] that enzymes can differentiate between the two primary carboxyl groups of *free* citric acid. Analogous results have been obtained with other substrates.

2. The role of the isotope

In the experiments mentioned and in numerous others, the asymmetry of the process was studied with isotopically labeled substrates. It is pertinent to inquire, therefore, what role, if any, the presence of atoms of different mass plays in the process of differentiation. It is known, of course, that the rate of bond formation or of bond cleavage varies considerably if the reaction involves different isotopes of hydrogen and to a much lesser extent in the case of the heavier elements. The mass difference should be the sole

```
    COOH               CH2OH              CH2OH               COOH
     |                  |                  |                   |
H—C—OH    ——>    H—C—OH         HO—C—H    <——    HO—C—H
     |                  |                  |                   |
   *CH2OH            *CH2OH             *CH2OH              *CH2OH
     V                  VI                 VII                 VIII
```

factor determining isotope distribution in the metabolite, if the enzyme possesses no stereospecificity. However, if the mechanism envisaged by Ogston should operate, mass difference would have no bearing on isotope distribution*. When the selective reactivity of the (a) groups in Caabd was derived from Fig. 1, no reference to isotopic labeling had to be made. Therefore, if there is a mass effect, a preparation which has the heavier atom at (A′) (Fig. 1) might react more slowly than its isotopic enantiomer, but this would not affect the isotope distribution in the products, since with the first preparation the reaction could take place only with the (a) group containing the heavier isotope, whereas if the second preparation were used, the reacting (a) group would contain only the lighter isotope. A critical test for this prediction would require the use of a pure enzyme to avoid possible complications from alternative pathways, alternative precursors, etc., but even with crude enzyme systems results have been obtained[6,7] which, within the limits of their consistency, bear out this consequence of the Ogston hypothesis. This may be illustrated by the following example.

D- and L-glyceric acid[7], (V, VIII) each labeled with ^{14}C in the primary carbinol group, were reduced to glycerol and each product (VI, VII) was incubated with rat-liver slices. The glycerol phosphate derived from VII was phosphorylated almost exclusively at the labeled, the one from VI at the unlabeled carbon atom. Hence, as envisaged in Fig. 1 the position of the (a) group relative to the remainder of the molecule rather than the mass effect, determined the stereospecificity. Although such findings[6,7] fully support the view which was expressed already in 1950 by Martius and Schorre[6] that the isotope merely serves a diagnostic purpose and is otherwise irrelevant for the process of discrimination, at least one investigator[8] has taken the position that the Ogston effect represents a second type of isotope effect. The reason, it was argued, stereodiscrimination can occur with molecules like labeled citric acid is that they no longer are symmetric if appropriately labeled. In the parallel case of glycerol this argument can be refuted even experimentally. If the phosphorylation of one of the primary carbinol groups of glycerol could occur selectively only if the molecule possessed isotopic asymmetry, the product of the same reaction with ordinary glycerol would not be the natural optically active form but a racemic mixture. The stoichiometric and stereochemical data of Bublitz and Kennedy[9], however, leave no doubt that the metabolite

* This statement should not be interpreted to mean that a reaction in which the isotope is being retained, cannot alter the amount of isotope per mole. If, as is frequently the case, only a fraction of all molecules contains the isotope and if only a fraction of all molecules is converted into the product, discrimination between labeled and unlabeled molecules is possible through an isotope effect. This is clearly unrelated to our assertion that a structurally and sterically homogeneous group of labeled molecules will react uniformly if they undergo a selective reaction of the type postulated by Ogston.

References p. 259

of unlabeled glycerol is the known optically active glycerol phosphate.

Possibly the main reason for the repeated discussions of the Ogston phenomenon in terms of isotopic asymmetry lies in the illusion that this would allow one to describe it in familiar terms and thereby "explain" it. Although it is valid of course to regard labeled glycerol (VI, VII) as an asymmetric molecule, its selective phosphorylation is not just a minor variant of the enzymatic differentiation between optical antipodes. If optical antipodes (*e.g.* D- and L-glyceraldehyde) are being differentiated, only one stereoisomer reacts, whereas in the case of labeled glycerol both the D and L form undergo the reaction. In other words in the case of glyceraldehyde the reaction depends on the configuration of the molecule whereas in the case of the labeled glycerol it does not.

3. Some non-enzymatic differentiations

The Ogston hypothesis was widely interpreted as saying that any discrimination, even a partial one, between the (a) groups of a molecule Caabd required its attachment to an enzyme at three points. This attitude is reflected by a terminology which speaks of the "biological asymmetry" of Caabd, as if a mysterious union between substrate and enzyme created a situation completely unrelated to the phenomena of classical stereochemistry. Actually, as was pointed out by Wilcox[10], a partial discrimination of two (a) groups had been reported already in 1904 by Marckwald[11] who found that the decarboxylation of ethylmethylmalonic acid as the monobrucine salt gave more of the *levo*-rotatory form of the resulting 2-methylbutyric acid. As the mechanism of this process was not fully elucidated[12], Schwartz and Carter[13] provided another example which will be discussed below (Section 9, p. 255). Such experiments show that partial discrimination does not require an enzyme or a three-point contact of substrate and asymmetric reagent.

4. The role of the substrate

Racusen and Aronoff[14] were the first to point out that the Ogston model does not allow discrimination of like groups in every compound as it would not permit *e.g.* the discrimination of the carboxyl groups in malonic acid. The important role played by the substrate in the process of discrimination, although implicit in this realization, was first clearly stated by Schwartz and Carter[13]. In the differentiation of the (a) groups of Caabd, the Ogston model can be looked upon not only as a mechanism for selective reactions, but also as a device for demonstrating the non-equivalence of seemingly identical groups. Moreover, since this process involves nothing more than matching the substrate with three labeled points on a piece of paper, the steric difference between the two (a) groups should be discernible also without the Ogston model. If one views a three-dimensional representation of Caabd (IX) in such a way that the (b) and (d) groups are towards the rear with the (b) group above the (d), then a given (secretly marked) (a) group will invariably appear on the same side of the observer. Another[13] and somewhat less

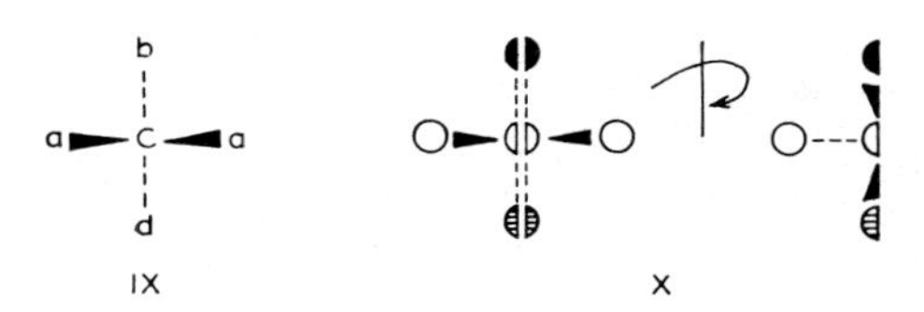

reliable[13,15] demonstration of the non-equivalence of the (a) groups lies in the fact that the plane of symmetry which Caabd possesses if all substituents of the central carbon atom are symmetrical, bisects the molecule into halves which are related like object to image but which ordinarily[13] are not identical because they cannot be superposed on each other (X). This situation resembles the one prevailing in those *meso* compounds which like *meso*-tartaric acid possess a plane of symmetry. Since this plane also bisects the molecule into non-superposable halves, Schwartz and Carter[13] proposed the term *meso*-carbon atom for a carbon with four substituents, two of which are alike but different from the two other dissimilar groups, and provided that all substituents have planes of symmetry. A *meso*-carbon atom Caabd so defined represents the simplest structural unit which permits discrimination of like substituents. As such the concept possesses considerable utility and has found wide application. However, it is not justified to conclude that all groups which can be differentiated are substituents of *meso*-carbon atoms[16]. For example, the aconitase reaction with citric acid selectively removes one of the four hydrogen atoms that are *vicinal* to the hydroxyl group[17]. The molecule has only one plane of symmetry. This plane bisects the central carbon atom and its hydroxyl and carboxyl substituents. Therefore, the central carbon is a *meso*-carbon atom but the two methylene carbons, which lie outside the mirror plane are not since they possess an asymmetric substituent ($-COH(COOH)CH_2COOH$). The rule of Schwartz and Carter, therefore, merely states the steric non-equivalence of the two methylene groups but not the steric non-equivalence of the hydrogen atoms attached to a single methylene group. The place of the *meso*-carbon atom in the problem of differentiation is not unlike that of the asymmetric carbon atom in the theory of optical isomerism. Similar considerations, therefore, seem to apply as were expressed by Jaeger[18] when he stated that "the whole concept of asymmetric atoms must be considered as an incomplete and rudimentary one. The fundamental

References p. 259

truth of the general principle underlying the phenomena of optical isomerism has been disturbed by bringing to the fore a mere special case of a more general principle, as if it were the fundamental and exhaustive one".

The criterion of Wilcox[10] is more widely applicable but again fails to cover all cases such as the one concerning the four hydrogens of citric acid[16]. Since the rule of Racusen and Aronoff[14] was shown to be incorrect[13,15], the only criterion applicable to all cases is believed to be the one proposed by the writer[15] in 1955. Aside from its theoretical implications, a general criterion has practical applications. It allows one to avoid needless experimentation if the result is predictable and may permit one to decide between two alternative pathways if only one of these would lead to random distribution of the isotopic tracer.

5. The superposition test and its relation to molecular symmetry

The criterion used in deciding which structures allow differentiation of like substituents and its relation to molecular symmetry was derived in much the same manner[15,16] as were the rules for the existence of optically active forms. Since texts and treatises on stereochemistry have presented these rules without showing their interrelationship, it seems desirable to retrace these steps.

A compound can exist in two antipodal forms only if its molecular model cannot be superposed on its mirror image. Although this axiomatic statement provides a sufficient criterion, it is often inconvenient to make the model and that of its image and to make sure that all possibilities for achieving superposition have been exhausted. A second criterion is, therefore, usually preferred. It is applicable to all cases which can be adequately represented by a rigid molecular model and is derived from the first criterion by merely analyzing the simplest series of steps that is required to achieve superposition, provided that this is possible. It has been shown by Leonhard Euler that two finite identical rigid objects which have one point in common can always be superposed by a single rotation around an axis which goes through the common point[19]. If one places a mirror through the center of gravity of a molecular representation, reflection in this mirror will of course produce the mirror image. Object and image must have one point in common, because the center of gravity like all points in the plane of the mirror will not change its position during the reflection. Therefore, if object and image are identical and not yet in superposition, they can be superposed by means of a rotation because they have at least one point in common. One can deduce, therefore, that a compound cannot exist in two enantiomeric forms if the molecular model upon reflection and if necessary a rotation can be converted into a model congruent with the original. It can be shown further[19], that the axis of rotation and the plane of reflection can always be chosen in such a manner that they are perpendicular to each other and intersect at the center of gravity. As explained in Vol. 1, Chapter IV this combined operation of reflection in a plane and rotation is called an alternating axis of symmetry and the well known criteria of the plane and of the center of symmetry are merely special cases differing in the angle of rotation (0° and 180° respectively)[19]. Since the operation which achieves superposition requires reflection, but may or may not require rotation, the symmetry possessed by molecules which cannot exist in optically active forms has been termed *reflective symmetry*[20]. It differs in kind from the symmetry which determines whether a compound can have substituents which cannot be distinguished in any reaction.

To facilitate the discussion we shall designate these structurally identical substituents as (a′) and (a″). If a molecular model of a compound M containing these groups can be superposed upon itself in such a way that the (a′) group of one representation coincides with the (a″) group of the other and every other atom and bond of the first representation coincides with a like atom and bond of the other, then these two representations are indistinguishable. Therefore, the chances are equal that the reagent will encounter either (a′) or (a″) and that the reaction will take place in either case. There is no conceivable mechanism for differential reactivity of the (a′) and (a″) groups if the molecule meets the superposition test specified. However, if it is not possible to achieve this kind of superposition, it will be equally impossible to superpose the product resulting from the interaction of the (a′) group with the reagent from that formed by its interaction with (a″). The nature of this product is irrelevant in this context. It may be a compound modifying both the reagent and the (a) group, a molecular compound, a complex held together by Van der Waals or similar forces, a transition state, etc. The fact that the products* (M—a′) · a′ · R and (M—a″) · a″ · R are not superposable and, therefore, not identical, does not in itself assure that the reaction will differentiate (a′) from (a″) because the two products could be related like object and image and, therefore, have equal probability of formation and equal reactivity. This situation, however, can be prevented easily by proper selection of the reagent. If it is optically active and retains its optical activity on reaction with M, the resulting products such as (M—a′) · a′ · (+R) and (M—a″) · a″ · (+R) cannot possibly be optical antipodes because the mirror image of (+R) is (−R). The products, therefore, are diastereomers** and as such must

* (M—a) is to indicate the radical resulting from the removal of an (a) group from the molecule (M).

** For definition see Vol. 1, Chapter IV, p. 192.

References p. 259

differ more or less in their chemical properties. Differentiation, therefore, can be expected* although it may be so slight that it cannot be detected. One can summarize, therefore, that *differentiation of structurally identical groups (a′) and (a″) can occur only if the molecular model cannot be superposed upon itself in such a way that the (a′) of the first representation coincides with the (a″) of the second and that every other atom coincides with a like atom, bound to its neighbors in the same manner*[16].

In order to relate this basic criterion to molecular symmetry we shall again assume that a single rigid model can adequately represent the compound and shall inquire into the simplest operation which will achieve superposition. Since the two representations with either (a′) or (a″) in a predetermined position are to be indistinguishable, their centers of gravity must coincide. Therefore, the Euler theorem predicts that superposition, if possible, can be achieved by a rotation around an axis through the center of gravity. An object which can be superposed upon itself in a new way by means of a rotation also conforms to the traditional definition of symmetry and this symmetry is called *rotational symmetry*[20]. We can state, therefore, that a molecule possessing rotational symmetry does not allow the differentiation of *those* groups which can be superposed on each other by operating the test for such symmetry[16]. The axis of such a rotation has been termed a simple axis of symmetry.

The importance of rotational symmetry to crystallography and spectroscopy has long been recognized, whereas organic chemists in their preoccupation with reflective symmetry have made use of the concept of rotational symmetry only on rather rare occasions (for some notable exceptions see Ref. 21) although there are other applications besides the problem of differentiation. This preoccupation with reflective symmetry has led to the frequently heard statement: *Although* citric acid is a symmetrical molecule, it can react in an asymmetrical manner, which explained nothing. We now can state: *Because* citric acid has no rotational symmetry, differentiation of the two primary carboxyl groups is possible. This analysis restores symmetry considerations to their proper place in the problem of deciding whether a given intermediate is compatible with the metabolic scheme under discussion. If such use is made of rotational symmetry, it is important to emphasize a difference between reflective and rotational symmetry: since a compound can have only one optical antipode, the presence of reflective symmetry invariably prevents the existence of an optically active form. One cannot similarly conclude that all structurally identical

* This expectation is based on the assumption that the optically active reagent participates in the rate-determining stage of the reaction. If it does not, as in an ideal $S_{N}1$ process and if the dissociation of (a′) or (a″) leads to the same product, no differentiation will occur.

substituents of a compound possessing rotational symmetry are indistinguishable because only those substituents (a′) and (a″) which can be superposed in the superposition test for rotational symmetry cannot be differentiated. For example, as will be shown below, succinic acid contains two sets of carbon-bound hydrogens which are indistinguishable among themselves but different from the other pair (*cf.* Section 7, p. 253).

When the superposition tests were related to either reflective or rotational symmetry, the assumption had to be made that the molecule could be represented by a rigid model. Although this view is unrealistic, because most molecules can assume various shapes, little difficulty arises from this if it is understood that the conformation selected for analysis should be as symmetric as possible. On occasion the model to be chosen does not represent an existing conformation but rather the average positions of the various nuclei as for example in the case of the cyclohexane derivatives which when depicted in the customary way as planar structures show higher symmetry than either of the two prevailing chair conformations. Occasionally, however, this device of "averaging conformations" is difficult to apply and then it is usually best to rely only on the superposition test with the understanding that permissible operations for superposition include not only motions of the rigid molecule but also those intramolecular motions (like rotations around single bonds) which proceed readily under prevailing conditions. An example of a non-resolvable compound which is best analyzed in this manner has been given by Mislow and Bolstad[22]. An analogous situation can exist in compounds which have no rotational symmetry for any conceivable conformation and which nevertheless possess indistinguishable substituents. This is illustrated by the prototype Caaa(+b), where the central carbon atom carries three identical substituents and a fourth one which is optically active (*e.g.* (+b) = (−Cefg)). If one tries to superpose (a′) on (a″) by rotation of the rigid model (XI), (g) would reach the original position of (f) and create a situation distinct from the

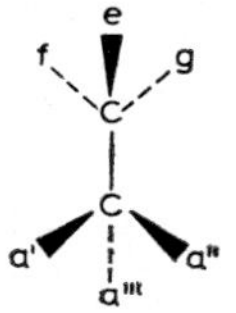

XI

original. The rigid model has no rotational symmetry. However, the superposition of (a′) on (a″) is easily accomplished without any detectable change if one rotates the bond linking the two central carbon atoms through 120°. Therefore if this motion proceeds readily in the actual compound, the three (a) groups are indistinguishable regardless of the structure of the remainder of the molecule.

References p. 259

Examples

The different implications of reflective and of rotational symmetry are best illustrated by examining a structural type which can show either form of symmetry, *e.g.*, the tetritols. Formula XII depicts an optically

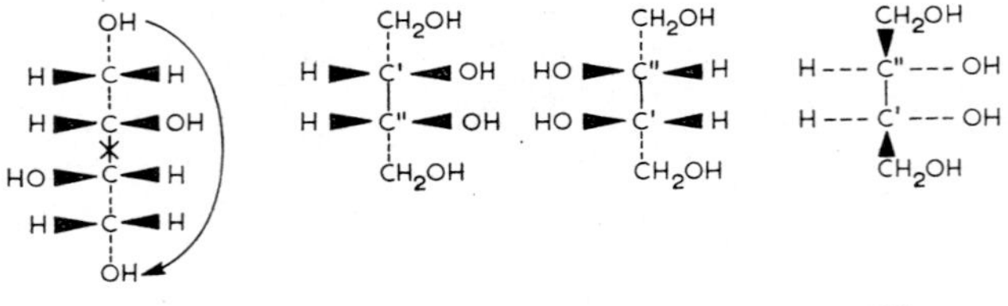

XII XIII a XIII b XIII c

active form (L-threitol) which of course lacks reflective symmetry. However, a rotation in the plane of the paper through 180° around an axis perpendicular to the central carbon–carbon bond superposes the top half of the molecule on the bottom half and *vice versa*. The molecule, therefore, has rotational symmetry and the two primary carbinol groups (or the two secondary) must be indistinguishable since they were superposed in the rotation described. A verification of this prediction was provided by Batt *et al.*[23]. In contrast, erythritol (XIIIa) has reflective symmetry but does not allow the superposition of the top half on the bottom half. Two unsuccessful attempts to achieve this by rotation are illustrated—neither XIIIb nor XIIIc are identical with XIIIa and hence all atoms of erythritol are distinguishable.

Apparently no metabolic studies with erythritol have been reported but a study has been carried out with a closely related structural type[24], Caa(+b)(−b) (XIV) which again has reflective but no rotational symmetry,

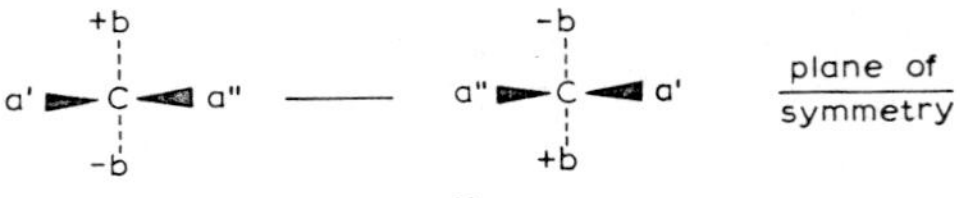

plane of symmetry

XIV a XIV b

since the rotation around an axis through the central carbon perpendicular to the plane of the paper which superposes (a′) on (a″) also brings (+b) to the site originally occupied by the non-superposable, antipodal substituent (−b). Therefore, neither the (b) nor the (a) substituents are sterically equivalent. A partial verification of this deduction can be seen in the selective decarboxylation of *meso*-α,α'-diaminopimelic acid to L-lysine by a *Sporosarcina* species[24]. On the other hand an optically active form like

Caa(+b)(+b) does not allow differentiation of its (a) or (+b) substituents.

The utility of the concept of rotational symmetry is particularly apparent in more complex situations, such as the ones provided by the inositols. Rotation by 180° of D-inositol (XV) around the axis shown gives a representation indistinguishable from the original and shows that the following pairs

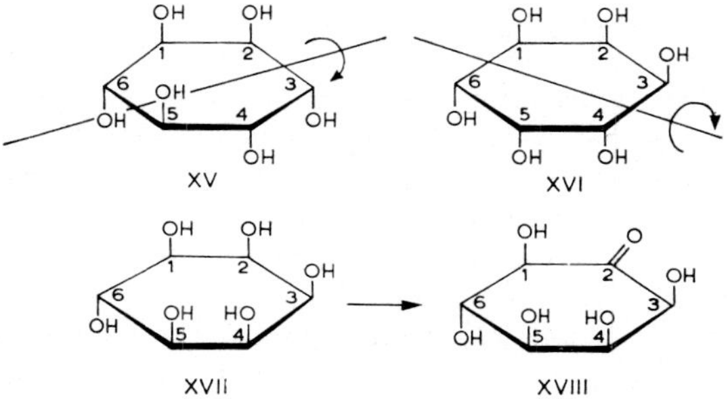

XV

XVI

XVII

XVIII

of carbinol groups cannot be differentiated: 1 from 4, 2 from 3, and 5 from 6. Similarly in *neo*-inositol (XVI) which has a center of symmetry, it is not possible to distinguish 1 from 6, 2 from 5, 3 from 4. This demonstrates that a *meso* structure is not always incompatible with rotational symmetry. Another *meso* compound, *epi*-inositol (XVII), however, lacks all rotational symmetry. It is converted by *Acetobacter suboxydans* by a selective oxidation of C-2 to the optically active *epi*-inosose (XVIII)[25].

Some of the best-known examples of stereoselectivity in enzymatic reactions do not involve differentiation of like substituents but the addition to double bonds from one or the other side. The formation of L-lactic acid from pyruvic or the hydration of fumaric to L-malic acid are typical examples. Schwartz and Carter[13] have pointed out that such addition reactions bear analogy to the differentiation of like substituents if one regards the "two bonds" of the double bond equivalent to the bonds towards the two (a) groups. This analogy allows one to use the same criterion for both situations and to state that bdC=a (XIX) can undergo stereoselective addition reactions because regardless of the nature of (a) it is not possible to

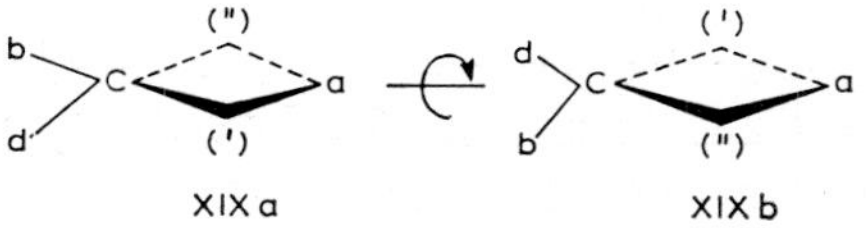

XIX a

XIX b

superpose the forward (′) on the rearward (″) bond without causing other changes if (b) and (d) are different substituents. The species bbC=a, on the

References p. 259

other hand, has rotational symmetry which prevents differentiation between the (b) groups and between the two "components" of the double bond. If the addendum to the unsaturated carbon atom of bdC=a has the same structure as one of the substituents already present, the stereospecificity of the process can be demonstrated only with isotopic tracers. Examples of such processes are the formation of citric from oxaloacetic acid, or the enzymatic reduction of acetaldehyde to ethanol[26].

Still another type of discrimination involves differentiation between two pairs of unshared electrons. An example of this was observed by Dodson *et al.*[46] who found that *Aspergillus niger* converts sulfides with dissimilar substituents of the sulfur (*e.g.*, phenyl benzyl sulfide) to the corresponding optically active sulfoxide. Since the sulfides are not linear, they lack rotational symmetry if the two substituents of the sulfur are different. The superposition test demonstrates the non-equivalence of the two pairs of unshared electrons marked ′ and ″ in XX. In the examples studied, the discrimination

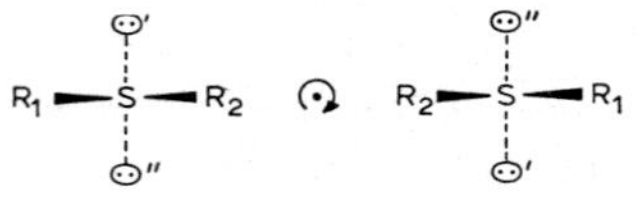

R_1—S—R_2 ⟳ R_2—S—R_1

XXa XXb

was only a partial one and reflective symmetry was restored in a second oxidation step which gave the sulfone.

The superposition test for rotational symmetry allows one to classify molecules into those which allow differentiation of certain structurally identical groups and those which do not allow such differentiation. This may appear on superficial consideration to be a contradiction since numerous metabolic interrelationships exist between the two classes. For example the primary carbinol groups are sterically distinct in glycerol but they are not in dihydroxyacetone. However, the reduction of the carbonyl group of dihydroxyacetone labeled in one of the carbinol groups cannot possibly lead to their discrimination in subsequent reactions because both enantiomeric forms of labeled glycerol must always be produced in equal amounts*.

6. Differentiation with optically inactive reagents

In deriving the criterion for differentiation of the substituents (a′) and (a″) which differ from each other only in their steric relationship towards the remainder of the molecule, it was pointed out that the process required an optically active reagent only if the products resulting from the interaction

* In this statement a possible minor differentiation due to a secondary isotope effect is being ignored since this is not the point at issue.

of one or the other of these (a) groups with an optically inactive reagent were related like object and image. If the product (M—a′) · a′ · R is the mirror image of (M—a″) · a″ · R then there must be an operation consisting of a reflection and if necessary* also a rotation which would superpose a′ · R on a″ · R and every atom of (M—a′) on a like atom of (M—a″). Therefore the operation, which interconverts the two products, converts (M) into itself. (M) consequently meets the criterion of reflective symmetry and one can state[16]: "If a molecule has structurally identical groups (a′) and (a″) *which can be differentiated according to the rotation test*, their differentiation requires an optically active reagent, only if the molecule has reflective symmetry and if (a′) and (a″) can be brought into coincidence by operating the test for such symmetry".

This rule can be illustrated by the case of citric acid which has no rotational symmetry. Therefore, all four carbon-bound hydrogen atoms are sterically distinct. The two hydrogens which in a Fischer projection (II) appear next to the hydroxyl group can be distinguished only by an optically active reagent since they occupy corresponding positions across the sole plane of symmetry of the molecule. The same holds true for the remaining pair of carbon-bound hydrogen atoms. On the other hand, it is theoretically possible to use a reagent with reflective symmetry to distinguish between the two hydrogen atoms that are attached to the same carbon atom since these lie on the same side of the mirror plane of citric acid. It is not certain to what extent this discrimination is realized in the dehydration of citric acid to *trans*-aconitic acid[27] by sulfuric acid since the *cis*-acid undoubtedly would isomerize under reaction conditions[28], but there is scarcely any question that such stereoselective processes occur in cases such as the dehydration of cyclohexanol which, depending on the nature of the optically inactive reagent, allows the removal of one member of the pair of hydrogens that is either *cis* or *trans* to the hydroxyl group. The two hydrogens at C-4 of cyclohexanol which lie within the plane of symmetry cannot be mutually superposed by reflection in the mirror plane and therefore should also be distinguishable by an optically inactive reagent. Of greater interest is the case of Caa(+b)(—b) (XIVb) since any reagent could qualify for differentiation of the structurally identical (a) groups whereas the agent that distinguishes between the antipodal (b) groups must be optically active. Examples of the use of optically inactive reagents for the differentiation of the two bonds of a carbonyl group of a *meso* compound of this type are provided by addition reactions[29] to *myo*-inosose-2.

---

* Euler's theorem[19] is applicable because the center of gravity of (M) is a common point of both products.

References p. 259

7. Methods and some applications

The recognition that two seemingly identical groups are distinguished in enzymatic reactions posed new problems in biological stereochemistry, namely which of the groups is the one acted upon by the enzyme. If the product is optically active and if the mechanism of the reaction has been elucidated, the configuration of the product would give the desired information. This, however, is only rarely the case and methods which utilize isotopic tracers are of much wider applicability. They are well-illustrated by the metabolic studies of glycerol[7] already cited. The first step consisted in the preparation of the two enantiomeric forms (VI, VII) which contained the tracers in one or the other of the two primary carbinol groups to be differentiated. Methods ordinarily used for the resolution of optical antipodes are of little use if the asymmetry is merely isotopic. The following procedure, however, is often applicable. The species Cabde is resolved into the two enantiomeric forms and both are converted separately to Caa*bd. If the configuration of the starting material is known and the conversion (e) → (a*) either does not affect the bond to the central carbon atom (*e.g.*, V → VI)[7] or if it has been determined whether the substitution proceeds with retention or inversion, the steric structure of the labeled product can be deduced. It does not matter, of course, whether (e) is already labeled as it was in the case of the glyceric acids[7] or whether the label is introduced during the conversion of (e) → (a*).

If the metabolic process leads to a structural differentiation between the labeled and the unlabeled group as in the case of the glycerokinase reaction, the location of the tracer by ordinary chemical means is usually quite straightforward. On the other hand, if the metabolic product has reflective symmetry except for the presence of the isotope, one of the following more complex methods can be used. If the product can undergo further biological transformation to a substance which permits the location of the isotope by ordinary chemical means, the results can be compared with those obtained with another labeled specimen of the product which was prepared synthetically and has known configuration. This approach was used by Hanson and Rose[50] in their investigation of the stereochemistry of the condensation reaction which yields citric acid from oxaloacetic acid and acetyl-coenzyme-A. If no reference sample with known isotopic configuration is available, conclusions might be based on analogous transformations by the same enzyme of related substances with known configuration. An example is a study of Rose[30] who analyzed the position of the hydrogen isotope introduced into dihydroxyacetone phosphate by the aldolase reaction. The product was converted to glycolic acid and then dehydrogenated by an enzyme preparation which discriminated between the two carbon-bound hydrogens and which could dehydrogenate L-lactic acid but not its optical antipode. It was inferred that the carbon-bound hydrogen of glycolic acid which was retained on dehydrogenation had the same orientation as the methyl group of L-lactic acid*. A third, non-enzymatic method is available, at least in principle. It apparently has not been used but may be illustrated as follows: Let the metabolic product be glycerol labeled in one of its primary carbinol groups. After dilution with carrier, it is oxidized (*via* its acetonide) to DL-glyceric acid which is resolved into the two enantiomeric forms. These are degraded individually to determine which antipode contains the label in the remaining primary carbinol group. If it is D-glyceric acid, the configuration of the labeled glycerol must have been that shown in VI.

A much more direct procedure consists in the measurement of the optical rotation which is associated with a carbon atom having hydrogen, deuterium and two different symmetrical substituents. It was used[48] in determining the probable configuration of ethanol-1-^{2}H which was obtained enzymatically from acetaldehyde-1-^{2}H. The observed rotation was very small ($[\alpha]_D$ −0.28°). Recently Cornforth *et al.*[49] reported that the rotation of monodeuterio-succinic acid increases very rapidly below 300 mμ and used this fact for the determination of the orientations of the deuterium which is transferred stereospecifically to NAD^+ by dehydrogenases of classes A and B. The required reference compound was prepared from 3-deuteriomalic acid of known configuration (see below) by successive substitutions of the dimethyl ester, OH → Cl → H, and hydrolysis. Since many compounds with reflective asymmetry show very large increases of optical rotation at lower wave-lengths, it is essential to guard against impurities when the optical rotations of isotopically asymmetric compounds are measured. Correlation between deuterium content and optical activity can provide an important safeguard[49].

If the two possible labeled metabolites are related like diastereomers, different physical methods can serve in locating the isotopic tracer. An example is the determination of the orientation of the hydrogen that is introduced into malic acid by the fumarase reaction. The analysis was based on the different nuclear magnetic resonance spectra which the *erythro* and *threo* forms of 3-monodeuterated malic acid possess[31,32]. The results showed that fumarase catalyzes the *trans* addition of D_2O because the resulting 3-deuterio-L-malic acid showed the *erythro* relationship between the two asymmetric centers (XXII).

* The certainty of stereochemical assignments by this general method is reduced by the observation that the antipodal stereospecificity of α-chymotrypsin is reversed with certain substrates (see section 9). However, such a reversal is most imprcbable in the present case because the result which was obtained with glycolate oxidase from tobacco leaves was confirmed with L-lactate dehydrogenase from muscle[30] and with D-lactate dehydrogenase from *Escherichia coli*[47].

This information helped to elucidate the stereochemistry of the aconitase reaction because the deuterium which was introduced into citric acid by the enzymatic steps XXI→XXIV, was removed by the action of aconitase. The phenomenon is stereospecific. These results of Englard[33] established the configuration of the deuterated methylene group of citric acid (XXIV) but provided no evidence for the configuration at C-3. The latter was elucidated* by Hanson and Rose[50] who prepared citric acid with a hydrogen isotope by a different method. Tritium was introduced into quinic acid (XXVIII) by enzymatic synthesis from 5-dehydroshikimic acid (XXVI) in tritiated water. Quinic acid (XXVIII) was oxidized with periodic acid and with bromine water to yield tritiated citric acid (XXX). In this preparation, the configuration of the methylene carbon was unknown but that of C-3 could be deduced

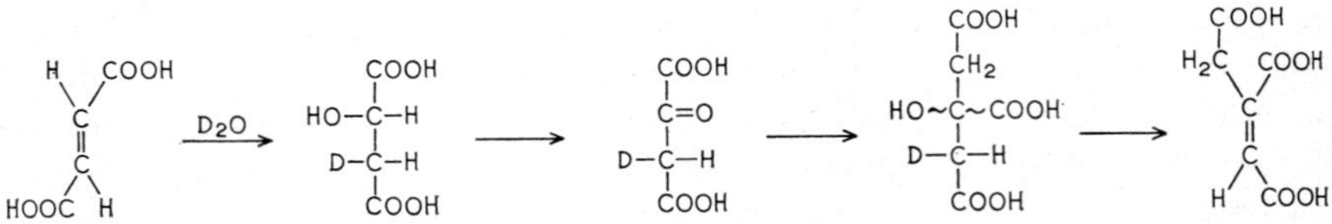

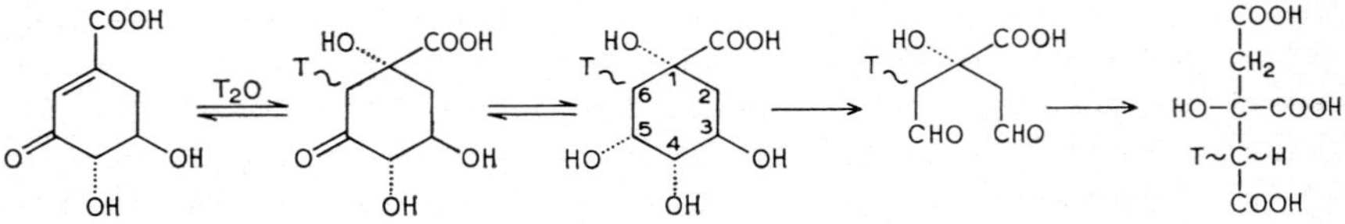

* Two other attempts at the solution of this problem have been widely cited. Both assigned configurations to labeled preparations of citric acid on the basis of the optical rotations of starting materials which had been converted to citric acid by unambiguous chemical reactions. The arguments used lead to opposite results and neither of them is considered to be conclusive. Martius and Schorre[6] prepared dideuterated citric acid (XXXV) from (−)-oxalocitromalic acid lactone (2-oxo-4-hydroxy-4-carboxyadipic acid 1,4-lactone). Its probable configuration was deduced by application of Hudson's lactone rule although the asymmetric carbon of Martius' lactone contained besides the nuclear substituents, not one but two carbon substituents (COOH and CH_2COOH). No reason was given for deciding which of these makes a rotatory contribution analogous to the hydrogen in Hudson's lactones. Martius' levorotatory lactone on exchange with D_2O and oxidation gave XXXV which retained its deuterium on metabolism to α-oxoglutaric acid. According to the results of Hanson and Rose[50] the configuration of XXXV and, therefore, of the lactone as originally proposed is correct. Gawron *et al.*[31] based their deduction on the presumed configuration of a chemical precursor of [^{14}C]-citric acid. This citric acid had been prepared by Wilcox *et al.*[34] who converted it enzymatically to α-oxoglutaric acid that contained ^{14}C in the carboxyl γ to the keto group. Since Gawron *et al.* based their deduction on the ^{14}C being α to the keto group, their conclusion must be reversed to be consistent with their analysis of the rotation. The conclusion is then the opposite of that reached by Hanson and Rose.

from the known configuration of quinic acid (XXVIII) at C-1 and from the known sequence of enzymatic reactions which had yielded it from dehydroshikimic acid (XXVI). Again the tritium was lost by the action of aconitase. This shows that the configurations of XXIV and of XXX agree at both asymmetric centers and are as shown* in XXXI. The results prove that the elimination of water from citric acid by aconitase is *trans* and fully elucidate

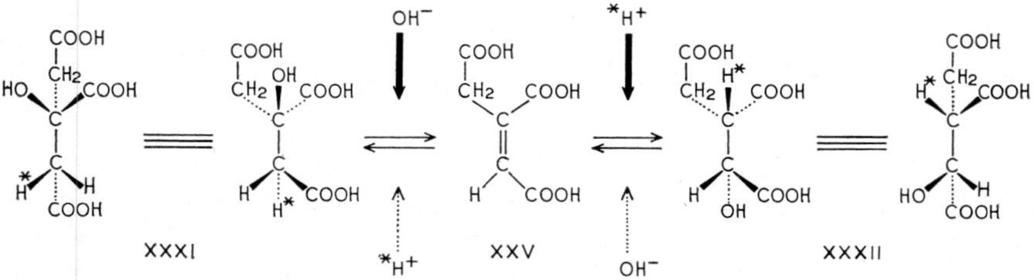

Fig. 2. Stereochemistry of the aconitase reactions. The starred hydrogen exchanges with the medium. (Here as elsewhere in this Chapter, the actual state of ionization of substrates, addenda and products is being ignored.)

the stereochemistry of the condensing reaction (I→II) because it had been shown that the methylene group of citric acid which is derived from oxaloacetic acid (I) is converted to the carbinol group of the isocitric acid (III). Finally the data shed further light on the mechanism of the aconitase reactions when considered jointly with the configuration of the isocitric acid which was recently shown[35,36] to be III=XXXII. The results eliminate the possibility that aconitase forms a single substrate–enzyme complex with *cis*-aconitic acid (XXV) which produces both citric (XXXI) and isocitric (XXXII) acid by the action of a single protonating and of a single hydroxylating locus. There are either two different attachments of the unsaturated acid to the enzyme which produce either citric or isocitric acid, respectively, or if there is only one substrate–enzyme complex, a given unsaturated carbon atom of *cis*-aconitic acid will receive from the same direction either a hydroxyl or a hydrogen to yield the two hydroxy acids (XXXI and XXXII) as is shown in Fig. 2.

A problem studied with rather different methodology concerns the conversion of succinic to fumaric acid. If either conformation XXXIIIa or XXXIIIc is subjected to the rotation test, the same conclusion is reached[15]: the hydrogen atom labeled (a′) is indistinguishable from (a′′′′), as is (a′′) from (a′′′). The two pairs, however, are sterically distinct and according to

* This fact also establishes that the tritium in XXVII and XXVIII must be *cis* to the hydroxyl at C-1 and consequently that the dehydration XXVII → XXVI must be a *cis* elimination. This unusual result should caution against unwarranted generalizations about the geometry of biological elimination reactions.

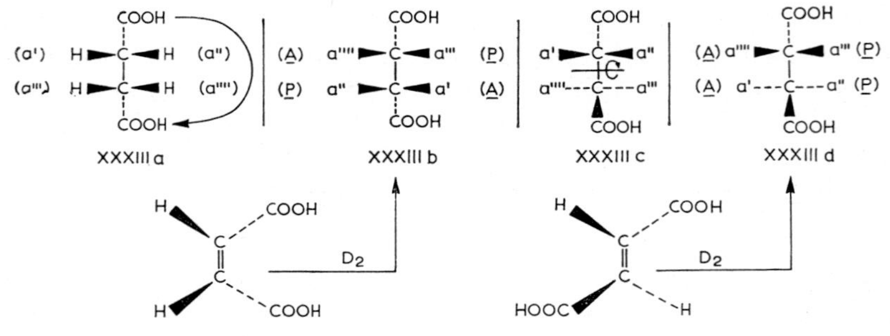

a general nomenclature proposal (Section 8) have been termed (*A*) and (*P*) hydrogens, respectively. Enzymatic dehydrogenation was found to remove both (*A*) and (*P*) hydrogens[37]. This might signify a process without stereospecificity or one which would remove from every individual molecule both an (*A*) and a (*P*) hydrogen. Tchen and Van Milligan[38] reached a decision between these two possibilities in the following manner: Deuteration of olefins with noble-metal catalysts usually results in *cis* addition. Secondary exchange reactions can also occur but evidently did not take place in the formation of the deuterated succinic acids from XXXIV and XXI because the two products were sterically distinct. Therefore, the deuterated succinic acid derived from fumaric acid (XXI) ought to be such that the two deuterium atoms of individual molecules are of the same kind, either (*A*,*A*) or (*P*,*P*), whereas the succinic acid prepared from maleic acid (XXXIV) would have only (*A*,*P*)-dideuterated molecules. If the enzymatic process was stereospecific, the second preparation would be the only one which could give dideuterated fumaric acid (by removal of the (*A*,*P*) ^{1}H atoms present in the labeled molecules). This was shown to be the case by mass spectrographic analysis.

8. Nomenclature

Experiments such as those which deal with the metabolism of citric acid require means of expressing the results besides pictorial representation. This can be done by stating the configuration of labeled substances and one can report, for example, the steric assignment suggested by Martius and Schorre[6] by saying that aconitase acts on C-4 of L-α,α-dideuteriocitric acid (XXXV) or on C-2 of D-α,α-dideuteriocitric acid (XXXVI), provided that it is understood that the configurational prefix refers to the hydroxyl rather than the carboxyl group at C-3, that the deuterated carbon is C-2, and that C-2 is shown above C-3. The major disadvantage of this type of nomenclature lies in the fact that it does not allow one to generalize

	XXXV	XXXVI
(1)	COOH	COOH
(2)	CD_2	CD_2
(3)	HO—C—COOH	HOOC—C—OH
(4)	CH_2	CH_2
(5)	COOH	COOH

and thus to state which carbon atom is acted upon in the unlabeled molecule. For this reason the writer[16] has proposed a stereospecific system of numbering carbon atoms and also a closely related system (*A*,*P*) for the designation of "identical" substituents which like hydrogen atoms are not ordinarily numbered. The system is a departure from convention, justifiable on the grounds that groups which are distinguished in chemical reactions are not identical and should not be treated in nomenclature as if they were identical. The system has been described in detail elsewhere[16]. It is based on the (*R*,*S*) system of Cahn *et al.*[39], which has been presented in Vol. 1, Chapter IV and allows one to state that the hydrogen removed from citric acid by aconitase is at C-4 and has the (*P*) orientation.

9. Mechanisms

Like the differentiation of optical antipodes, the discrimination of two seemingly identical groups or bonds depends on the diastereomeric relationship which the two transition states (or products) bear to each other (Section 5). In order to recognize more clearly the role which rotational asymmetry plays in creating this diastereomeric situation, it may be helpful to examine the example studied by Schwartz and Carter[13]. They found that the *levo*-rotatory α-methylbenzylamine (1-phenylethylamine)[40] reacted preferentially (3 : 2) with one of the carbonyl groups of 3-phenylglutaric anhydride to form the monoamide. It is not hard to visualize that an amine with groups of varying sizes (hydrogen, methyl, phenyl) at the asymmetric center may have a better fit with one of the carbonyl groups if the attack were from the side indicated in Fig. 3. Therefore, one of the resulting addition compounds[41] would be expected to form (or react) more readily than the other. The resulting discrimination would be completely vitiated, however, if the attack from the other side were equally feasible. This state of affairs is prevented by the rotational asymmetry of the anhydride which carries on opposing sites a small hydrogen atom and a much larger phenyl group.

It is not likely that mechanisms which allow a fair measure of con-

References p. 259

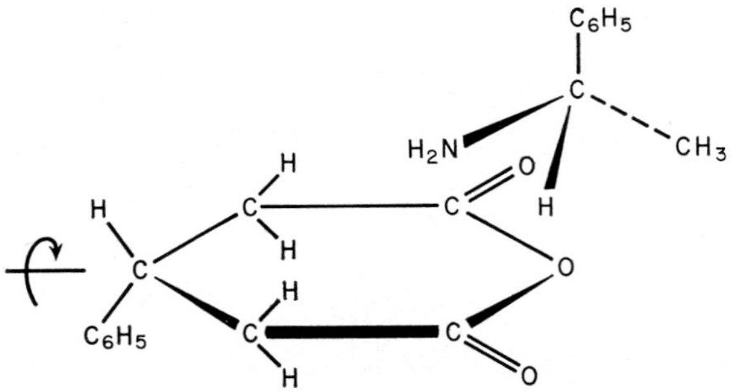

Fig. 3. 3-Phenylglutaric anhydride and (−)-α-methylbenzylamine. This schematic drawing is given merely to facilitate the discussion and with no claim that it represents the preferred alignment of the molecules in the transition state. (It is not known which carbonyl group is attacked preferentially.)

formational freedom could account for the complete stereospecificity which many but not all[42] enzyme reactions possess. Many investigators have stated, therefore, that the stereospecificity of any enzyme reaction proves that the substrate was attached to the enzyme at three or more sites. It may well be that complete stereospecificity can result only in the event that only one of the (a) groups can reach the active site, but one may question whether this can be achieved only by attractive forces at three points. A planar surface as in Fig. 1 does not seem to provide a very realistic picture of a protein[43] and the role of steric hindrance[15,34,44] deserves closer scrutiny than it has received. It may be well to heed Ogston's[45] suggestion that the three-point attachment ought not to be taken as a literal description of the forces acting between the two molecules. In this sense three-point attachment is merely a convenient term to describe a fixed alignment between substrate and enzyme. If the term is used in its literal sense, it should be noted that even attracting forces which involve three separate atoms of the substrate do not necessarily assure a fixed alignment with the enzyme. The theorem that the position of any rigid object is fully defined by the position of any three of its points which do not lie in a straight line, is applicable only if the sites of attachment are so distributed that the attachment adequately curtails the conformational freedom of the substrate. Clearly, two hydrogen bonds each to an oxygen atom of a catechol group will not constitute two sites of attachment in the sense of the Ogston model if *e.g.* the reaction takes place in the side-chain of epinephrine.

If the conclusion is drawn that the fixed alignment is caused only by binding forces, evidence beyond the demonstration of the stereospecificity of the reaction will be required. In some cases repulsive forces such as compression or charge effects seem to be unimportant. The stereospecificity of glycolic acid oxidase towards lactic acid remained unimpaired[30] when the largest substituent, the methyl group, was replaced by one, hydrogen, which had similar polarity and which was no larger than the smallest substituent of the asymmetric carbon of lactic acid. Retention of stereospecificity in such situations suggests that the fixed alignment of substrate and enzyme is caused by attracting forces at three or more sites. Kinetic studies of α-chymotrypsin[51], on the other hand, indicated that the attachment of esters of aromatic *N*-acyl-L-α-amino acids involves significant binding forces at only two sites which usually attract the aromatic side-chain and the ester group. The optical antipodes are also bound to the same active center but are usually not hydrolyzed. To explain the usually very high stereospecificity of ester hydrolysis and the lack of stereospecificity of binding, a steric hindrance effect of the *N*-acyl amino group of the substrate was postulated which in the D configuration would interfere not with binding but with the enzymatic reaction.

α-Chymotrypsin assumed great importance for the study of the stereochemistry of enzymatic processes when it was shown that the antipodal specificity of hydrolysis could be reversed with certain substrates[51–53]. The D-form of 1-oxo-3-carbomethoxytetrahydroisoquinolin was hydrolyzed about 2800 times faster than its epimer[51]. Esters of the *O*-acetyl derivative of D-lactic acid[52] and of the *N*-picolinyl derivative of D-alanine[53] were hydrolyzed faster than the corresponding L-forms although the reverse is true with other *N*-acyl derivatives (acetyl, benzoyl) of alanine esters. These startling results have been discussed extensively by the original discoverers and others. Unfortunately, the predictive value of several specific explanations for these anomalies has been rather low. In the most general and not necessarily mutually exclusive terms, one can postulate that the binding sites of the enzyme are not invariant or that their affinities can be determined by factors other than the nature of the atoms which are directly linked to the asymmetric center of the substrate or perhaps even that the

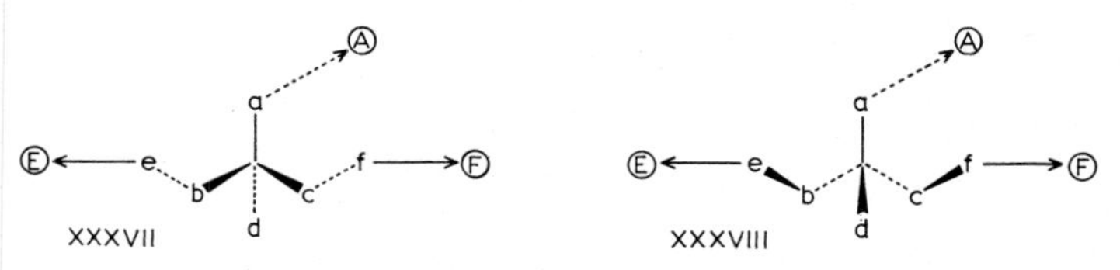

Fig. 4. Reversal of stereospecificity without change in binding interactions. Although the configurations of XXXVII and XXXVIII are enantiomeric, the positions of (a), (e), (f) of XXXVII and XXXVIII are the same. These three atoms are assumed to be bound to the three enzymatic sites (A), (E), and (F). (As the distances of (b), (c) and (d) from the enzyme are different in XXXVII and XXXVIII, one expects that some other factor such as steric hindrance ordinarily prevents such ambiguity of attachment. This again emphasizes the complexity of forces which may be involved in the stereospecificity of "three-point attachment".)

References p. 259

forward or rearward directions of bonds of the asymmetric carbon of the substrate can be reversed in the active complex with certain substrates. The third mechanism can be operative only if the atoms bound to the enzyme are not directly bonded to the asymmetric center of the substrate (Fig. 4).

α-Chymotrypsin is of particular interest in a discussion of the Ogston phenomenon since it can distinguish not only between antipodal configurations but also between structurally identical substituents of a substrate. Some like diethyl 3-hydroxyglutarate were hydrolyzed with good stereospecificity to the optically active monoester[54]. These dual manifestations of stereospecificity which have also been observed with other enzymes, are not surprising since both presumably depend on a fixed alignment of substrate and enzyme which places the reacting group at the active site. Therefore, the essential *difference* between the two manifestations of enzymatic stereospecificity does not lie in the role of the enzyme but solely in that of the substrate. Discrimination between optical antipodes depends on their reflective asymmetry, whereas the discrimination between like substituents depends on the rotational asymmetry of the substrate with respect to these substituents.

ACKNOWLEDGEMENT

The author acknowledges support from the U.S. Public Health Service through grant C-1679 and a Research Career Award.

REFERENCES

1 A. H. Beckett, in E. Jucker (Ed.), *Progress in Drug Research*, Vol. 1, Birkhäuser, Basel, 1959, p. 455.
2 A. G. Ogston, *Nature*, 162 (1948) 963.
3 E. A. Evans Jr. and L. Slotin, *J. Biol. Chem.*, 141 (1941) 439; H. G. Wood, C. H. Werkman, A. Hemingway and A. O. Nier, *J. Biol. Chem.*, 142 (1942) 31.
4 H. A. Krebs, *Nature*, 147 (1941) 560.
5 V. R. Potter and C. Heidelberger, *Nature*, 164 (1949) 180.
6 C. Martius and G. Schorre, *Ann. Chem.*, 570 (1950) 140, 143.
7 M. L. Karnovsky, G. Hauser and D. Elwyn, *J. Biol. Chem.*, 226 (1957) 881.
8 S. Aronoff, *Techniques of Radiobiochemistry*, The Iowa State College Press, Ames, 1956, p. 12.
9 C. Bublitz and E. P. Kennedy, *J. Biol. Chem.*, 211 (1954) 951.
10 P. E. Wilcox, *Nature*, 164 (1949) 757.
11 W. Marckwald, *Chem. Ber.*, 37 (1904) 349.
12 F. Eisenlohr and G. Meier, *Chem. Ber.*, 71 (1938) 997; J. Kenyon and W. A. Ross, *J. Chem. Soc.*, (1952) 2307.
13 P. Schwartz and H. E. Carter, *Proc. Natl. Acad. Sci. U.S.*, 40 (1954) 499.
14 D. W. Racusen and S. Aronoff, *Arch. Biochem. Biophys.*, 34 (1951) 218.
15 H. Hirschmann, in S. Graff (Ed.), *Essays in Biochemistry*, John Wiley and Sons, New York, 1956, p. 156.
16 H. Hirschmann, *J. Biol. Chem.*, 235 (1960) 2762.
17 S. Englard and S. P. Colowick, *J. Biol. Chem.*, 226 (1957) 1047.
18 F. M. Jaeger, *Spatial Arrangements of Atomic Systems and Optical Activity*, McGraw-Hill, New York, 1930, p. 40.
19 A. Schoenflies, *Theorie der Kristallstruktur*, Bornträger, Berlin, 1923, pp. 3–8, 17, 20, 31–37.
20 H. Weyl, *Symmetry*, Princeton University Press, Princeton, 1952, pp. 43, 44, 66.
21 D. H. R. Barton and K. H. Overton, *J. Chem. Soc.*, (1955) 2639; J. D. Roberts, C. C. Lee and W. H. Saunders Jr., *J. Am. Chem. Soc.*, 76 (1954) 4501.
22 K. Mislow, *Science*, 120 (1954) 232; K. Mislow and R. Bolstad, *J. Am. Chem. Soc.*, 77 (1955) 6712.
23 R. D. Batt, F. Dickens and D. H. Williamson, *Biochem. J.*, 77 (1960) 272.
24 M. Antia, D. S. Hoare and E. Work, *Biochem. J.*, 65 (1957) 448.
25 T. Posternak, *Helv. Chim. Acta*, 29 (1946) 1991; B. Magasanik and E. Chargaff, *J. Biol. Chem.*, 174 (1948) 173.
26 F. A. Loewus, F. H. Westheimer and B. Vennesland, *J. Am. Chem. Soc.*, 75 (1953) 5018.
27 W. F. Bruce, *Org. Syn.*, 17 (1937) 1.
28 R. Malachowski and M. Maslowski, *Chem. Ber.*, 61 (1928) 2521.
29 T. Posternak, *Helv. Chim. Acta*, 24 (1941) 1045; 25 (1942) 746; 27 (1944) 457.
30 I. A. Rose, *J. Am. Chem. Soc.*, 80 (1958) 5835.
31 O. Gawron, A. J. Glaid III and T. P. Fondy, *J. Am. Chem. Soc.*, 83 (1961) 3634.
32 F. A. L. Anet, *J. Am. Chem. Soc.*, 82 (1960) 994.
33 S. Englard, *J. Biol. Chem.*, 235 (1960) 1510.
34 P. E. Wilcox, C. Heidelberger and V. R. Potter, *J. Am. Chem. Soc.*, 72 (1950) 5019.
35 T. Kaneko and H. Katsura, *Chem. Ind. (London)*, (1960) 1188; O. Gawron, A. J. Glaid III, A. LoMonte and S. Gary, *J. Am. Chem. Soc.*, 80 (1958) 5856.
36 A. L. Patterson, C. K. Johnson, D. van der Helm and J. A. Minkin, *J. Am. Chem. Soc.*, 84 (1962) 309.
37 S. Englard and S. P. Colowick, *J. Biol. Chem.*, 221 (1956) 1019.
38 T. T. Tchen and H. van Milligan, *J. Am. Chem. Soc.*, 82 (1960) 4115.
39 R. S. Cahn, C. K. Ingold and V. Prelog, *Experientia*, 12 (1956) 81.
40 W. Leithe, *Chem. Ber.*, 64 (1931) 2827.
41 M. L. Bender, *Chem. Rev.*, 60 (1960) 53.
42 M. Bergmann, L. Zervas, J. S. Fruton, F. Schneider and H. Schleich, *J. Biol.*

Chem., 109 (1935) 325; J. E. SNOKE AND H. NEURATH, *Arch. Biochem. Biophys.*, 21 (1949) 351.
43 J. C. KENDREW, *Federation Proc.*, 18 (1959) 740.
44 B. VENNESLAND, *J. Cellular Comp. Physiol.*, 47, Suppl. 1 (1956) 201.
45 A. G. OGSTON, *Nature*, 181 (1958) 1462.
46 R. M. DODSON, N. NEWMAN AND H. M. TSUCHIYA, *J. Org. Chem.*, 27 (1962) 2707.
47 G. KRAKOW AND B. VENNESLAND, *Biochem. Z.*, 338 (1963) 31.
48 H. R. LEVY, F. A. LOEWUS AND B. VENNESLAND, *J. Am. Chem. Soc.*, 79 (1957) 2949.
49 J. W. CORNFORTH, G. RYBACK, G. POPJÁK, C. DONNINGER AND G. SCHROEPFER JR., *Biochem. Biophys. Research Commun.*, 9 (1962) 371.
50 K. R. HANSON and I. A. ROSE, *Proc. Natl. Acad. Sci. (U.S.)*, 50 (1963) 981.
51 G. E. HEIN AND C. NIEMANN, *J. Am. Chem. Soc.*, 84 (1962) 4487, 4495; *Proc. Natl. Acad. Sci. (U.S.)*, 47 (1961) 1341.
52 S. G. COHEN, J. CROSSLEY, E. KHEDOURI, R. ZAND AND L. H. KLEE, *J. Am. Chem. Soc.*, 85 (1963) 1685.
53 J. R. RAPP AND C. NIEMANN, *J. Am. Chem. Soc.*, 85 (1963) 1896.
54 S. G. COHEN AND J. CROSSLEY, *J. Am. Chem. Soc.*, 86 (1964) 1217; S. G. COHEN AND E. KHEDOURI, *J. Am. Chem. Soc.*, 83 (1961) 4228.

Chapter VIII

Enzyme Structure and Function with Particular Reference to Bovine Ribonuclease and Chymotrypsin

C. H. W. HIRS*

Department of Biology, Brookhaven National Laboratory, Upton, Long Island, N.Y. (U.S.A.)

1. Introduction

The exceptional specificity and efficiency that are the most notable attributes of enzymatic reactions have been discussed in other Chapters of this book. The interpretation of these attributes at the molecular level has been given serious attention in recent years as knowledge of the structure of proteins and of enzymes in particular, has begun to accumulate. The problems have not been greatly simplified by the recognition that the region of the surface of an enzyme at which interaction with substrate takes place, the active site, perforce represents but a small fraction of the total surface of the molecule, for the highly demanding specificity requirements of many enzymes make it evident that detailed knowledge of the stereochemical relationships at the active site, *and* of the dependence of these relationships on the structure of the enzyme molecule as a whole, will be required to formulate a quantitatively satisfactory interpretation of enzyme action. At present our knowledge of protein structure, particularly of the structure of proteins in solution, falls far short of the degree of completeness necessary for the attainment of this goal. Nonetheless, at lower levels of resolution some noteworthy progress has been made in relating certain features of structure with function in enzymes.

2. The Michaelis complex

The first aspect of enzyme action to which attention must be directed is the

* Work at Brookhaven National Laboratory performed under the auspices of the United States Atomic Energy Commission.

References p. 278

adsorption of substrate molecules at the active site to form the enzyme–substrate complex. The variety of amino acid side-chains that can be presented to the external environment by the enzyme surface makes possible a range of different types of interactions between the surface and substrate molecules. These include electrostatic interactions between oppositely- and like-charged groups on the substrate and the enzyme surface, hydrogen-bonding, and cohesion due to dispersive forces between non-polar portions of the substrate molecules and similar regions on the enzyme surface. A combination of such interactions can bring about a relatively firm attachment of the substrate and may hold substrate molecules in specific orientations relative to the enzyme surface. Since most enzyme-catalyzed reactions are bimolecular, a pair of substrate molecules frequently must be adsorbed.

Fig. 1. Model of the sperm-whale myoglobin molecule. The large sphere represents the iron atom of the heme group; the model also shows a water molecule immediately adjacent to the iron atom. The white cord traces the course of the polypeptide chain through the structure.

Attachment at the active site therefore affords the possibility of orienting substrate molecules in precisely the correct relation to one another to maximize the probability for reaction. Even when relatively simple substrate molecules are involved, reaction paths that are likely to yield a fruitful encounter may be limited to a narrow region about the optimal path. The ability to hold substrate molecules in a position favorable for reaction is undoubtedly one of the principal factors responsible for the remarkable efficiency of enzyme action[1].

An indication of the type of interactions that may contribute to the formation of an enzyme–substrate complex is provided by the structure of the myoglobin molecule[2,3]. Myoglobin is, of course, not an enzyme, but the ferroheme prosthetic group responsible for the binding of molecular oxygen by this protein may for the purposes of illustration be considered as a substrate molecule for which the Michaelis constant, K_m, is very small. As Fig. 1 shows, the heme group in myoglobin is located in a cavity on the surface of the protein molecule. The central iron atom forms a co-ordinate link on one side of the planar heme group with the imidazole side-chain of a histidine residue (at position 91 in the amino acid sequence) and a second co-ordinate link on the opposite side of the heme group with a water molecule, itself hydrogen-bonded to another imidazole side-chain (contributed by the histidine residue in position 61). The bonds formed by the iron atom in the complex are octahedrally distributed: the bonds to the imidazole side-chain at position 91 and to the water molecule are co-linear and directed normal to the plane of the porphyrin ring. Electrostatic interaction between one of the propionic acid side-chains of the heme group and an arginine side-chain on the protein (at position 39) assists in the binding of the heme group at a point near the surface of the protein molecule. The side of the heme group possessing methyl and vinyl side-chains is most distant from the surface and appears to be associated with a region rich in hydrocarbon-like side-chains, *i.e.*, it is hydrophobically bonded to the protein*. The combination of interactions positions the heme group with great precision in the cavity into which it fits. Some impression of the sensitivity of the stereochemical relationships is gained from an example taken from the hemoglobin series. The abnormal hemoglobin associated with the familial disorder called methemoglobinemia possesses an α-chain in which the imidazole side-chain responsible for water binding (at position 61) is replaced by a phenolic group (tyrosine residue). The addi-

* Detailed examination of the structure of myoglobin, as revealed by X-ray crystallographic analysis, has shown that the great majority of polar side-chains occur at the surface of the molecule, and that the interior structure appears largely to be determined through the interaction of groups that come within normal hydrophobic bonding distances of one another[3].

References p. 278

tional volume required by the phenolic side-chain over that of the imidazole side-chain in the normal human protein is apparently sufficient to prevent the entrance of a water molecule: the iron atom is directly bonded to the phenolic hydroxyl group, remains in the ferric state, and molecular oxygen cannot displace the phenolic group to form a complex with iron.

The ferroprotoporphyrin moiety may be removed under controlled conditions from myoglobin with acidified acetone. The apo-protein recombines with the prosthetic group to form a product virtually indistinguishable from myoglobin. The apo-protein is readily denatured and is then incapable of recombination with heme. It is likely that dissociation of the prosthetic group from the conjugated protein leaves an apo-protein the configuration of which must be similar if not identical with the configuration of the conjugated protein itself. Removal of the heme group may be associated with relatively small rearrangements in the protein, but these must be reversible in order to permit the reconstitution of the conjugate. Such considerations indicate that if myoglobin were an enzyme its active site would be a cavity inside which very precise orientation of the heme group is achieved by coordinate, electrostatic, and hydrophobic bonding to specific side-chains of amino acid residues brought together in the site by the structural configuration of the molecule from widely separate regions of the amino acid sequence. It is quite certain that this imaginary active site would be a rather rigid one in which the side-chains contributing to the binding of the substrate (the binding sites) would only be capable of small fluctuations in orientation and position. Such a set of relatively inflexible binding sites with the planar iron–protoporphyrin complex undoubtedly represents an unrealistic extreme. Very few of the substrates normally encountered in enzyme reactions have the unusual shape, dimensions, and rigidity of the heme group. Moreover, it is becoming increasingly certain that in many enzymes the binding sites are not as inflexibly positioned as they are in the myoglobin molecule. When such flexibility exists, formation of the enzyme–substrate complex may be accompanied by conformational readjustments not only in the substrate but at the binding sites as well. The implications of substrate-induced conformational changes during the formation of the enzyme–substrate complex are of importance to an understanding of enzyme specificity[4].

By forming the enzyme–substrate complex certain functional groups at the active site that may be contributed by a variety of amino acid side-chains (thiol, imidazole, hydroxyl, etc.) are brought into apposition with the groups about to undergo reaction in the substrates. For convenience, the effective side-chains on the enzyme may be called catalytic side-chains to distinguish them from side-chains purely concerned with binding; but it will be recognized that attempts to distinguish between side-chains on the basis of their participation in either binding or catalysis may be quite arbitrary.

3. Activated complex

Catalysis can be the consequence of direct intervention by the catalytically important side-chains with the formation of covalent bonds, even if only transitorily, between these side-chains and the substrates or fragments thereof. Covalent bond formation is not a requisite for catalysis. The catalytically significant side-chains can assist the reaction by indirect participation, such as through the process of polarizing bonds about to undergo scission, or by the stabilization of a particularly favored transition state. It is therefore of some importance to recognize that preliminary formation of an enzyme–substrate complex is an essential pre-requisite for reaction not only because an opportunity is afforded for the appropriate orientation of the substrate molecules relative to one another, but also because the catalytic side-chains are thereby poised in their proper dispositions with regard to the complex to assist in the redistribution of chemical bonds that accompanies the reaction.

As familiar examples of reactions in which enzyme catalysis is associated with covalent bond formation between enzyme and substrate, or fragments of the substrate, the hydrolysis of *p*-nitrophenyl acetate by chymotrypsin[5], and the interconversion of glucose 1- and glucose 6-phosphate by phosphoglucomutase may be considered. The chymotrypsin-catalyzed reaction proceeds in two stages. In the first (1) the enzyme attacks the substrate to

$$\text{E–X:} + NO_2\text{—}C_6H_4\text{—O—CO—}CH_3 \rightarrow NO_2\text{—}C_6H_4\text{—}O^- + \text{E–X—CO—}CH_3 \quad (1)$$

$$\text{E–X—CO—}CH_3 + H_2O \rightarrow {}^-\text{O—CO—}CH_3 + \text{E–X:} \quad (2)$$

displace nitrophenolate ion with formation of acetyl-chymotrypsin. In the reaction shown in Eqn. 1 X represents a nucleophilic side-chain at the active site and E represents chymotrypsin. In the second step (2), acetyl-chymotrypsin is attacked by a water molecule to displace acetate ion with regeneration of the enzyme. In the phosphoglucomutase reaction the phosphorylated enzyme is an intermediate in a two-stage process (3, 4) which has been written with G-1,6-P_2, G-1-P, and G-6-P, to represent glucose 1,6-diphosphate, glucose 6-phosphate, and glucose 1-phosphate, respectively; E and X have the same significance as they had in Eqns. 1 and 2.

$$\text{E–X:} + \text{G-1,6-}P_2 \rightleftharpoons \text{E–X—}PO_3H_2 + \text{G-1-P} \quad (3)$$

$$\text{G-6-P} + \text{E–X—}PO_3H_2 \rightleftharpoons \text{G-1,6-}P_2 + \text{E–X:} \quad (4)$$

In both chymotrypsin[7] and phosphoglucomutase[8] the group X is the hydroxyl group of a serine residue at the active site. Whether the hydroxyl groups of the serine residues are the sole sites of acyl–enzyme formation in these reactions is still the subject of critical investigations, and it is possible, in the more general context of enzyme action, that such reactions may involve several covalent intermediates in a scheme of the type suggested by Eqn. 5.

$$
\begin{aligned}
&\text{E–X:} + \text{A—B} &&\rightarrow \text{E–X–A} + \text{BH}\\
&\text{E–X–A} &&\rightarrow \text{E–Y–A}\\
&\text{E–Y–A} &&\rightarrow \text{E–Z–A, etc.}\\
&\text{E–N–A} + H_2O &&\rightarrow \text{E–X:} + \text{A—OH}
\end{aligned}
\qquad (5)
$$

Failure to detect covalent intermediates does not rule out their existence as stages in the catalytic mechanism. Moreover, certain side-chains may exert a catalytic effect either by direct covalent participation or, indirectly, through general acid or general base catalysis. Imidazole side-chains exemplify this possibility. In the hydrolysis of a carboxylic ester by an esterase an imidazole side-chain may directly attack the ester at the carbonyl carbon atom with displacement of alkoxide and formation of a typical acyl–enzyme

$$\text{E–Im–N:} + \text{R–C(=O)–O–R}' \longrightarrow \text{E–Im–N–CO–R} + \text{HO–R}' \qquad (6)$$

$$\text{E–Im–N–C(R)=O} + \text{H–O–H} \longrightarrow \text{E–Im–N:} + \text{R–CO–OH} \qquad (7)$$

(Eqn. 6). The latter is attacked (7) subsequently by water to displace carboxylate ion with regeneration of the esterase. Alternatively, the imidazole side-chain can participate in the reaction by general base catalysis, whereby attack of a water molecule on the ester carbonyl group is facilitated by the removal of a proton from the water molecule (8). In this mechanism only prototropic changes are undergone by the enzyme molecule.

$$\text{E–Im–N:} \;\; \text{H–O(H)} \;\; \text{R–C(=O)–O–R}' \longrightarrow \text{E–Im}^{\oplus}\text{–N:H} \;\; \text{HO–C(R)(O–R}')\text{–O}^{\ominus} \longrightarrow \text{R–CO–O}^{\ominus} + \text{HO–R}'$$

4. Ribonuclease

Only for a few enzymes is precise but by no means complete knowledge at hand concerning the side-chains present at the active site. Where knowledge of this kind exists, assignment of a role in the catalysis to such residues is often subject to considerable uncertainty. Insight into the function of different side-chains in the catalysis can be provided by studies on substrate specificity, isotope effects and isotope redistribution, enzyme kinetics, and modification reactions. Such mechanistic studies are treated in many parts of this book. The emphasis here must be on structural considerations. At the present time the enzymes ribonuclease and chymotrypsin have probably been the objects of the most comprehensive studies aimed at the correlation of what is understood about their structure with their known functions. The remainder of this Chapter will be concerned with a summary of the present status of these studies.

Pancreatic ribonuclease catalyzes the hydrolysis of ribonucleic acid at pyrimidine nucleotide phosphodiester linkages in a two-step process (9, 10)

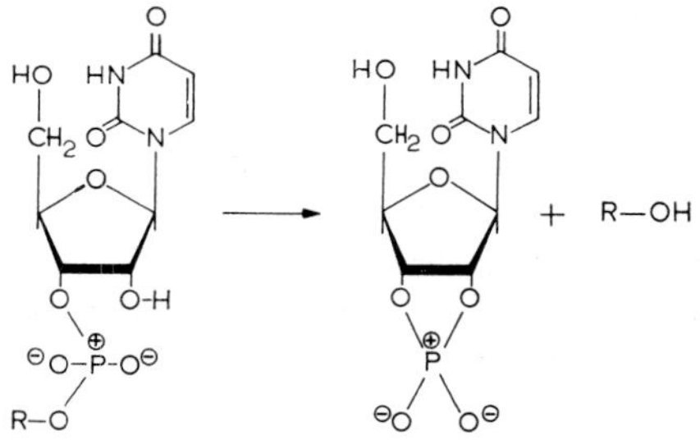

(9)

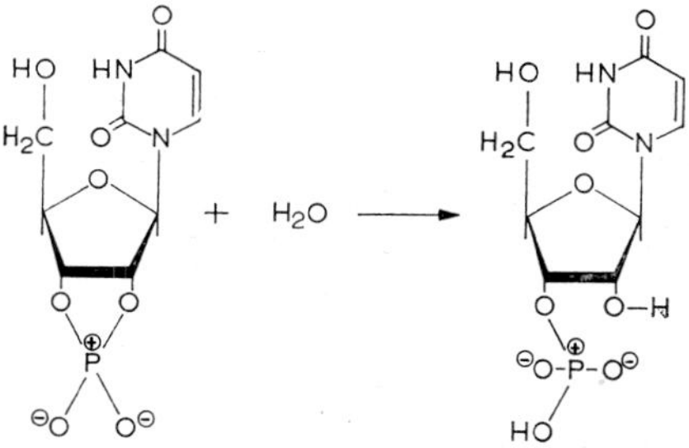

(10)

in which nucleoside-2′:3′-cyclic phosphates are intermediates. The first step is reversible, and ROH may be replaced by other alcohols or nucleotides[9]. The enzyme has a molecular weight of 13 683. The covalent structure[10–15] is shown in Fig. 2. X-ray crystallographic studies of the structure

References p. 278

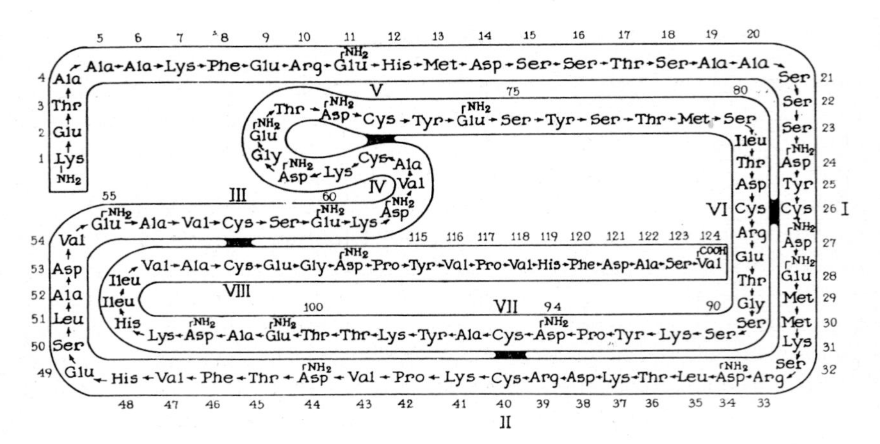

Fig. 2. The covalent structure of bovine pancreatic ribonuclease.

of the protein are in progress[16], but unfortunately were not at a sufficiently definitive stage at the time of writing to permit the incorporation of the results into the present Chapter.

Physically the protein is characteristically stable. Its crystals are unusually dense and hard and give sharp X-ray diffraction patterns to Bragg[16] spacings of 1.1 Å. There seems little doubt that the ribonuclease molecule contains only a small percentage of α-helix, approximately 15%; yet the structure is extremely compact. For instance, deuterium-exchange studies[17,18] have shown that of the 245 exchangeable hydrogen atoms in the molecule, 175 exchange rapidly at 0°, 25 exchange slowly at 0°, and 25 more exchange slowly if the temperature is increased to 38° for 24 h. The remaining 20 hydrogen atoms do not exchange with solvent hydrogen atoms unless the protein is heated[19] above 70°. Heating to 70° disrupts the native structure[20]; and the transition is fully reversible on cooling[19]. At neutral pH and low ionic strength the transition temperature[17] is 65°.

When the four disulfide bonds are ruptured by performic acid oxidation the native structure is abolished: the enzyme is inactivated, a large increase in viscosity is observed[20], and deuterium-exchange becomes essentially instantaneous[18]. The structural transition at 65° also has a pronounced effect (large negative increase) on the optical rotatory properties in the direction of denaturation[20]. Titration studies have shown that the carboxyl groups in ribonuclease have an unusually low pK_a, and that three of the six phenolic groups fail to titrate until a pH of 12 is attained[21]. The anomalous titration behavior is not observed when the protein is dissolved in solutions that contain high concentrations of urea or guanidinium chloride[22,23]. Examination of solutions of the enzyme in these solvents shows that the intrinsic viscosity of the protein approaches that of performic acid-oxidized ribonuclease[20]. The spectral properties of the molecule are altered at the same time. Difference spectra obtained from solutions of ribonuclease in buffer and similar solutions at equal concentration of protein under various denaturing conditions have been attributed to alterations in the environment of the tyrosine residues. Difference spectra obtained by comparison of solutions at low pH with solutions in the neutral range demonstrate an alteration in the environment of one of the tyrosine residues that fails to titrate normally in the alkaline range; while difference spectra obtained in solvents like 8 *M* urea suggest that all three of the anomalous tyrosine residues attain a normal solution environment under extreme conditions of denaturation[24–26]. Significantly, various polyanions and substrates are able in part to prevent the development of a difference spectrum in 8 *M* urea[27].

A noteworthy property of ribonuclease is its resistance to attack by trypsin and chymotrypsin at temperatures well below the transition range[17]. Both these enzymes catalyze extensive hydrolysis of the performic acid-oxidized protein[28,29], and attack ribonuclease in solutions containing high concentrations of urea or guanidinium chloride[11]. When ribonuclease is heated in aqueous solution above 40° unfolding of the molecule commences, and is apparently sufficiently extensive in certain regions of the structure to permit attack by trypsin and chymotrypsin[17]. These enzymes are being used to detect such regional unfoldings in the molecule[30]. At 60° attack by trypsin at the carbonyl bonds of residues 31 and 33 has been established, and the products maintain some ribonuclease activity. With chymotrypsin at 60° attack at residue 25 is particularly facilitated, and the product formed is inactive. Secondary cleavages also take place at residues 79, 97, 35, 76 and 46 (in decreasing prevalence), and possibly at residue 73, but it has yet to be established that these cleavages all represent independent processes.

Scission of the peptide bond between residues 20 and 21 may be effected at neutral pH values with the bacterial protease subtilisin[31]. The modified protein formed is fully active and may readily be separated from the parent enzyme. It is called ribonuclease-S. The 20-residue amino-terminal portion of ribonuclease-S has no covalent attachment to the body of the molecule, but it remains firmly bound. Dissociation may be achieved in solutions containing trichloroacetic acid or urea in high concentrations, when the peptide fragment (S-peptide) may be separated from the remainder of the molecule (S-protein). Neither fragment is enzymatically active, but on mixing ribonuclease-S is again formed. Extensive modification studies with the S-peptide[32] have revealed that its binding to S-protein does not depend significantly on charge interactions between cationic groups on the peptide (residues 1, 7, 10) and charged groups on the S-protein moiety. Hydrophobic bonding around the methionine residue at position 13 contributes

References p. 278

importantly to the binding of S-peptide, as modification of the thioether function by oxidation to the sulfone (with a large change in polarity) markedly diminishes the binding affinity.

Ribonuclease-S, unlike the parent enzyme, is readily attacked by trypsin[33]. The molecule is, therefore, not as compact as that of ribonuclease itself. This attribute is also revealed by difference spectra in the acid range: ribonuclease-S unfolds at higher pH values than the parent protein[32]. The S-peptide is readily attacked by trypsin to form fragments which, individually or in combination, no longer reconstitute an active enzyme with S-protein. Carboxypeptidase removes the carboxyl-terminal amino acids from S-peptide[34]. Residues 18, 19 and 20 may be removed from S-peptide without diminishing the ability of the modified peptide to regenerate an active enzyme with S-protein; more extensively degraded S-peptide does not possess this capacity.

Ribonuclease is inactivated by carboxypeptidase action. Residues 122, 123 and 124 may be removed without effect, but further attack at the carboxyl terminus destroys the activity of the enzyme[35]. Controlled hydrolysis with pepsin near pH 2 (with the ribonuclease molecule partially unfolded) furnishes a modified protein from which the carboxyl-terminal tetrapeptide has been removed[36]. This pepsin-modified ribonuclease is enzymatically inactive and exhibits a difference spectrum that suggests the removal of the carboxyl-terminal tetrapeptide is responsible for a partial unfolding of the molecule[37].

Ribonuclease may be fully reduced with mercaptoethanol to an inactive product that contains 8 thiol groups. The reduced protein may be re-oxidized in dilute solution, when fully active ribonuclease is regenerated in good yield[38]. The recombination of the proper pairs of thiol groups in the reduced protein demonstrates that side-chain interactions must be able to specify critical segments of the structure. The correct re-assembly of the molecule on re-oxidation of fully reduced ribonuclease is inhibited by a variety of substances all of which could be imagined to be effective in competing with the formation of hydrophobic bonds[34]. It is noteworthy that ribonuclease (in phosphate-containing buffers) is modified on treatment with *N*-carboxy-DL-alanine anhydride to an active product in which 7 of the 10 ε-amino groups in the molecule carry an average of 6 to 7 polypeptidyl side-chains[39]. This poly-alaninated derivative of ribonuclease may be fully reduced with mercaptoethanol like the parent protein, and is regenerated when the reduced protein is re-oxidized[39]. The location of 7 cationic charges in the structure is therefore unimportant in determining both the catalytic activity and the manner in which the reduced protein refolds on oxidation[34]. These 7 ε-amino groups are undoubtedly "external" in the same sense as the 18 ε-amino groups in the sperm-whale myoglobin molecule, all of which are found in the solution environment of the molecule[3].

Modification of ε-amino groups in ribonuclease may also be effected with *O*-methyl-iso-urea, whereby guanido groups are formed. At least 8 of the 10 ε-amino groups in ribonuclease may be so modified without affecting the activity of the enzyme[40]. The modification of an ε-amino group that reacts much more slowly than the others, however, destroys the activity[40]. It has been proposed that the ε-amino group that reacts slowly with *O*-methyl-iso-urea is normally inaccessible to the reagent and that an inactivating conformational rearrangement of the enzyme molecule is responsible for the unmasking of this group. It appears almost certain that the 7 ε-amino groups that readily react with *N*-carboxy-DL-alanine anhydride are also groups that become guanidinated rapidly with *O*-methyl-iso-urea[40].

The knowledge summarized to this point leads to an impression of the enzyme molecule as an extremely compact structure in the folding of which hydrophobic bonds play a critical role. Some regions of the structure appear to be less compact, particularly at higher temperatures. Of the groups involved in hydrogen ion equilibria, at least 7 of the 10 ε-amino groups are on the outside of the molecule, probably most of the carboxyl groups, and 3 of the 6 phenolic groups. The S-peptide region and the carboxyl terminus probably contain elements of the active site or contribute to the stabilization of the structure of that site.

Chemical modification studies of yet other kinds permit a refinement of this picture. In the guanidination of ribonuclease with *O*-methyl-iso-urea, the ε-amino group necessary for activity is protected from modification by the presence of uridylate, a strong competitive inhibitor of ribonuclease[40]. This and similar observations on the alteration of side-chain reactivity by competitive inhibitors of the enzyme are usually interpreted to mean that the side-chains in question are located at the active site. It appears that the structure of the active site of ribonuclease is dependent upon elements involving at least one masked ε-amino group[40]. A similar conclusion may be drawn from knowledge of the consequences of subjecting the enzyme to the action of fluorodinitrobenzene. The ε-amino group at position 41 is unusually reactive towards the reagent, and substitution at position 41 is accompanied by inactivation of the enzyme[41]. The reaction of the ε-amino group at position 41 is strongly inhibited by typical competitive inhibitors of ribonuclease such as cytidylate and phosphate ions[41]. Modification at position 41 makes the ε-amino group at position 7 available to the reagent: both these amino groups have significantly greater reactivities than ε-amino groups in the rest of the molecule[42]. It appears likely that the ε-amino group at position 7 is the group critical for activity in the reaction of the protein with *O*-methyl-iso-urea[42].

Further substantiation for the involvement of residues 7 and 41 in the

References p. 278

activity of ribonuclease comes from an extension of the alanination studies noted earlier[34]. In the experiments described before, reaction with *N*-carboxy-DL-alanine anhydride was carried out in the presence of phosphate buffer. Phosphate is a competitive inhibitor of ribonuclease, and its presence in the reaction medium modifies the reactivity of some ε-amino groups. Study of the reaction in bicarbonate buffer demonstrates that the enzyme is readily inactivated with *N*-carboxy-DL-alanine anhydride, and that two ε-amino groups, those at positions 7 and 41, react more rapidly than other ε-amino groups in the molecule[34]. In the presence of phosphate ion these two groups are among the three that are essentially resistant to modification. Protection of the ε-amino groups at positions 7 and 41 by phosphate ion against modification by fluorodinitrobenzene and *N*-carboxy-DL-alanine anhydride implies that these groups are connected with a region of the molecule where binding of phosphate ion takes place. Dinitrophenylation of the ε-amino group at position 41 is also inhibited by the nucleoside uridine[42]. Uridine is a competitive inhibitor of ribonuclease and its binding to the protein apparently involves attachment at a site the center of which is at least 6.5 Å removed from the center of the phosphate-binding site. Protection of a group at the phosphate-binding site may be regarded as evidence that uridine is bound in a specific orientation on the enzyme surface[50] as to permit the attached ribose moiety to interfere with attack at the phosphate-binding site. Such orientated binding of uridine requires interaction between several sites on the enzyme with regions of the inhibitor[42].

Ribonuclease is inactivated by the anionic reagents iodoacetate[43], imidazole diphosphate[44], and cyanate ion[45], all of which modify ε-amino groups. It is noteworthy that inactivation is achieved when at the most two ε-amino groups are modified. Since these reagents are undoubtedly attracted to the same anion-binding site responsible for phosphate binding, it is likely that the inactivation they cause is due to reaction with the exceptionally reactive ε-amino group at position 41. The unusual reactivity of the ε-amino group at position 41, and of the ε-amino group at position 7 once it is exposed, have occasioned some speculation[42]. It is possible that the phosphate-binding site, with which these groups are associated, contains several cationic groups. The electrostatic interaction between several closely situated cationic groups would reduce the pK_a of an ε-amino group, and thereby increase its susceptibility to alkylation and similar reactions[42].

Alkylation with iodoacetate at lower pH values has also been studied extensively[43]. In acid solution ($pH \leqslant 3$) where the ribonuclease molecule is partially unfolded, methionine side-chains are readily and exclusively modified to sulfonium salts[46]. The alkylation is accompanied by inactivation in all likelihood because the hydrophobic regions associated in the native structure with the environment of the thioether side-chains of methionine cannot be reconstituted when these side-chains become polar in consequence of sulfonium salt formation. It has already been mentioned that modification of the methionine side-chain in position 13 to the sulfone greatly diminishes the affinity of the S-peptide for S-protein[32]. A similar explanation is also invoked to account for the inactivation brought about by peroxide in acid solution, when the thioether side-chains are modified to the sulfoxides[47].

It is noteworthy that alkylation of the thioether function in methionine is not markedly pH-dependent[49]. At pH 5.5, with ribonuclease in the native configuration, the over-all rate of inactivation by iodoacetate is the same as it is under comparable conditions at pH 2.8. However, as would be expected if the methionine side-chains are involved in internal hydrophobic bonding, methionine residues are not alkylated at pH 5.5 and the inactivation is due almost exclusively to modification at histidine residues[43]. In 8 *M* urea at pH 5.5, on the other hand, methionine alkylation proceeds to the exclusion of alkylation at histidine[49].

The imidazole side-chains substituted with concomitant inactivation at pH 5.5 in the iodoacetate reaction[50,51] are those at position 12 and 119. The reaction with the side-chain at position 119 is the more rapid and is unusual in that the imidazole side-chain is substituted in the 1 position exclusively rather than in both the 1 and 3 positions, as in simple model compounds[49]. Since the inactivation of ribonuclease by bromoacetate at pH 5 is strongly inhibited by cytidylate these side-chains are located in the active site[50]. The alkylation of histidine residues does not normally take place at an appreciable rate at pH 5.5. It is also noteworthy that iodoacetamide does not inactivate ribonuclease under the same conditions[49]. The special properties of the imidazole side-chains at position 12 and 119 are undoubtedly occasioned by their environment in the structure and may in part be attributed to the proximity of the cationic center that constitutes the phosphate-binding site[49]. The imidazole side-chain at position 119 is specifically orientated to restrict alkylation to the 1 position in the ring. A possible explanation for this property comes from a study of the myoglobin structure, in which some of the histidine side-chains are located in such a way that only one of the nitrogen atoms in the imidazole ring is accessible to the solution environment[37].

The structural knowledge summarized earlier coupled with the results obtained in the search for the residues concerned in the activity permit an extension of the picture of the ribonuclease molecule outlined before. At least three sections of the covalent fabric contribute to the active site: the region between residues 7 and 16, the region around residue 41, and the region around residues 119 and 121.

The recognition of histidine at the active site of ribonuclease has led to

References p. 278

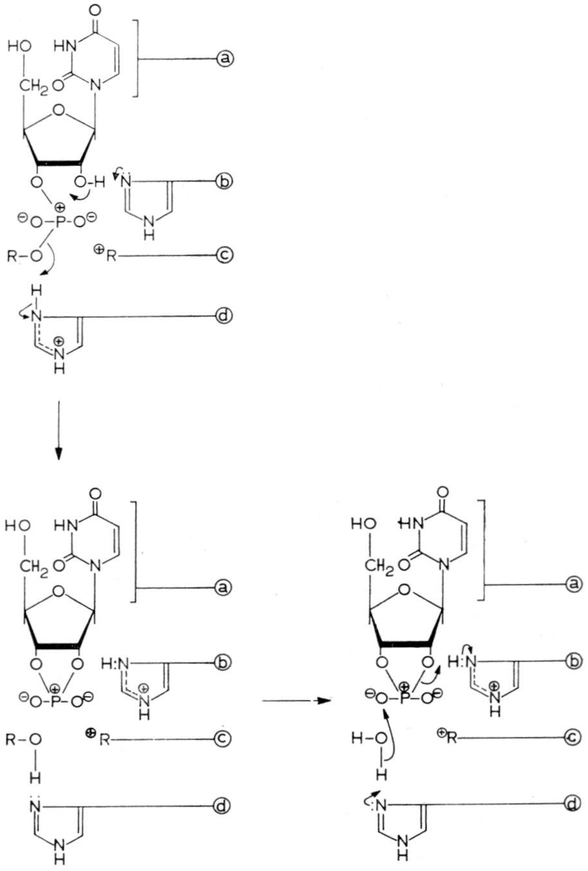

Fig. 3. Hypothetical mechanism of action for ribonuclease[55]. *a*, binding sites for pyrimidine ring; *b*, imidazole side-chain at position 119; *c*, cationic center capable of binding anionic portion of substrate: involves ε-amino group of lysine at position 41; *d*, imidazole side-chain at position 12.

the postulation of several mechanisms for the catalysis that involve imidazole participation (Fig. 3). Kinetic studies[52,53] indicate the existence of a group RH^+ at the active site with a pK_a of 6.8 in the cyclization step, and a second group RH^+ with the pK_a of 5.2 in the hydrolytic step*.

* In the mechanism given above these groups would be the histidine side-chains at positions 12 and 119, respectively. It should be emphasized that at present divergent findings in kinetic studies[54] remain to be reconciled, and that under the circumstances the mechanism given here should be regarded as one of several possible working hypotheses.

5. Chymotrypsin

Present knowledge of the structure of chymotrypsin[56] is provided by Fig. 4. As with ribonuclease the results of X-ray crystallographic studies of the protein are being awaited with considerable expectation. Preliminary results at 5 Å resolution of the structure of chymotrypsinogen A[57] have shown that only a small fraction of the peptide chain is present in structures that may prove to be α-helices when the resolution is improved. The molecular weight of the enzyme is approximately 25 000; but physico-chemical studies of the protein have not provided the detailled knowledge available for ribonuclease.

The serine residue capitalized in Fig. 4 is the residue to which the di-isopropylphosphoryl group is attached when chymotrypsin is inactivated with diisopropylphosphorofluoridate[58]. It has been shown that the same serine residue is acetylated when acetyl chymotrypsin is isolated from a solution containing *p*-nitrophenyl acetate and the enzyme[59].

One of the two histidine residues is implicated in the activity of chymotrypsin. Analysis of the kinetics of inactivation in consequence of photo-oxidation in the presence of methylene blue has revealed that the specific rate of the inactivation agrees precisely with the sum of the specific rates of photo-oxidation of one of the two imidazole side-chains and one of the two methionine side-chains[60]. Moreover, reaction of chymotrypsin with the

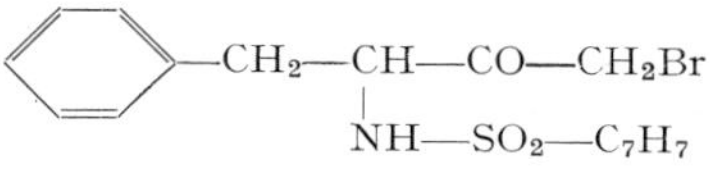

$$C_6H_5—CH_2—CH(NH—SO_2—C_7H_7)—CO—CH_2Br$$

(I)

substrate analog (I) of L-phenylalanine inactivates the enzyme by alkylation of one of the two imidazole side-chains[61]. Alkylation of the histidine side-chain by the bromoketone is inhibited by β-phenylpropionic acid, a typical competitive inhibitor of chymotrypsin; and it is noteworthy that the analog does not attack histidine in diisopropylphosphoryl chymotrypsin or chymotrypsinogen A. These results indicate that the histidine residue alkylated is part of the active site and must lie close to the serine residue that is acetylated in the hydrolysis of *p*-nitrophenyl acetate by the enzyme. Experiments with similar inhibitors have also demonstrated the significant requirement for compounds of the L series[62].

The methionine side-chain that is most readily photo-oxidized (with sulfoxide formation) has been identified[63] and is underlined in Fig. 4. The substrate analog (II) inactivates chymotrypsin in a reaction in which one

References p. 278

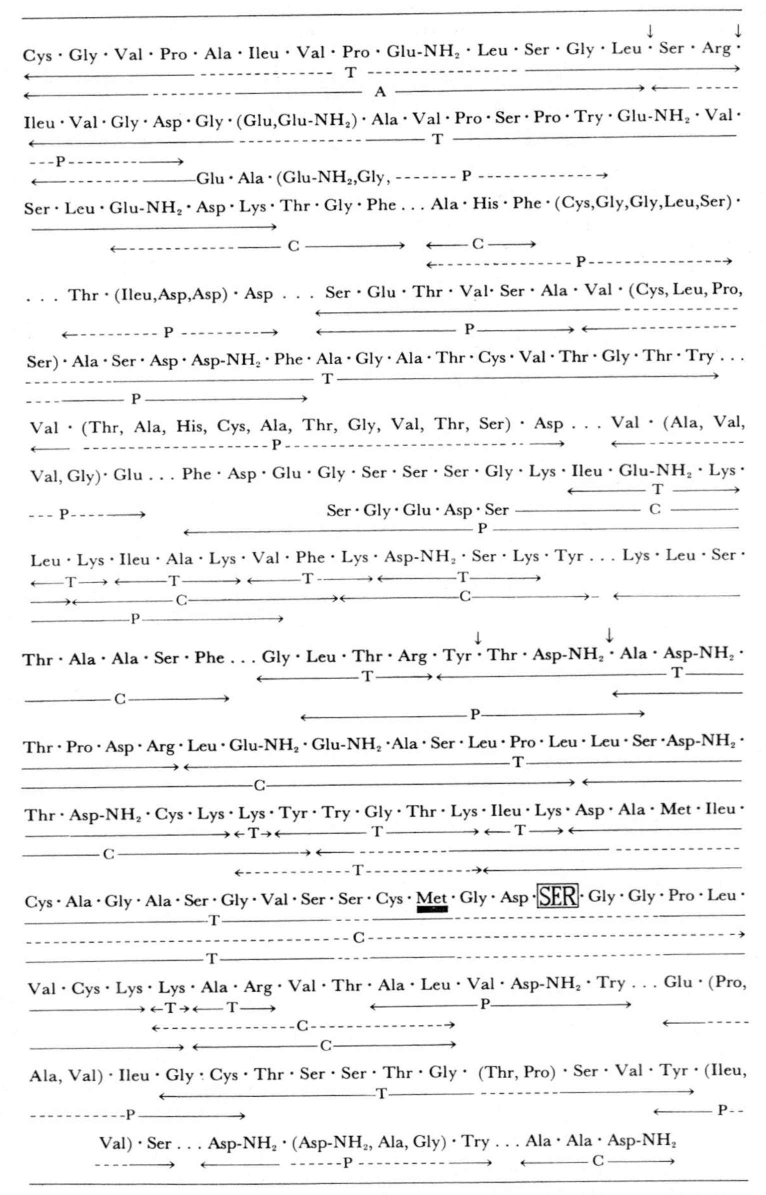

Fig. 4. Partial covalent structure of bovine chymotrypsinogen. The peptides formed on activation of the zymogen are indicated by the vertical arrows. Tryptic peptides are designated by T; chymotryptic and peptic peptides by C and P, respectively. The A-chain of chymotrypsin is represented by A.

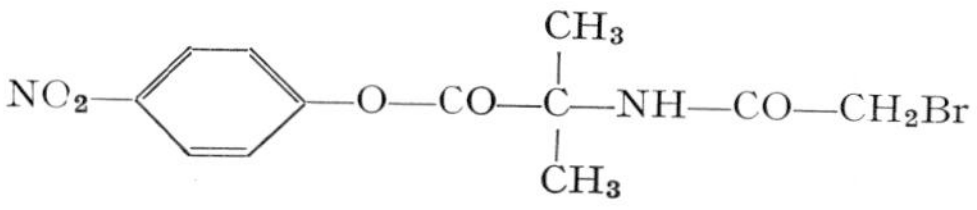

$$NO_2\text{—}C_6H_4\text{—O—CO—}\underset{CH_3}{\overset{CH_3}{\underset{|}{\overset{|}{C}}}}\text{—NH—CO—}CH_2Br$$

(II)

of the two methionine side-chains is alkylated[64]. In the initial step the analog is adsorbed to the enzyme and acyl-enzyme formation with attendant *p*-nitrophenolate ion displacement ensues. In the second step the bromoacetyl moiety alkylates the methionine side-chain with formation of a sulfonium salt. Finally, in the third step, attack by water displaces the acyl group, and leaves the protein modified at the methionine residue with the side-chain:

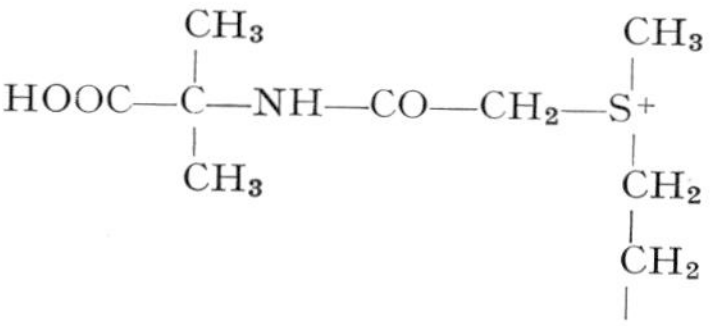

$$HOOC\text{—}\underset{CH_3}{\overset{CH_3}{\underset{|}{\overset{|}{C}}}}\text{—NH—CO—}CH_2\text{—}\underset{\underset{\underset{|}{CH_2}}{\underset{|}{CH_2}}}{\overset{CH_3}{\underset{|}{\overset{|}{S^+}}}}$$

The analog does not attack diisopropylphosphoryl chymotrypsin. The need for acyl–enzyme formation prior to attack at the methionine residue is emphasized by the observation that the corresponding acid does not inactivate chymotrypsin. It is significant that modification of the enzyme by the analog is blocked by the presence of indole-propionic acid, a competitive inhibitor of chymotrypsin. The methionine side-chain is therefore at the active site and must be adjacent to the side-chain(s) at which acyl–enzyme formation takes place. The final product of the reaction between the analog and chymotrypsin is not completely inactive, but like the parent enzyme, may be completely inactivated with diisopropylphosphorofluoridate. It has a Michaelis constant approximately 11-fold larger than chymotrypsin itself. Further work will be required to determine whether this methionine side-chain plays a part in the binding of the substrate.

As with ribonuclease, the illuminating modification studies being performed with chymotrypsin are demonstrating that the active site of the enzyme is built from elements of the covalent fabric contributed by widely separated portions of the amino acid sequence.

References p. 278

REFERENCES

1 D. E. Koshland, *J. Theoret. Biol.*, 2 (1962) 75.
2 J. C. Kendrew, H. C. Watson, B. E. Strandberg, R. E. Dickerson, D. C. Phillips and V. C. Shore, *Nature*, 190 (1961) 666.
3 J. C. Kendrew, *Brookhaven Symp. Biol.*, 15 (1962) 216.
4 D. E. Koshland, *J. Cellular Comp. Physiol.*, 54, Suppl. 1 (1959) 245.
5 B. S. Hartley and B. A. Kilby, *Biochem. J.*, 56 (1954) 288.
6 V. A. Najjar and M. E. Pullman, *Science*, 119 (1954) 631.
7 N. K. Schaffer, S. C. May and W. H. Summerson, *J. Biol. Chem.*, 202 (1953) 67.
8 D. E. Koshland, W. J. Ray and M. J. Erwin, *Federation Proc.*, 17 (1958) 1145.
9 F. H. Westheimer, *Advan. Enzymol.*, 24 (1962) 441.
10 C. H. W. Hirs, W. H. Stein and S. Moore, *J. Biol. Chem.*, 235 (1960) 633.
11 D. H. Spackman, S. Moore and W. H. Stein, *J. Biol. Chem.*, 235 (1960) 648.
12 D. G. Smyth, W. H. Stein and S. Moore, *J. Biol. Chem.*, 237 (1962) 1845.
13 D. G. Smyth, W. H. Stein and S. Moore, *J. Biol. Chem.*, 238 (1963) 227.
14 J. T. Potts, A. Berger, J. A. Cooke and C. B. Anfinsen, *J. Biol. Chem.*, 237 (1962) 1851.
15 E. Gross and B. Witkop, *J. Biol. Chem.*, 237 (1962) 1856.
16 H. P. Avey, C. H. Carlisle and P. D. Shukla, *Brookhaven Symp. Biol.*, 15 (1962) 199.
17 H. A. Scheraga and J. A. Rupley, *Advan. Enzymol.*, 24 (1962) 161.
18 A. Hvidt, *Biochim. Biophys. Acta*, 18 (1956) 306.
19 C. L. Schildkraut and H. A. Scheraga, *J. Am. Chem. Soc.*, 82 (1960) 58.
20 W. F. Harrington and J. A. Schellman, *Compt. Rend. Trav. Lab. Carlsberg., Sér. Chim.*, 30 (1956) 21.
21 C. Tanford and J. Hauenstein, *J. Am. Chem. Soc.*, 78 (1956) 5287.
22 O. O. Blumenfeld and M. Levy, *Arch. Biochem. Biophys.*, 76 (1958) 97.
23 C. Y. Cha and H. A. Scheraga, *J. Am. Chem. Soc.*, 82 (1960) 54.
24 H. A. Scheraga, *Biochim. Biophys. Acta*, 23 (1957) 196.
25 C. C. Bigelow, *Compt. Rend. Trav. Lab. Carlsberg., Sér. Chim.*, 31 (1960) 305.
26 C. C. Bigelow, *J. Biol. Chem.*, 236 (1961) 1706.
27 M. Sela and C. B. Anfinsen, *Biochim. Biophys. Acta*, 36 (1959) 471.
28 C. H. W. Hirs, S. Moore and W. H. Stein, *J. Biol. Chem.*, 219 (1956) 623.
29 C. H. W. Hirs, W. H. Stein and S. Moore, *J. Biol. Chem.*, 221 (1956) 151.
30 J. A. Rupley, T. Ooi and H. A. Scheraga, *Biochem. Biophys. Res. Commun.*, 8 (1962) 147.
31 F. M. Richards, *J. Cellular Comp. Physiol.*, 54, Suppl. 1 (1959) 207.
32 F. M. Richards and P. J. Vithayathil, *Brookhaven Symp. Biol.*, 13 (1960) 115.
33 J. E. Allende and F. M. Richards, *Biochemistry*, 1 (1962) 295.
34 C. B. Anfinsen, *Brookhaven Symp. Biol.*, 15 (1962) 184.
35 M. Sela, C. B. Anfinsen and W. F. Harrington, *Biochim. Biophys. Acta*, 26 (1957) 502.
36 C. B. Anfinsen, *J. Biol. Chem.*, 221 (1956) 405.
37 C. C. Bigelow and M. Ottesen, *Biochim. Biophys. Acta*, 32 (1959) 574.
38 C. B. Anfinsen and E. Haber, *J. Biol. Chem.*, 236 (1961) 1361.
39 C. B. Anfinsen, M. Sela and J. P. Cooke, *J. Biol. Chem.*, 237 (1962) 1825.
40 W. A. Klee and F. M. Richards, *J. Biol. Chem.*, 229 (1957) 489.
41 C. H. W. Hirs, M. Halmann and J. H. Kycia, *First IUB/IUBS Symp. on Biological Structure and Function, Stockholm, 1960*, Vol. 1, Academic Press, New York, 1962, p. 41.
42 C. H. W. Hirs, *Brookhaven Symp. Biol.*, 15 (1962) 154.
43 H. G. Gundlach, W. H. Stein and S. Moore, *J. Biol. Chem.*, 234 (1959) 1754.
44 G. Taborsky, *J. Biol. Chem.*, 234 (1959) 2915.
45 G. R. Stark, W. H. Stein and S. Moore, *J. Biol. Chem.*, 235 (1960) 3177.
46 W. H. Stein, *Brookhaven Symp. Biol.*, 13 (1960) 104.
47 N. P. Neumann, S. Moore and W. H. Stein, *Biochemistry*, 1 (1962) 68.

[48] H. G. Gundlach, S. Moore and W. H. Stein, *J. Biol. Chem.*, 234 (1959) 1761.
[49] G. R. Stark, W. H. Stein and S. Moore, *J. Biol. Chem.*, 236 (1961) 436.
[50] W. D. Stein and E. A. Barnard, *J. Mol. Biol.*, 1 (1959) 350.
[51] A. M. Crestfield, W. H. Stein and S. Moore, *J. Biol. Chem.*, 238 (1963) 2413.
[52] D. G. Herries, *Biochem. Biophys. Res. Commun.*, 3 (1960) 666.
[53] D. Findlay, D. G. Herries, A. P. Mathias, B. R. Rabin and C. A. Ross, *Nature*, 190 (1961) 781.
[54] M. Litt, *J. Biol. Chem.*, 236 (1961) 1786.
[55] F. H. Westheimer, *Fifth Intern. Congr. Biochem. Symp., Moscow, 1961*, Vol. 4, Pergamon, London, 1961, p. 1.
[56] B. S. Hartley, *Brookhaven Symp. Biol.*, 15 (1962) 85.
[57] J. Kraut, L. C. Sieker, D. F. High and S. T. Freer, *Proc. Natl. Acad. Sci. U. S.*, 48 (1962) 1417.
[58] N. K. Schaffer, L. Simet, S. Harshman, R. R. Engle and R. W. Drisko, *J. Biol. Chem.*, 225 (1957) 197.
[59] J. A. Cohen, R. A. Oosterbaan, H. S. Jansz and F. Berends, *J. Cellular Comp. Physiol.*, 54, Suppl. 1 (1959) 231.
[60] W. J. Ray and D. E. Koshland, *Brookhaven Symp. Biol.*, 13 (1960) 135.
[61] G. Schoellmann and E. Shaw, *Biochem. Biophys. Res. Commun.*, 7 (1962) 36.
[62] B. Kallos, *Brookhaven Symp. Biol.*, 15 (1962) 124.
[63] D. E. Koshland, D. H. Strumeyer and W. J. Ray, *Brookhaven Symp. Biol.*, 15 (1962) 101.
[64] W. B. Lawson and H. J. Schramm, *J. Am. Chem. Soc.*, 84 (1962) 2017.

Chapter IX

Some Aspects of Enzyme Theory

I. B. WILSON

Department of Biochemistry, College of Physicians and Surgeons, Columbia University, New York, N.Y. (U.S.A.)

Although the distinction between a description and an explanation is arbitrary, it is surely fair to say that our knowledge of enzyme mechanisms is descriptive rather than explanatory. Much of our information, which is often wonderous, is described under individual enzymes in this book so that here we shall briefly consider only some general aspects of enzymatic catalysis. Some special features which are not generally well known will also be considered.

The description of enzyme kinetics begins with the enzyme–substrate complex. This loose addition compound explains the observed limiting value for the reaction velocity with increasing substrate concentration

$$E + S \rightleftharpoons E \cdot S \rightarrow E + \text{products}$$

The complex is believed to lie along the reaction path as indicated above; that is if we could watch the individual molecules we should see them come together, the substrate combining with a specific portion of the large protein molecule. Sometimes the complex dissociates and sometimes it reacts further to form products. Actually, as far as the kinetics are concerned, an inert complex would serve just as well. A scheme such as

$$E + S \rightleftharpoons E{\cdot}S \text{ (inert)}$$

$$E + S \rightarrow E + \text{products}$$

also explains the enzyme saturation effect but it does not offer the same possibilities for understanding the reaction.

Once we accept the enzyme–substrate complex as a necessary intermediate we can easily imagine how specificity might be achieved through the application of weak forces. A substrate offers a constellation of varying kinds of chemical groupings; some parts of the molecule are polar, others non-polar, some parts have dipoles, others may bear electrical charges; some parts may have hydrogen atoms suitable for forming hydrogen bonds, other parts may be (Lewis) acids or bases. The active site of the enzyme also offers a constellation of chemical groupings and if in forming the enzyme–substrate complex, the enzyme and substrate bring complementary features into opposition, a number of small forces will be summed to yield a relatively strong bond. If complementarity is not complete some repulsive forces will develop and the complex will be less stable. The summation of just a few, say four weak energies of interaction each of which corresponds to a binding factor of say seven, leads to an increase in binding of 2500 times over a similar molecule lacking these interactions.

Depending on the extent of interaction, some complexes will be quite stable and highly defined with respect to the relative orientation of substrate and enzyme whereas others may be very loose. We note that a strong interaction with a functional group say between the ester function of a substrate and an esterase cannot by itself lead to specificity, for then all esters would interact strongly. The secret of specificity lies in summing up a number of weak interactions. A single strong-positive interaction can lead to specificity only if there are repulsive forces which exert selectivity. This is a rather more difficult situation and could not function to exclude a small substrate molecule. However, repulsive forces are sometimes involved along with attractive forces in determining specificity. A non-selective enzyme such as alkaline phosphatase might utilize a single strong interaction with the phosphate group for binding. In this case, phosphate itself should be bound and in fact phosphate is a competitive inhibitor of this enzyme. There is, however, another plausible explanation for the non-selectivity of alkaline phosphatase.

Hydrophobic interactions are receiving considerable attention both for the formation of complexes and for stabilizing the tertiary structure of proteins. Here a non-polar portion of a substrate imparts an extra driving force for a substrate molecule to leave the water and separate out on the protein if the protein offers a complementary area. Experimental analysis of the driving force shows that the energy change in transferring a non-polar molecule from water to a non-polar solvent is small. Surprisingly enough the non-polar molecule, far from decreasing the extent of water–water interaction, actually promotes it and the gain in solvation energy in the transfer barely compensates for the decrease in interaction amongst water molecules. The driving force for the transfer is the increased entropy arising it is believed from the dissolution of an ordered mantel of water molecules surrounding the hydrophobic group.

Similarly the interaction of two oppositely charged groups to form a salt bond in water is not exothermic but endothermic. The driving force is the increased entropy derived from freeing the water molecules which by virtue of their high dipole moments are oriented about the ions.

Evidently the forces of interaction between substrates and enzymes derive very much from the structure of water. But this point of view should not be overemphasized because it is a fact that some enzymes function quite well in media in which most of the water has been replaced.

While the specificity of enzyme action often derives from specificity in forming the enzyme–substrate complex it is also true that there is usually specificity in the maximum velocity. How is specificity in the maximum velocity achieved? At present we have very little experimental help here. We might enquire first why the formation of the complex should be helpful. The very fact that the complex is more stable than the reactants would by itself increase the free energy of activation, not decrease it. Evidently the forces of interaction must stabilize the transition-state complex at least as well as the enzyme-substrate complex. Merely bringing the two substrates together will not help. This is immediately obvious in the case of hydrolytic enzymes, for here the substrate is already completely surrounded by water molecules.

The idea has been proposed, perhaps most enthusiastically by Koshland and by Lumry, that the interaction of substrate and enzyme involves a large change in conformation of the protein whereby the latter is in effect converted into the enzyme only upon forming the enzyme–substrate complex. We represent this reaction

$$\mathrm{P} + \mathrm{S} \rightleftharpoons \mathrm{E} \cdot \mathrm{S}$$

where P is the protein and E is the altered configuration with catalytic activity. It pays to analyze this idea in a different but equivalent way. We can say that P and E are initially in equilibrium, with P overwhelmingly the predominant form. But S is bound far more strongly by E than by P and the equilibrium is thereby shifted

$$\mathrm{P} \rightleftharpoons \mathrm{E}$$

$$\mathrm{E} + \mathrm{S} \rightleftharpoons \mathrm{E} \cdot \mathrm{S}$$

In this way we see that a large amount of free energy of binding is used up in converting P to E. If, for example the ratio P/E is initially 100, the binding constants for S with E are in actuality 100 times greater than we measure. The purpose of this hypothesis is to account for low catalytic activity which enzymes often show toward molecules which are very much smaller than the preferred substrates, even when the former are present in enzyme-saturation concentrations. The small size rules out any explanation based upon the inability of the substrate to interact freely with the active site. However, a ready explanation is inherent within the older framework. It is only necessary to suppose that the extra binding features of a good substrate which are lacking in the small substrate orient the substrate in a position relative to the catalytic groups of the enzyme, favorable for the ensuing reaction, and that these same interactions persist in the transition state. The "induced-fit" hypothesis is an intriguing idea which deals with the formation of the catalytic entity; it does not of course explain catalytic activity but only specificity.

There is some experimental evidence which perhaps favors the "induced-fit" hypothesis. Acetylcholine, the normal substrate for acetylcholinesterase contains a substituted ammonium group as well as an ester function. During the catalytic process choline is split out and an acetyl–enzyme is formed which in turn reacts rapidly with water to yield acetic acid and regenerate the active enzyme. This acid-transferring process occurs also with other hydrolytic enzymes. There are many substances which react readily with the active site of acetylcholinesterase (and other hydrolytic enzymes) to form a derivative analogous to the normal acetyl–enzyme but a derivative which does not readily react with water. Organo-phosphorus anti-esterases such as diisopropyl fluorophosphate belong to this class; they react to form relatively stable phosphoryl–enzyme derivatives. Methanesulfonyl fluoride is another such compound. It too inhibits acetylcholinesterase by forming a stable methanesulfonyl–enzyme derivative. I have called such inhibitors, acid-transferring inhibitors. Now in the case of methanesulfonyl fluoride (and also dimethylcarbamyl fluoride) the rate of reaction with the enzyme is greatly increased in the presence of substituted ammonium ions: the rate is 35 times greater in the presence of tetraethylammonium ion. This is especially suggestive because the normal substrate is a quaternary ammonium ion. Since the ammonium ion is not joined to the reactant, the binding and orienting effect would appear to be lost and this experiment then suggests that a reshaping of the protein may be involved. However, there are discrepancies between the hypothesis and some of these observations; for example, tetraethylammonium ion is five times more effective than tetramethylammonium ion, yet the substrate analogous to acetylcholine containing ethyl groups rather than methyl groups is three times poorer than acetylcholine as a substrate. Perhaps these discrepancies are not important. An explanation is possible without invoking "induced fit". While the ammonium ion could not directly contribute to the binding of methane sulfonyl fluoride, it is possible that it might control orientation in that only certain orientations would allow the simultaneous binding of both substances. Under these circumstances the maximum velocity would be increased if the orientation were favorable but the effect on the rate measured under first-order conditions (the actual experimental conditions) would be just offset by a decreased binding constant since the limitation upon the relative orientation of the reactants would correspondingly diminish their binding. We should then have to assume that there is an additional increase in V_{max} resulting from an additional stabilization of the transition state even though the ammonium function is not part of the substrate molecule. This stabilization might involve a small change in configuration.

This hypothesis begins to resemble the induced-fit hypothesis but there are some very imporant differences. In the latter hypothesis all the protein in combination with the substrate has a much altered conformation but in the former only the extremely small fraction in the transition-state complex is altered and the change may be very small. The former hypothesis has the added burden of explaining how the extra stabilization occurs.

While the question of a possible extra stabilization in the transition state comes to mind in the usual catalytic reactions of enzymes, there are only a few experiments such as these special instances, where an added substance increases the rate of reaction, that there is evidence that it may be necessary. If the induced-fit hypothesis applies, it is not necessary. We have discussed one example. Two others are known. Some amines greatly increase the rate of reaction of trypsin with the small and extremely poor substrate acetylglycine ethyl ester (this compound may be an acid-transferring inhibitor) and the rate of hydrolysis of acetylchymotrypsin is increased by indole.

One of the earliest ideas concerning enzymatic mechanisms is that the reaction is essentially the same as in the absence of enzyme but the functional group of the substrate molecule is in a highly strained configuration in the enzyme–substrate complex and could therefore react more readily with the second substrate. The strain is of course to be paid for by binding forces, for otherwise the complex would not form. This engaging idea is still discussed in various forms. But the amount of strain would have to be quite large — at least 15 kcal/mole to account by itself for the greater rate of reaction. If "strain" is one of a number of contributing catalytic components its magnitude might be much less, perhaps 2–3 kcal/mole. Before analyzing this question we might briefly consider the kinetic consequences of the formation of a covalent enzyme intermediate during catalytic activity. It is clear now that acyl–enzyme intermediates occur with acetylcholinesterase and chymotrypsin and probably with many if not all hydrolytic enzymes. Covalent enzyme intermediates also probably occur with many other types of enzymes exemplified by sucrose phosphorylase, phosphoglucomutase, aldolase, and 3-phosphoglyceraldehyde dehydrogenase. In other cases (notably with several transferases) where such intermediates might be suspected, attempts to demonstrate an exchange reaction failed and it appears therefore that an enzyme intermediate does not occur. The scheme for a hydrolytic reaction involving an acyl–enzyme during the hydrolysis of an ester, S, is as follows

$$\mathrm{E} + \mathrm{S} \underset{k_2}{\overset{k_1}{\rightleftharpoons}} \mathrm{E \cdot S} \overset{k_3}{\rightleftharpoons} \mathrm{E' + P_1}$$

$$\mathrm{E'} \xrightarrow[\mathrm{H_2O}]{k_4} \mathrm{P_2}$$

where E′ is the acyl–enzyme, P_1 is an alcohol and P_2 is an acid. The rate equation has the Michaelis–Menten form

$$v = \frac{kE^0}{1 + \frac{S}{K_m}}$$

with

$$k = k_3 \Big/ \left(1 + \frac{k_3}{k_4}\right) \qquad V_{max} = kE^0$$

and

$$K_m = \frac{k_2 + k_3}{k_1} \Big/ \left(1 + \frac{k_3}{k_4}\right)$$

We note that V_m and K_m are determined in part by k_3/k_4; if k_3/k_4 is large the maximum velocity is k_4 and the value of K_m is decreased. Even if $k_2 \gg k_3$ (which is probably the case with these enzymes) there is still a relationship between K_m and V_m. It is quite possible for K_m to have a much lower value than k_2/k_1, the dissociation constant for the enzyme–substrate complex. At low values of S, $S \ll K_m$ and $E^0 = E$ we have

$$v = \frac{k}{K_m} E \times S = \frac{k_3 \cdot k_1}{k_2 + k_3}$$

that is, the second-order rate constant for the acylation of the enzyme is given by k/K_m.

We return now to the question of strain in the enzyme–substrate complex, using acetylcholinesterase as an example. The substituted ammonium function of acetylcholine is a highly important factor in the determination of specificity. This is illustrated by comparing acetylcholine ($K_m = 9 \cdot 10^{-5}$, $k = 100$) with ethyl acetate ($K_m = 0.5$, $k = 13$) as substrates.

Two different lines of evidence indicate that k_3 for acetylcholine is greater than k_4 probably by a factor of about six. Analyzing the data in terms of the above equations we find that the k_3 for acetylcholine is 50 times greater than the k_3 for ethyl acetate. Is this difference caused by extra strain in the enzyme–substrate complex? The dissociation constants of the complexes, k_2/k_1, are given by K_m $(1 + k_3/k_4)$ since it is now generally admitted that

$k_3 \ll k_2$ for hydrolytic enzymes. We get $6.5 \cdot 10^{-4}$ for acetylcholine and 0.55 for ethyl acetate, values differing by a factor of $8 \cdot 10^2$. For comparison we now calculate the expected difference in the dissociation constants if no extra strain is involved in the binding of acetylcholine as compared to ethyl acetate. To do this we use the dissociation constant for the binding of dimethylammonium ion which has the value $2.6 \cdot 10^{-2}$ *M*. This dissociation constant, rather than the one for trimethylammonium ion, corresponds to the extra binding energy of acetylcholine because one methyl group in acetylcholine projects into the solution and so does not contribute to the binding energy of the complex. This group does contribute a statistical factor of three because the non-binding methyl group in acetylcholine can be selected in three ways. Finally we have to consider the loss in entropy of mixing, 8 e.u. or a factor of 55, when two separate molecules are bound rather than one. Thus the dissociation constants for the two substrates should differ by a factor of $55/(2.6 \cdot 10^{-2} \cdot 3)$ equals $7 \cdot 10^2$. The agreement with the experimental values (which is fortuitously, extremely good), clearly indicates that there is little difference in strain in the two complexes.

It would seem that enzymes work by providing a facile path to the transition state which may or may not be stabilized by extra interaction over the enzyme–substrate complex. The facile path results from the binding and orientation of the substrate. The highly specific orientation of the substrate is shown by the stereospecificity of enzyme reactions even when the substrate is not asymmetric. The decarboxylation of citric acid and the dehydrogenation reaction of reduced pyridine nucleotides are outstanding examples. It is sometimes possible to add a second substance such as NH_2OH or CH_3OH to compete with water as an acceptor for the acyl group. Considerable extra information can then be obtained. In the case of chymotrypsin or acetylcholinesterase, hydroxylamine reacts with the acyl–enzyme to yield a hydroxamic acid:

$$E'\text{—}\begin{cases} \xrightarrow[k_5]{NH_2OH} R\text{—}\overset{O}{\overset{\|}{C}}\text{—}NHOH \\ \xrightarrow[H_2O]{k_4} R\text{—}\overset{O}{\overset{\|}{C}}\text{—}OH \end{cases}$$

It is evident that the ratio of hydroxamic acid to carboxylic acid must be precisely constant for a series of esters RCOOR′ in which only the alcohol residue R is changed. This was found to be true with 11 esters of hippuric acid. Actually, this demonstration is also a sufficient proof that an acyl–enzyme is formed, because in the scores of reaction series that have been studied the relative rates of reactions with two reagents, even when they are very similar, has never been observed to be in a constant ratio. This method of testing for a covalent enzyme intermediate could in principle be applied to many enzymatic reactions.

A second acceptor also enables us to evaluate both k_3 and k_4. If we call v the rate of disappearance of substrate (into both products) the effect of the second acceptor is the same as an increase in k_4. This increase is known precisely from the ratio of products k_5/k_4. Since k_3 remains constant (if the addition of the acceptor does not have some non-specific solvent effect, etc.) it is possible to evaluate k_3 and k_4 from the change in k. The value of k_4 must be the same for all esters of the same acid.

The value of the standard free energy of hydrolysis of the acyl–enzyme can also be evaluated kinetically with the aid of a second acceptor. Consider the reaction of *N*-acetyltyrosine hydroxamic acid at very low concentrations with chymotrypsin in the presence of hydroxylamine, then

$$E + S \underset{k_2^\circ}{\overset{k_1^\circ}{\rightleftharpoons}} E' + \text{hydroxylamine} + H_2O$$

The equilibrium constant for the reversible reaction of the enzyme with the hydroxamic acid is given by k_1^0/k_2^0. Since these constants can be evaluated and since the free energy of hydrolysis of the hydroxamic acid is known, the problem is solved. The value of k_1^0 is given by k/K_m for the hydroxamic acid as a substrate. The value of k_2^0 is the value of k_5 which can be determined from the ratio of k_5/k_4 for any ester of *N*-acetyltyrosine and from the value of k_4 which can be determined as we have already described. It has already been indicated in the case of acetylcholinesterase that the acyl–enzyme was at least as stable as an ester.

Work with chymotrypsin indicates that the free-energy level of the acyl–enzyme relative to hydrolysis is about that of a hydroxamic acid. The acyl–enzyme tends to hydrolyze in water at pH 7.0 in the presence of high concentrations of carboxylic acid only because ionization of the acid pulls the reaction. In the case of alkaline phosphatase the phosphoryl enzyme is surprisingly stable relative to hydrolysis, and in this case the phosphoryl–enzyme forms in the presence of phosphate. The relative stability of the phosphoryl–enzyme, because it tends to make k_3 large and k_4 small, tends to make dephosphorylation the rate-controlling step in the hydrolysis. If this tendency should prevail, a large number of substrates would have the same V_m even though their k_3 values may be quite different. As we have seen, this will also make K_m values small. The enzyme will appear to be non-specific. These deductions are in fact in agreement with the kinetic properties of this enzyme.

The catalytic importance of forming a covalent intermediate followed by a second transfer of a group rather than a single transfer to the final acceptor is not clear. From the discussion we do see that by introducing another dimension of variability the quantitative possibilities are broadened and the versatility of enzymes as a group is increased. The formation of a covalent intermediate also makes substrate inhibition possible. When the first product of hydrolysis contains important binding features of the substrate as for example the quaternary ammonium function in acetylcholine, the formation of the acetyl–enzyme, in this case, leaves the complementary structure of the enzyme unoccupied. This unoccupied site (anionic site) can bind the quaternary ammonium function of a second acetylcholine molecule. Under these circumstances the proper approach of a water molecule is prevented and catalysis cannot proceed. There is no evidence, at present, that substrate inhibition is physiologically important in the case of acetylcholinesterase but substrate inhibition is physiologically important in the ATPase activity of actomyosin. Aside from the possibility of enhancing the versatility of enzymes it would appear that the formation of a quite stable intermediate, as in the case of alkaline phosphatase, would place an extra burden on the overall catalytic process.

The advantage of a two-step transfer would seem to lie in the fact that while the enzyme is called upon to bring about a reaction between substances which are of necessity kinetically relatively stable, there is no necessary limitation on the activity of the functional structure of the enzyme. The activity of the enzyme permits reaction with a kinetically stable substrate to yield a covalent enzyme intermediate which still retains lability. The trouble with this argument is that it is hard to see why there are many enzymes which do not form such intermediates.

Push-pull mechanisms, such as combined acid–base catalysis, though going back many years, received special impetus from the experiments of Swain on the mutarotation of tetramethylglucose catalyzed by 2-pyridone. In this case the catalyst has the special property that an interaction with either the acidic or basic group facilitates interaction with the other. Even before this work, this kind of mechanism had been proposed for hydrolytic enzymes. While there is abundant evidence of a nucleophilic role for hydrolytic enzymes (and some evidence for a general base) there was not until very recently any strong evidence that an electrophilic mechanistic component existed. Evidence comes from studies which show that fluorides such as diphenylcarbamyl fluoride react much more rapidly with hydrolytic enzymes than do the chlorides. This reversed order of reactivity can be explained either by the formation of a tetrahedral intermediate or by an electrophilic catalysis. Because the hydrolysis of benzoyl fluoride and other reactions of fluorides are acid-catalyzed whereas the reactions of chlorides are not, the electrophilic mechanism seems the more likely explanation.

Reaction rates are sometimes analyzed in terms of thermodynamic parameters. The reaction rate is translated into a free energy of activation $\Delta F^{\pm}$, the difference in standard free energy between the reactants and the transition state. This quantity is then divided up into $\Delta H^{\pm}$ which is approximately the same as the energy of activation and $T\Delta S^{\pm}$ where $\Delta S^{\pm}$ is the entropy of activation. The energy of activation corresponding to the first-order reaction of the E·S complex is found to be rather small for enzymatic reactions which suggests that there is some extra stabilization of the transition state. However, the relatively low $\Delta H^{\pm}$ is not sufficient to account for the high reaction rate and $\Delta S^{\pm}$ although negative is therefore relatively more positive. In fact, a relatively more favorable $\Delta S^{\pm}$ is expected with good substrates because they form more rigid E·S complexes than poorly bound substrates. This thermodynamic view of kinetics involving $\Delta S^{\pm}$ might lead one to think that the orientation of the E·S complex need not resemble the transition state complex; all that would seem to be required for a relatively favorable $\Delta S^{\pm}$ is that E·S be rigid. Compounds such as

$$C_2H_5O-\overset{\overset{\displaystyle O}{\|}}{C}-CH_2CH_2-\overset{+}{N}(CH_3)_3$$

in which the ammonium function is in the acid moiety of the ester are not substrates for acetylcholinesterase even though they bind strongly with the enzyme. The answer is, of course, that the complex formed with such a compound is not free to explore possibilities of existence which include the transition state, and a thermodynamic treatment presupposes that this is possible. Similar orientation in the E·S complex and in the transition-state complex would seem to be necessary. The binding of the substrate brings it into proper orientation relative to the constellation of catalytic functional groups (in the case of a hydrolytic enzyme nucleophile, general base, general acid, etc.). Is this enough? Does the simultaneous operation of a number of catalytic components lower the activation energy or is there some extra stabilization in the transition state? What kind of extra stabilization might occur? It would seem possible that something equivalent to a solvent effect might occur. For example, suppose the transition-state complex is more polar than E·S complex. Then the close proximity of highly polar side-chains or water would be advantageous but the proximity of non-polar residues would be detrimental. This kind of solvation effect might be controlled by binding features in the substrate. Its effect would appear in the transition state. Even if one should wish to call this a conformational change, it is clear that it is very different from the kind of change envisaged in the induced-fit hypothesis. The question of an extra boost to catalysis is only at a discussion stage — there is only some evidence that such an effect may occur as we have already indicated.

SUBJECT INDEX

PRINTED IN THE NETHERLANDS